MW00654094

THE NEW HUMAN REVOLUTION

VOLUME 11

THE NEW HUMAN REVOLUTION

VOLUME 11

DAISAKU IKEDA

ILLUSTRATIONS BY
KENICHIRO UCHIDA

World Tribune
——*Press*——

Published by World Tribune Press
606 Wilshire Boulevard
Santa Monica, California 90401

Complete Set   ISBN 978-0-915678-33-4
Volume 11   ISBN 978-0-915678-43-3

Interior and cover designed by Gopa & Ted2, Inc.

10 9 8 7 6 5 4 3

Contents

Chapter 1: Light of Dawn   1

Chapter 2: Pioneering New Frontiers   85

Chapter 3: Ever-Victorious   177

Chapter 4: Dynamic Advancement   269

Index   341

More on Nichiren Buddhism
and Its Application to Daily Life   355

Editor's Note

The citations most commonly used in this book have been abbreviated as follows:

♦ GZ refers to the *Gosho Zenshu*, the Japanese-language compilation of letters, treatises, essays and oral teachings of Nichiren Daishonin.

♦ LS refers to *The Lotus Sutra*, translated by Burton Watson (New York: Columbia University Press, 1993). The citation usually appears as (LSXX,xx), where XX refers to the chapter number and xx is the page number.

♦ WND refers to *The Writings of Nichiren Daishonin* (Tokyo: Soka Gakkai, 1999).

♦ OTT refers to *The Record of the Orally Transmitted Teachings* (Tokyo: Soka Gakkai, 2004).

Light of Dawn

BREAK THROUGH the darkness! Surmount pre-
cipitous peaks! Then, the glorious, hope-filled vista
of a new era will enfold before you.

The date was March 10, 1966, and Shin'ichi Yamamoto
flew through the predawn sky above the South American
continent. His destination was Rio de Janeiro, Brazil. Most
of the other passengers seemed to be asleep, but Shin'ichi
hadn't been able to sleep a wink. He had come down with
a fever in New York two days earlier and it was still with
him. Though he felt somewhat under the weather, his
mind was strangely clear.

I also wasn't feeling well last time... he thought. The memory of his previous trip to Brazil, which had also been his first, came back to him. He had been very sick then, too.

Five-and-a-half years earlier, in October 1960, he had suffered from a persistent fever, due no doubt to the physical toll taken by his long journey, and the day before he was scheduled to fly from New York to São Paulo, his exhaustion reached its limit. The leaders accompanying him desperately urged him to cancel his trip to Brazil. They thought that if Shin'ichi went there in his condition he would surely collapse.

But Shin'ichi was adamant. "I'm going," he insisted. "The members there are expecting me. I absolutely refuse to cancel my plans when everyone is waiting.... Did President Toda ever once retreat in the middle of a struggle? I am his disciple. I am going, no matter what. If I collapse, then so be it!"

Shin'ichi thus made his first trip to Brazil. Summoning every ounce of his strength, he devoted himself to offering guidance and encouragement to the Brazilian members. During that visit, he also established the first chapter outside Japan there.

Kosen-rufu is the will and decree of the Buddha of the Latter Day of the Law. This path dedicated to realizing world peace and happiness for all humanity is far from easy. The path of kosen-rufu has always been one buffeted by adversity and filled with life-and-death struggles, a path that people have ridiculed and called impossible. Against all odds, however, the Soka Gakkai has striven earnestly to advance this movement, braving fierce storms and scaling arduous peaks to pitch the flags of glorious victory. This is the Gakkai's noble history.

Now, in 1966, the organization's membership in Brazil, where the flow of kosen-rufu had been fervently set in motion by Shin'ichi, had grown to eight thousand member-households. A grand culture festival was scheduled to be held in São Paulo on March 13, which was the reason for Shin'ichi's visit to Brazil this time.

SHIN'ICHI set off on his trip to North and South America on March 6. After a brief stop in San Francisco, he flew to Los Angeles where he stayed one night before heading to New York, arriving there around half past five in the late afternoon on March 7.

That evening, he paid his first visit to the Soka Gakkai's New York Community Center, which had opened two-and-a-half years earlier. The next morning, he met with local members at the center, giving himself wholeheartedly to answering their questions and offering guidance.

It was about this time that Shin'ichi began to feel ill, and he came down with chills and a fever. On the evening of March 8, he was scheduled to have dinner with representatives of a number of Japanese companies with which the Soka Gakkai had business relations, but he asked General Director Hiroshi Izumida and other leaders in his party to take his place so that he could rest.

Shin'ichi's wife, Mineko, who was also traveling with him, nursed him diligently, making him take medicine and placing cold compresses on his forehead to reduce his fever. The next day, the fever had subsided somewhat but not completely.

Mineko looked at Shin'ichi with worry etched on her face, but he said to her cheerfully: "I'm fine now. I can go to Brazil!"

In his heart, he was already on his way there.

At ten that evening, Shin'ichi and his party left New York and headed for their first stop in Brazil: Rio de Janeiro.

Shin'ichi, who spent the night in the plane wide awake, closed the book he was reading and pressed his forehead against the window to look outside. The horizon was beginning to glow faintly, and he could see a great river weaving through the vast continent below. He was sure it was the Amazon.

Eventually the sun began to rise. A sea of green stretched out endlessly before his eyes, as if warmly enveloping the world. In the sparkling light of dawn, he renewed his resolve: "I will open the way for the flow of an eternal river of kosen-rufu in Brazil, as timeless as the mighty Amazon!"

Shin'ichi arrived in Rio de Janeiro just before ten o'clock in the morning on March 10. Several local Gakkai leaders were at the airport to welcome him and his party. They included Yasuhiro Saiki, South America Headquarters leader, and his wife, Setsuko, the Headquarters women's division leader. Soka Gakkai Women's Division Leader Katsu Kiyohara and other leaders from Japan who had reached Brazil ahead of Shin'ichi were also on hand to greet them.

It was about seven months since Shin'ichi had last met Mr. and Mrs. Saiki. "The culture festival is finally here," Shin'ichi said to them. "Let's bring the flowers of culture, peace and happiness to bloom in Brazil. Let's open a new page of history."

A FTER CHECKING IN at the hotel, Shin'ichi and his party held a meeting to discuss their schedule in Brazil. As they spoke, the telephone rang. Kiyoshi Jujo picked up the receiver and quickly passed it to Shin'ichi. It was Vice General Director Ittetsu Okada, who had come to São Paulo ahead of the others to prepare for Shin'-ichi's visit.

Okada's voice was tense as he spoke: "Sensei, I have learned that the Soka Gakkai is faced with an extremely volatile situation here in Brazil. Yesterday, I visited the Japan Cultural Association in São Paulo and met with a leader there who happens to be from Okayama Prefecture, where I was born. We were able to have a very frank conversation and he told me how the Brazilian secret police views the Gakkai.

"According to what he said, they think we are actually a political movement masking itself as a religious organization, and that your visit is in preparation for the establishment of a political party here. They see us as a dangerous organization that will undermine social order. That is why, while they are permitting the Brazilian members to hold meetings and other events, it is under strict surveillance, and they will not hesitate to make arrests if anything happens."

"How has this come about?" Shin'ichi asked.

"One reason is that around two-and-a-half years ago a famous US magazine published a highly prejudicial article on the Soka Gakkai. The Brazilian mass media accepted as true the magazine's claims that the Gakkai aims to take the world and published the same sort of stories here. It seems that the Brazilian government and police also believe those reports.

"In addition, various religions, including some of the established Buddhist schools from Japan, have already been introduced to Brazil, and a fair number of influential Japanese Brazilians associated with those schools regard us as an enemy. Apparently, it is they who have spread rumors among the authorities that we are allied with the communists and are an extremely dangerous organization."

On March 31, 1964, the civilian government of Brazil, led by President João Goulart, was toppled in a coup and taken over by a military junta. Castelo Branco, chief of staff of the army, then became the new president. While working to fight inflation and encourage Brazil's economic development, the new administration also adopted a strong anticommunist policy and placed harsh restrictions on freedom of speech, thought and political activities. Consequently, many intellectual and cultural figures in Brazilian society were driven into exile.

WHEN MEMBERS of the governing party suffered a substantial loss in gubernatorial elections held in Guanabara and other Brazilian states in October 1965, President Branco became increasingly dictatorial. He suspended all existing political parties and drafted a new constitution, changing the system of presidential election from national plebiscite to indirect voting.

This was part of the background behind the Brazilian government's sensitive reaction to the preposterous reports and false information that the Soka Gakkai was bent on world domination and what led to its tightened surveillance of the organization.

Brazil remained under military rule for twenty-one years, until a civilian government was finally reestablished in 1985.

When Shin'ichi heard Okada's account, he replied: "I see. Let's proceed cautiously but at the same time courageously." He then hung up the phone.

After he had communicated Okada's message to the other leaders, Shin'ichi said to Saiki: "The Brazilian organization has experienced tremendous growth and set sail on the great sea of kosen-rufu. It is only natural that it should be buffeted by strong winds and rough waves.

"The Gosho states: 'As practice progresses and understanding grows, the three obstacles and four devils emerge in confusing form, vying with one another to interfere' (WND, 770). Because the Brazilian members' faith has developed to the extent it has, it can be said that these obstacles have arisen according to plan."

It was true that the organization in Brazil had grown remarkably in recent years. At the start of 1965, just a year earlier, there were only twenty-five hundred member-households. By August there were fifty-six hundred and by the end of the year, sixty-eight hundred. The members' propagation efforts picked up even more steam, and in the last three months, from the beginning of 1966, twelve hundred member-households had joined, bringing the total to approximately eight thousand member-households.

Shin'ichi continued: "No matter what happens, we mustn't be afraid or cowardly. If the true value of the Soka Gakkai becomes known, our organization will definitely come to be highly praised and respected by the government and society at large. After all, only Buddhism can bring genuine prosperity and happiness to Brazil.

"The time for struggle is at hand. Let's advance into the storm. With earnest prayer, penetrating wisdom and determined action we can turn this situation around."

Mr. Saiki nodded as he listened to Shin'ichi, his eyes shining with firm resolve.

Shin'ichi then said in a powerful voice: "All right then, let's get to work! At present, every minute, every second, is worth months or even years. Let's start by sending a message of encouragement to the members rehearsing for the culture festival."

Shin'ichi began composing a message on the spot: "Thank you for all the hard work you have been putting into rehearsals. Please chant abundantly. And remember the importance of unity. If you work together, your success will be assured."

A LIGHT RAIN FELL as Shin'ichi arrived in Rio de Janeiro, a place he had long dreamed of visiting. But the next day, the clouds gradually cleared, and a bright summer sun began to shine in the sky.

Shin'ichi was scheduled to do some sightseeing around the city that day. Just as he was about to set out, however, a well-known Brazilian journalist turned up at the hotel and said he wished to interview President Yamamoto. The journalist had previously written an article for a Brazilian magazine criticizing the Soka Gakkai, and it had been filled with errors.

Hiroshi Izumida and Kiyoshi Jujo met with the journalist first, and they reported to Shin'ichi that he seemed to be seriously interested in finding out the truth about the Soka Gakkai.

"I'll meet with him then," Shin'ichi said. "We need to correct prejudices and misunderstandings toward the Soka Gakkai, and the way for us to do that is to speak with people directly. Through such efforts, we can eliminate anxiety and unnecessary apprehension and build trust in society. That's why it's important to actively reach out and meet with people."

The interview, which was conducted with the aid of an interpreter, began.

Shin'ichi greeted the journalist politely and said with a smile: "Please ask anything you wish. We are prepared to answer all of your questions so that you will gain a correct understanding of the Soka Gakkai. May I ask a question first, though?"

The journalist looked inquiringly at Shin'ichi and said, "Go ahead."

"I am wondering about the sources on which you based your previous report on the Soka Gakkai," Shin'ichi remarked. "The information contained in the article was far removed from the truth and many people who read it gained a false impression of our organization. Isn't it a journalist's responsibility to report the truth?"

Visibly taken aback, the journalist asked: "Was it that off the mark?"

Izumida leapt in: "It sure was. For example, you stated that our first president, Tsunesaburo Makiguchi, was arrested as a war criminal and died in prison, but nothing could be further from the truth. He was actually persecuted and died in prison for his beliefs as a result of his resistance to the military government, which was carrying out the war with State Shinto as its spiritual pillar."

IZUMIDA spoke rapidly and with some passion, but perhaps because of his personality, his tone remained friendly: "To call President Makiguchi a war criminal is to turn the situation completely on its head. Brazil may be located in the southern hemisphere on the opposite side of the world from Japan, but that's no excuse for confusing the truth so blatantly. There were many other grievous errors in your article as well."

The journalist looked at Shin'ichi and asked: "Is what he says true?"

"Yes," Shin'ichi replied.

With a serious expression, the journalist said: "If that's the case, I have made a grave mistake. I obtained my information from Japanese Brazilians who said they knew a lot about the Soka Gakkai. However, while involved with other Japanese religions, none of them were actually Soka Gakkai members. I also referred to books and materials on the Soka Gakkai they supplied me with, as well as the article featured in the US magazine that came out some time ago.

"I would have preferred to travel to Japan to interview members of your organization in person, but time constraints made that impossible. Then, when I heard of your visit to Rio de Janeiro, I thought it would be a good opportunity to speak with you, so I came to your hotel.

"But if my reporting contained misinformation that caused trouble for you, I am very sorry. I would like to write another article based on today's interview and introduce the Soka Gakkai to the Brazilian people correctly."

Sensing the sincerity of the journalist, who had admitted his error and apologized for it, Shin'ichi felt kindly toward him.

"Everyone makes mistakes," Shin'ichi said. "I'm glad you have recognized yours in this case. Shall we begin?"

The interview started with questions about the history of the Soka Gakkai and went on to cover various topics, including the organization's goals and principles. But what the journalist was most interested in was the relationship between the Soka Gakkai and the Clean Government Party. His questions hinted at the suspicion that the Gakkai was making plans to gain political control of governments around the world.

THE JOURNALIST asked Shin'ichi: "Can you tell me why the Soka Gakkai, a religious organization, has become involved in politics?"

Shin'ichi nodded and replied: "What is the purpose of religion? Leading people to happiness, bringing peace to the world and building a better society—this is religion's fundamental mission. Thus, a religion that is indifferent to and ignores people's suffering and the problems facing society must be called a dead religion.

"The Lotus Sutra, Buddhism's quintessential teaching, sets forth the way of compassion. It also elucidates that the life of the Buddha is inherent in all people and expounds the dignity and equality of life. The purpose of the Soka Gakkai is to put these Buddhist principles into practice in the spheres of culture and education, and indeed all realms of human endeavor, thereby contributing to the happiness and peace of humanity. Based on that thinking, we have encouraged members to enter the political realm and formed a political party."

Without pause, the journalist then asked: "Does that

mean that the Soka Gakkai seeks the unification of Nichiren Buddhism and the state—in other words, a union of government and religion?"

"No, it doesn't," Shin'ichi replied. "All governments require a firm political philosophy and political principles. Without them, they have no solid foundation and simply flow along passively with changing circumstances like driftweed; this only brings anxiety and suffering to the people. We founded the Clean Government Party with the aim of realizing a government with the Buddhist principles of compassion and respect for life as its basis.

"This is different, however, from direct religious involvement in government. The Clean Government Party is a political party that seeks to contribute to the well-being of the Japanese people as a whole, and a distinct line has been drawn between its operation and that of the Soka Gakkai. While both groups share the same fundamental goal of achieving peace and happiness for all humanity, their roles are different.

"Religion cultivates the soil of the human spirit. The rich vegetation that sprouts, blooms and bears fruit on that vast earth is culture in the broadest sense, and it includes government. We have tilled the spiritual soil and planted the seed for a tree, in other words, a political party. We intend to continue supporting it wholeheartedly in the future, but how it grows and the kind of fruit that it produces is ultimately up to the tree, the party, itself."

THE JOURNALIST then asked pointedly: "I gather from what you've said so far that you believe religion must by necessity concern itself with the political realm.

Does this mean you are planning on establishing a political party in Brazil?"

It seemed that this was the question he most wanted to ask.

With a smile, Shin'ichi Yamamoto replied: "When it comes to matters of faith, I am always ready to offer advice, but how Soka Gakkai members handle political issues in their respective countries is something they must discuss and decide amongst themselves. This is not something that I, as a Japanese citizen, could decide or mandate, and in fact I believe it would be wrong for me to do so. With that said, however, I personally don't think there is any need whatsoever for the Soka Gakkai to establish political parties in Brazil or any other country."

The reporter's next question came without a moment's hesitation and delved further into the matter: "Earlier you said that the purpose of religion is to build a better society. If that's the case, why isn't it necessary to establish political parties in other countries?"

"The social mission of practitioners of Buddhism is to create a better world, a better society," Shin'ichi responded. "And it is true that government deeply affects people's lives and plays a significant role in determining the direction of our societies. But this does not mean that as a religious organization we must unite politically and take such action as forming a political party.

"The aim of the Soka Gakkai is for its members to enrich and develop their lives and to achieve victory through their Buddhist practice. In other words, it is to enable people to develop their character as individuals so that they can realize genuine happiness. This is called human revolution.

"If we are to live happily as human beings, we must transform society in a positive direction. Toward that end, we of the Soka Gakkai strive to contribute to our communities as good citizens, based on personal convictions that derive from our religious faith. I believe that fostering such human character is one of the important roles of religion. It thus follows that in regard to politics, it is the responsibility of each Soka Gakkai member to take action in accord with his or her personal political beliefs with a view to creating a better society."

The reporter quickly fired off his next question: "Why, then, in Japan did you send Soka Gakkai members into politics and go on to form the Clean Government Party?"

THE QUESTION STRUCK to the very heart of the matter.

Shin'ichi's reply came in a strong tone: "There are several reasons for that, all of which are unique to the situation in Japan. One is the issue of Japan's military rearmament. After World War II, Japan made a new beginning with a constitution that renounced war. But at the urging of the United States, the country established a National Police Reserve, which later became the National Safety Forces, and then in 1954 the Self Defense Forces. The defense of the nation is an extremely important issue, but my mentor and second Soka Gakkai president Josei Toda was deeply concerned about this sudden rearmament of Japan.

"Despite the fact that Japan had in the past invaded other parts of Asia, it has never genuinely repented its military aggression. Under those circumstances, what would be the outcome of increasing the strength of Japan's armed forces? President Toda feared that the country might once again become a major military power and head in the wrong direction.

"President Toda also believed that, amid the Cold War's intensifying threat of nuclear weapons, it was the responsibility of Japan, as the only nation that had been the victim of a nuclear attack, to speak out against that threat and become a messenger of world peace. In order for Japan to rise to that role, he strongly felt that political leaders with a global consciousness—an awareness that we are all members of the same global community, which he called global citizenship—were indispensable.

"But the East-West rivalries of the Cold War were in fact brought into the Japanese political arena just as they were. The platforms of Japan's established political parties and the positions of its leaders all had a strong ideological coloring, yet no one exhibited a concern for humanity as a whole or upheld a genuine philosophy of peace."

The journalist's eyes shone as his pen raced across his notepad.

"In addition, while there were some parties in Japan at the time that protected the interests of the major industries and their owners, and other parties that supported the cause of unionized employees of big companies, there was no representation for the nonunionized workers of small factories and shops. But it was those people who were actually in the majority and who were forced to struggle the most.

"We believed that society would never truly prosper unless the government was made to benefit ordinary people and power was restored to their hands. With that in mind, President Toda proposed sending several of his disciples into the political arena by having them stand as candidates in the local elections of 1955. The following year, after much discussion, we supported candidates in the House of Councilors (Upper House) election. This was also the strong wish of a large majority of our members."

SHIN'ICHI continued: "Initially, the Soka Gakkai members who were elected to office didn't belong to any political party, and they carried out their activities as independents. They soon understood, however, that the reality of Japanese party politics did not afford them as independents the influence they needed to reflect the voice of the people in government.

"At the same time, public opinion strongly supported the establishment of a new political organization, which led to the formation of the Clean Government Political Federation and, from there, the Clean Government Party."

As if seeking confirmation, the reporter then inquired: "I understand the process through which you established a political party in Japan. Though I have already asked this, let me repeat my question once again: Your present trip to Brazil is not part of preparations to form a political party, then?"

"Absolutely not!" Shin'ichi declared.

Shin'ichi had answered all the journalist's questions cordially and directly. The course of the hour-and-a-half interview, the journalist began to smile and show approval of Shin'ichi's remarks. Before taking his leave, he said: "I think I understand your ideas and the Soka Gakkai's stance now. It seems I really did have a mistaken idea of your organization. I'm very glad to have had the chance to meet you today."

An article based on the interview later appeared in an influential Brazilian weekly magazine under the title "O Mundo Limpo do Senhor Yamamoto" (The Clean World of Mr. Yamamoto). It was an extremely objective piece of journalism, taking the form of a rebuttal to the criticism of the Soka Gakkai as fascist or somehow dangerous. Shin'ichi's points were presented accurately and the reality of the Gakkai was conveyed.

The truth must be spoken. If we remain silent, misunderstandings and prejudices will persist. In the end, such inaction is the same as accepting and even affirming falsehood.

After completing the interview, Shin'ichi was given a tour of Rio de Janeiro by some of the local members. Brazil's second largest city after São Paulo, Rio had flourished as the nation's capital from the time of its independence from Portugal in 1822 until the capital was transferred to Brasília in 1960.

Shin'ichi and his party drove to the top of Morro do Corcovado, from where they could enjoy a panoramic view of the city. After driving up the steep, winding road, they parked their cars and walked up to the observation spot at the very peak of the mountain.

SHIN'ICHI took a walk with Masatada and Misako Kono, the Rio de Janeiro chapter leader and chapter women's leader, asking them about their life in Brazil.

The couple became Soka Gakkai members in 1957 in

Shizuoka Prefecture. In July of 1960, Masatada, an engineer, was sent to live and work in Rio as a permanent resident by his employer, a ship manufacturer. His wife, Misako, and their children joined him there five months later. Before her departure, Misako visited the Soka Gakkai Headquarters to report that she would be leaving. At that time, she was able to meet with President Yamamoto, who had just returned from his first visit to Brazil.

Hearing the news that the Konos would be living in Rio de Janeiro, Shin'ichi said to Misako: "On my trip to Brazil I was told that there are no Gakkai members in Rio. That means that your family will be the first ones there. As long as you are going there, I hope you will become pioneers of kosen-rufu and establish a record of achievement that will endure forever. Do you think you can do that?"

"Absolutely," Misako replied enthusiastically.

"Such determination is crucial," Shin'ichi said. "I will be chanting for you with all my might. I'll definitely be going to Brazil again, so let's meet in Rio when I do."

Life began for the Konos in their new homeland. Since the couple could not speak Portuguese, the official language of Brazil, they sought out Japanese Brazilians to whom they could introduce Buddhism in Japanese. Eventually a number of people took faith, but unlike São Paulo, there were relatively few Japanese Brazilians in Rio, and very soon they had run out of people with whom they could share Buddhism.

In addition, many of the Japanese Brazilians who did live in Rio were workers on temporary assignment from Japan, so even if they did start practicing, after several years they would eventually return home. The Konos realized that if they were really going to advance kosen-rufu in Rio, they would have to expand their propagation efforts beyond Brazilians of Japanese descent. Somehow or other they had to introduce their faith to the wider community.

Neither dramatic growth nor future development can be achieved by merely repeating the methods of the past.

The Konos began to perceive that they could only make new advances through new ideas and new endeavors. They started studying Portuguese in earnest. Using gestures to supplement their limited vocabulary, they set about enthusiastically introducing Buddhism to the *Carioca*— the native residents of Rio de Janeiro.

THE KONOS' lives seemed to transform completely as they endeavored wholeheartedly each day to spread the Daishonin's teachings. Although they found it challenging to convey their message in Portuguese, they refused to be discouraged. They chanted strongly and made propagation efforts a part of their daily routine.

Before long, a number of people started learning to recite the sutra and as a result were able to overcome illness or break through financial difficulties. Seeing these new members joyfully turn their lives around inspired others to embrace faith as well. As the members came to understand what the Konos were trying to communicate in their broken Portuguese, some began interpreting it into language that was more readily accessible. In this way, a wide spectrum of Brazilians in Rio started practicing Nichiren Daishonin's Buddhism.

Morro do Corcovado rises 2,330 feet above sea level and on its summit is a towering statue of Christ with outstretched arms. The sculpture was built to commemorate the centennial of Brazilian independence in 1822, and was completed in 1931. Standing ninety-eight feet in height atop an twenty-eight-foot base, it is a world-renowned landmark.

From the mountain, Shin'ichi and his companions took in the grand view of Rio and Guanabara Harbor below. The cobalt sea seemed to embrace the city and its many tall buildings. In the distance, they could see a high, cragged cone-shaped peak on the tip of a cape jutting out into the water. It was the famous Pão de Açúcar or Sugar Loaf Mountain.

Commenting on the city's beauty, Shin'ichi turned to Masatada Kono and asked: "How many districts are there in Rio now?"

"We have 166 member-households in three districts

and ten groups," Masatada replied. "It's been five years since we arrived here, but I'm embarrassed to say that we haven't made much progress in our efforts to advance kosen-rufu."

He believed it was his family's responsibility to bring happiness to all the people of Rio de Janeiro, which was why he felt frustrated and disappointed that Rio had so few members compared to the thousands in São Paulo. The development of kosen-rufu depends on just such a sense of responsibility.

Shin'ichi smiled warmly as he spoke: "The growth you have achieved in a mere five years from a single household is truly wonderful. Your membership has increased 166 times! There's no need to be impatient."

A S THE HOT tropical sun burned brightly in the sky over Rio de Janeiro, Shin'ichi addressed both Mr. and Mrs. Kono: "To realize success in any endeavor takes time. At the bottom of this mountain, I noticed that a small sapling had been planted. In ten or twenty years, that sapling will grow into a tall tree. The organization here in Rio may be small now, but if you chant in earnest and work hard, it is certain to see tremendous development.

"The important thing is always to maintain your original determination and build a solid record of achievement in which each day is marked by advancement and personal victory without a single regret. In other words, it is important to continuously ask yourselves: 'What is my goal today?' 'What is my goal right now?' and to challenge yourselves resolutely and take action.

"This is what is meant by the Lotus Sutra passages: 'At all times I think to myself: / How can I cause living beings

/ to gain entry into the unsurpassed way / and quickly acquire the body of a Buddha?' (LS 16, 232) and 'I have never for a moment neglected [the Buddha's work]' (LS 16, 226). That is to say, the ceaseless struggle for kosen-rufu is in itself the noble practice of carrying out the Buddha's work and the way to absolute happiness.

"The future of this beautiful city of Rio de Janeiro rests on your shoulders. Let us strive together to create a golden new page of history!"

The Konos voiced their firm commitment to that goal.

When Shin'ichi visited Brazil for the third time eighteen years later, membership in Rio de Janeiro had increased to six thousand member-households.

When Shin'ichi returned to the hotel from his tour of the city, reporters from several newspapers were waiting to interview him. Because Shin'ichi had some writing to complete, it was decided that Hiroshi Izumida and Kiyoshi Jujo would meet with the reporters in his stead. Having observed the way Shin'ichi interacted with the journalist earlier, they were able to respond to the reporters' questions with confidence.

During a meeting later that evening, Izumida said to Shin'ichi: "The fact that those journalists visited us at the hotel means that the police are aware of our activities and watching us. Maybe we should change our schedule."

The leaders all looked at Shin'ichi, waiting for him to speak.

"What need is there to do that?" he asked. "It's of course important to be cautious, but we're not doing anything wrong, so let's just proceed with our schedule as planned. Besides, to make changes at this point is only likely to rouse suspicion."

SHIN'ICHI sensed that the leaders accompanying him were feeling uneasy. His voice was forceful as he said: "You must never allow the immediate situation to make you lose sight of essential matters. If you do, you cannot be called a leader. The most important thing right now is how we can encourage the Brazilian members and enable them to develop great conviction in Nichiren Buddhism.

"If the roots of faith are strong and deep in our lives, even the most powerful winds of opposition will not topple us. But if those roots are weak, we will be felled by the slightest breeze. The key to realizing great victory in any endeavor is to stand up, to struggle and to win based on faith.

"Tomorrow we'll be in São Paulo. That is where our real struggle begins!" Shin'ichi declared decisively.

The leaders felt a strong fighting spirit in Shin'ichi's voice. He was so energetic that it seemed impossible he had been suffering from a high fever just a few days before.

Izumida thought to himself: *President Yamamoto's firm resolve to protect the members in Brazil has driven out the devil of illness. This is without a doubt the determination of a leader of kosen-rufu!*

On the following day, March 12, Shin'ichi's visit to Brazil was given extensive coverage in several Rio de Janeiro newspapers. It seemed that the reporters had gained a correct understanding of the organization through their direct contact with Soka Gakkai representatives, as their articles were free of prejudice or criticism.

When Shin'ichi was informed of this by Yasuhiro Saiki, the South America Headquarters leader, he said to those accompanying him: "If you meet with people, you can promote mutual understanding. From now on, let us all take every opportunity possible to convey the greatness of our cause to the world."

At half past ten that morning, when Shin'ichi and his party arrived at the airport, the flight that was scheduled to take off before theirs was still on the ground. Learning that there were some empty seats on that flight, they decided to take it instead. The journey to São Paulo from Rio took about fifty minutes. Most likely because they reached São Paulo's Congonias Airport earlier than planned, there were no journalists and hardly any members there to meet them. Shin'ichi did notice, however, three men in suits standing behind a pillar a little distance away, watching them intently. They were officers of the secret police.

WHEN SHIN'ICHI and his group arrived at their hotel in São Paulo, they held a meeting to discuss the expansion of the Brazilian organization and then went to view the buildings that Yasuhiro Saiki had proposed for a new Soka Gakkai community center and temple.

In São Paulo, there was already a South America Community Center. The decision to establish this center had been made in August 1964 and it opened in January of the following year. But the building was a rented private home and the largest room could hold only forty or fifty people at most. This made it too small to serve as the main center of the Brazilian organization, which now had more than eight thousand member-households, and so the purchase of new facilities was being considered.

Later that day, Shin'ichi went to the South America Community Center to interview prospective leaders for

newly created positions and to attend a local leaders meeting. At that meeting, he announced the organization's latest developments as well as the new leadership lineup and
personnel appointments, saying: "Until now Brazil has had
one general chapter, but with the increased membership
I would like to propose splitting the present general chapter into three. What do you think?"

A hearty round of applause, expressing everyone's
approval, filled the room. Shin'ichi then began to introduce the personnel appointments.

Mr. Saiki was appointed leader of General Chapter No.
1, and Aoi Chida was appointed to General Chapter No.
2 leader as well as South America Headquarters young
men's division leader. Chida had been sent to Brazil from
the Soka Gakkai Headquarters in Japan to serve as the
administrative officer for the South America Headquarters in November 1964.

Women's division leaders were also appointed, as were
leaders to the newly established young men's and young
women's divisions in each of the three new general chapters. In addition, seven new chapters, including Brasília and
Itatiba, were created.

Shin'ichi then announced the acquisition of the buildings that would serve as the new community center and
temple: "I understand that many members have expressed
a wish for a larger community center as well as a temple.
Today I visited the buildings that have been proposed for
that purpose. I would like to take this opportunity to
inform you that after serious consideration, we have decided to make the purchase. The lot is seventy-nine hundred square feet and is located in a residential area near the

São Paulo city center. It has two buildings, the larger of which has two stories. The other is situated at the back of the lot. The larger building will become the new South America Headquarters, and one of the rooms inside will house temple facilities."

The leaders applauded excitedly.

REFERRING to the Buddhist principle that earthly desires are enlightenment, Shin'ichi stated that although our lives may be filled with suffering and hardship, genuine happiness can be found through our efforts to challenge and overcome every obstacle based on faith. He also emphasized that faith is a struggle against the devilish forces that seek to cause us suffering and to obstruct our practice of Buddhism.

Shin'ichi was determined to enable the members to establish a core of unshakable faith deep in their lives. He continued: "The Daishonin clearly states that when we exert ourselves earnestly in accord with the correct teaching and work for kosen-rufu, the three obstacles and four devils are certain to arise and challenge us. This is comparable to the air resistance and turbulence an airplane experiences as it takes flight and makes its ascent. It follows that if we become fearful and retreat halfway through, we will never reach our goal. On the other hand, if we boldly continue our advance, just as an airplane reaches cruising altitude, we will without a doubt soar powerfully into the future.

"The Daishonin states: 'Something uncommon also occurs when an ordinary person attains Buddhahood. At such a time, the three obstacles and four devils will invariably appear, and the wise will rejoice while the foolish will retreat' (WND, 637). By persevering in faith through every obstacle and battling against the devilish functions, we can transform our karma and achieve a state of absolute happiness.

"In other words, to struggle against hardship is the direct path to our personal development and elevating our state of life. It is a springboard that leads to our human revolution. Life and faith are like an obstacle race. Overcoming each obstacle is a source of joy.

"I hope all of you will stand up courageously as true disciples of Nichiren Daishonin!"

This was Shin'ichi's sincerest hope, his earnest prayer and his heartfelt call.

"At any rate, the foundations of faith are chanting Nam-myoho-renge-kyo, reciting the sutra and participating in Soka Gakkai activities. They are like the rotation of earth on its axis and its revolution around the sun. Just as these two actions combined make up the earth's motion, the practice for oneself that consists of chanting and the practice for others that takes the form of spirited Gakkai activities together result in the establishment of a happy life and a peaceful and prosperous society.

"I would like to close my remarks today by expressing my hope that you will persist in faith valiantly throughout your lives undaunted by anything."

Everyone applauded vigorously. Shin'ichi's guidance struck a chord deep in the hearts of the members, who were all aware that Brazil's military government regarded the Soka Gakkai as a dangerous organization. It filled them with solid determination.

ON MARCH 12, the Kyodo News Service distributed an article datelined from São Paulo stating that the activities of the Soka Gakkai in various Latin American nations were regarded as a social problem. The article reported the arrival of President Yamamoto and other Soka Gakkai leaders in São Paulo, relating that the Brazilian secret police, the military and leading intellectuals were suspicious that the organization was a political association masquerading as a religious group and therefore considered it ill-suited to Brazilian society. The article also said that on March 8 the secret police had presented the Japanese consul general with a document containing forty-two questions concerning the Soka Gakkai.

It further stated that not only in Brazil, but in other Latin American countries as well, public concern about the Gakkai was growing, with some sources going as far as to predict that in the next five or six years the Clean Government Party would control Japan's cabinet and an ultra-nationalist government such as existed during World War II would be revived.

The article, published in several regional Japanese newspapers on March 14, enraged Soka Gakkai members. At a district planning meeting in Kanagawa Prefecture, the issue of the article's content came under discussion. One women's division member remarked: "It's absurd to say that a Clean Government Party cabinet would result in an extreme rightist government of the kind that existed under Japan's wartime military regime. How can a political party that upholds democracy and whose slogan is to speak with the people, to fight for the people and to die among the people ever be called rightist?"

A young men's division member then said: "Exactly. Wasn't the Soka Gakkai, which founded the Clean Government Party, the very group that upheld the freedom of religion and directly challenged the oppression of the military government during the war? And our first president Makiguchi even died in prison for those beliefs!"

Nodding, a men's division member added: "The Soka Gakkai has always striven to realize world peace. In his Declaration for the Abolition of Nuclear Weapons, President Toda proclaimed that in order to protect the basic human right to life, no nation could ever be permitted to use nuclear arms. He initiated a movement that championed the idea of nuclear disarmament.

"The Clean Government Party is working to establish those ideals in the realm of government. One can only assume that those who claim it is a right-wing organization are completely blinded by prejudice."

Hearing this, a young women's division member commented: "And now President Yamamoto has gone to Brazil to encourage the members there. Is it really safe for him to be there?"

A women's division member then said: "That's why we must chant. Let's chant earnestly for the safety of President Yamamoto and all the members in Brazil. That's the only thing we can do."

MARCH 13, the day after Shin'ichi's arrival in São Paulo, was the day of the South America Culture Festival. It was scheduled to begin at three o'clock in the afternoon. As Shin'ichi and the others made their way from the hotel to the venue, the São Paulo Municipal Theater, they were followed by a few tough-looking men who kept a close eye on them. These men were obviously members of the secret police.

Photographers from the press were lined up in front of the theater, and when Shin'ichi and his party arrived, there was a burst of flashlights. Police officers were stationed at the theater entrance, scrutinizing each person who entered. The atmosphere was tense and threatening as if martial law were in effect.

Nobuhiro Uda, who had been appointed the young men's division leader of South America No. 3 General Chapter at the leaders meeting the previous day and who was accompanying Shin'ichi as his interpreter, addressed the officer who appeared to be in charge, asking: "Why are there so many police officers here? The Soka Gakkai isn't doing anything wrong, and it isn't a dangerous group. This is outrageous!"

Glaring at Uda, the officer replied harshly: "We're here to provide security so that your meeting proceeds safely. After all, President Yamamoto is said to be an important man who is going to rule the world some day."

It was clear, however, from his contemptuous and bearing attitude that providing security was not their real concern.

When Uda then protested, "We didn't ask for any police protection!" the officer responded with a thin smile, saying, "Do you have a problem with our being here?"

Shin'ichi remained unperturbed. Smiling at the youth division members who were working as event staff as well as at the police officers standing behind them, he called out to everyone: "Thank you for your assistance! Thank you!" and ascended the stairs.

He had prepared himself for anything. Believing that persecution incurred for the sake of kosen-rufu was a badge of honor, he was ready to be unjustly arrested if necessary. He was completely unafraid.

Shin'ichi was determined to do everything he could to protect the Brazilian members. As they entered the theater, he spoke to Uda softly, trying to calm him down: "I know you must be angry, Mr. Uda, but you mustn't become emotional. The slightest mistake on our part might offer them the perfect excuse to crack down on us."

AS UDA SHOOK with anger. Shin'ichi gently chided him: "Mr. Toda often used to say, 'Don the armor of endurance.' This means enduring insult and other such attacks. It's important to be patient now. What matters is that we triumph ten years or twenty years down the road."

"I understand," Uda said, looking straight at Shin'ichi as tears welled up in his eyes.

Uda was a hardworking young man with a strong sense of justice. He was a second-generation Japanese Brazilian and the eldest son of six children in his family. His father immigrated to Brazil as a youth of nineteen, and his mother had come when she was an infant. Aside from being taught the Japanese syllabaries by his grandfather, Uda grew up speaking Portuguese and knew hardly any Japanese.

Uda's father had joined the Soka Gakkai first, in 1961. He had taken faith when the plantation he had built by cultivating a tract of forest was hit with financial difficulties and he was forced to give up his livelihood.

Uda decided to try practicing himself after observing his father, who had grown terribly depressed and had lost all hope for the future because of these dire circumstances, become more vibrant with each passing day through chanting. He was among the first non-Japanese-speaking second-generation Japanese Brazilians to join the Soka Gakkai. Before long, he started to participate in Gakkai activities, but the fact that most of the published materials were in Japanese was a major stumbling block for him.

In May 1965, a Portuguese-language Soka Gakkai journal titled *Nova Era* began publication, and Uda became its editor. He attempted to translate Nichiren Daishonin's writings and President Yamamoto's guidance into Portuguese, but was deeply chagrined at not being able to understand Japanese sufficiently to do so on his own.

In August of this same year, with a strong seeking spirit toward Buddhism burning in his heart, Uda had attended a summer training course at the head temple in Japan. But no matter how intently he listened to the Japanese leaders' guidance, he couldn't understand what they were saying. When he was called on to read aloud during a study session, it was all he could do to skip over the Chinese characters, which were beyond his comprehension, and read the phonetic syllabary in between. The other members praised his halted reading, knowing that the young man had come all the way from Brazil, but Uda was frustrated and dissatisfied with himself.

THE MORNING after the study session, Uda was still brooding. During his free time that day, he took a walk around the head temple grounds.

I have an important responsibility to produce the Brazil Soka Gakkai journal, he thought. *The job requires mastery of Japanese. But I can't even understand the guidance being given or read the Daishonin's writings. Japanese is a difficult language. It's too difficult. The enormous responsibility of editing the Brazilian journal may simply be too much for me.*

Just as he was pondering these thoughts, someone tapped him on the shoulder.

"Why, it's Mr. Uda from Brazil!" a voice said. When Uda turned around, Shin'ichi was standing there.

The day before, Shin'ichi had offered encouragement to the overseas members attending the summer training course and shaken each person's hand. At that time, he had made a point of memorizing Uda's face and name.

"Sensei," Uda said, deeply moved that President Yamamoto had remembered him. He went on to share everything he was feeling in his broken Japanese.

Shin'ichi nodded sympathetically as he listened and then said briefly: "You can do it. Just don't give up! Don't be defeated! You are a pioneer of kosen-rufu in Brazil!"

Shin'ichi's warm and confident words caused Uda's worry to evaporate and he felt a surge of courage. Hot tears flowed from his eyes. Shin'ichi then grasped his hand and said: "Please realize tremendous growth. I'll be waiting for you."

Uda clasped Shin'ichi's hand tightly and made a vow to himself: "I will overcome this language barrier no matter what it takes and work to open the path of kosen-rufu for the rest of my life."

After returning to Brazil, Uda began studying Japanese single-mindedly. He would ask one of the members who understood Japanese to help him pronounce all the words in a Soka Gakkai publication and then he would read and reread it dozens of times. Even if he didn't know the words' meanings, he memorized their pronunciation first. Later he would learn their definitions and study them word by word. Often when studying at night, he would become so absorbed that he would continue right through until morning, without realizing the passing of time.

In this way, Uda's Japanese-language ability improved tremendously in just a few months time and he was assigned to interpret for President Yamamoto on his visit to Brazil in 1966.

THE MUNICIPAL THEATER, the venue for the South America Culture Festival, was a time-honored building, which had been the site of performances by international opera and ballet troupes. The intricately carved hand railings and pillars decorating its interior added to the theater's dignified and elegant atmosphere.

By around half past two in the afternoon, thirty minutes before the festival was scheduled to begin, the hall was filled to capacity with some seventeen hundred Soka Gakkai members from throughout Brazil and numerous guests, who included representatives of the São Paulo Japanese Cultural Association and members of the press.

After Shin'ichi took his seat on the theater balcony, he looked around and saw several police officers in uniform as well as plainclothes officers of the secret police stationed throughout the hall. The culture festival would be conducted under heavy police surveillance. Rather than a disadvantage, however, to Shin'ichi this seemed an excellent opportunity for the government agents to witness firsthand what the Soka Gakkai was really about.

The culture festival soon commenced, with emcees speaking in both Japanese and Portuguese. When the curtain rose, the Fife and Drum Corps began to play. In their red and white uniforms and berets, the young women seemed like figures out of a children's fairy tale. Their sweet charm brought a sigh of delight to many in the audience.

The Brass Band performed next, gallant in their pristine white uniforms. This was followed by a chorus of women's division members in exquisite green dresses and then a modern dance performance by members of the young women's division. Holding large floral rings, the young women moved rhythmically to the strains of Tchaikovsky's *The Waltz of the Flowers,* transforming the stage into a gorgeous flower garden. The audience gasped in wonder at the colorful spectacle.

This piece had actually been the most challenging part of the program. Though the choreography required a considerable degree of skill, most of the performers had little experience. Two days before the festival, they were having trouble synchronizing their steps and the routine hadn't come together. The leaders didn't know what to do. But the choreographer who had been brought in to instruct the dancers, while not a member, was firmly confident that the performance would be a success.

She declared: "Your performance is going to be a great success. Individually you may not be experienced dancers, but because you are all eager to have President Yamamoto see your performance and are determined to do your best, you are certain to create strong unity, and in the end the dance will be magnificent. Your passion will overcome all difficulties."

And just as she predicted, the dance performance by the young women's division members drew rousing applause.

NEXT was a Japanese dance titled "Seasons" performed by members of the women's division. The dancers held cherry-blossom branches as they conveyed the mood of spring to the sounds of the koto, while that of summer was performed to the *shamisen* (a traditional Japanese stringed instrument). The audience applauded enthusiastically for this refined expression of the spirit of the seasons.

Young women's division members then presented a ballet, leaping through the air like beautiful snow fairies. This was followed by a stirring choral performance by the young men's division. The festival came to a close after an hour-and-a-half with a grand finale of Soka Gakkai songs passionately sung by all the performers.

Shin'ichi leaned forward in his seat and gazed at each of the performers as he clapped in rhythm to the music. Amid busy daily routines and straitened financial circumstances, they had done their utmost to attend rehearsals and prepare for the culture festival. Determined to communicate the essence of Buddhism and the true spirit of the Soka Gakkai through their performances, these ordinary people had been able to create a historic production flowing with joy.

The performers' faces glistened with tears. Each person was filled with confidence and pride, their eyes aglow with the exultation of total victory.

Deeply moved, one guest remarked that though the performers were amateurs, their presentation was equal to any professional show.

Shin'ichi gave the performers a standing ovation. Seeing this, everyone on stage cheered and waved. Shin'ichi waved back and then bowed deeply to the performers as well as the audience before taking his leave.

As he exited the hall, Shin'ichi said to Yasuhiro and Setsuko Saiki: "Congratulations! It was really a wonderful culture festival. Let's do it again. On a scale of one to one hundred, I'd give today's performance ninety-eight points. It was a great success."

Shin'ichi's reason for not giving the festival a perfect score had nothing to do with the performance itself. It was to inspire the members to strive even harder the next time.

When he entered the theater lobby, Shin'ichi addressed the secret police officer who had been keeping an eye on him all day: "I appreciate how busy you are and am profoundly grateful for your efforts today. Were you able to see the festival?"

Nobuhiro Uda interpreted Shin'ichi's remarks for the officer, who, clearly taken aback by this unexpectedly sincere greeting, said: "Well, yes, I was. Thank you. Thank you very much." And he made a slight bow.

AFTER LEAVING the municipal theater, Shin'ichi headed for the Pacaembu Gymnasium, about ten minutes away by car. Five thousand members, filled with youthful vigor, had joyfully gathered there and were awaiting Shin'ichi's arrival. The municipal theater was an old, distinguished building, but it had a capacity of less than two thousand. This meant that with the culture festival alone, only a limited number of members would have the chance to meet Shin'ichi.

Realizing this, Yasuhiro Saiki and other Brazilian leaders discussed the matter and decided to rent the spacious Pacaembu Gymnasium to hold another meeting that Shin'ichi would attend after the performance. When Saiki informed him of this plan, Shin'ichi said: "I definitely want to meet as many of the members as possible. I'll be glad to participate."

The Pacaembu Gymnasium was also under strict police surveillance. Police officers surrounded the building and were positioned here and there inside as well. When Shin'-ichi arrived at the gymnasium, cheers and thunderous applause rang out from the waiting members.

Saiki was the first to take the podium. His voice rang with excitement as he called out: "President Yamamoto has just come here from the culture festival! The festival was a great success. All of the performances were superb and drew enthusiastic applause and cheers from the audience. This is all due to your strong unity and support. Thank you very much!"

Jujo and other leaders who had accompanied Shin'ichi from Japan offered brief remarks, and then Shin'ichi quietly stepped up to the microphone. "I am so happy to see you all in such good health and spirits," he said. "I have just come from viewing the culture festival. It was a wonderful event, and I was deeply and sincerely impressed by the tremendous growth and development of the organization here in Brazil.

"I am sorry that, because of the theater's size, only a limited number of members could attend the festival. As I wasn't able to deliver a speech there, however, I have come here to speak to you all instead. I hope that makes everything fair. What do you think?"

The members' laughter, cheers and applause filled the gymnasium with an atmosphere of warm camaraderie.

THE MEMBERS listened intently, their eyes shining with strong seeking spirit.

"I'm only thirty-eight years old," Shin'ichi said. "I am far too inexperienced to be your president, so I deeply appreciate your support. The Soka Gakkai is an organization of members who are all equally striving in earnest to practice Buddhism in accord with the Daishonin's teachings. While I am the president, I am not a prophet. I am just an ordinary youth.

"What, then, is the guidance offered by the Soka Gakkai? In short, it is to continue chanting to the Gohonzon, polish oneself, attain genuine happiness and make positive contributions to society. This guidance is not something I alone uphold. It is also followed by Mr. Izumida, Mr. Jujo, Mr. Saiki and every other leader of the Soka Gakkai. It is the shared ideal and goal of every member of our organization.

"Basing ourselves entirely on the teachings of Nichiren Daishonin, we encourage each other and work together to develop ourselves as we aim to achieve our personal human revolution. I wish to declare that we are the most democratic of organizations."

A vigorous round of applause shook the gymnasium once again.

Shin'ichi continued, pouring his whole life into his speech, as if directly addressing the secret police and the Brazilian government: "There are religions that try to milk their followers for all their money and property and force them to blindly serve the leader as if they were slaves. But religion originally exists for the sake of human beings. Human beings are the driving force for creating prosperous societies and achieving world peace.

"Nichiren Buddhism teaches the path of human revolution that enables each individual to shine as bright as the sun and to illuminate their family, society and the world with the light of hope and happiness. How can we create a flourishing society? How can we realize peace for future generations? I am convinced that if world leaders are seriously concerned about these questions, they cannot help but take note of the Soka Gakkai, a religious organization committed to human revolution."

It was a bold declaration made while under full view of the police. Just as lion cubs are roused by the roar of the lion, Shin'ichi's call stirred a wave of passion and courage in the members' hearts. The sight of Shin'ichi at this moment brought to the minds of Izumida, Kiyohara and the other pioneer leaders present memories of first Soka Gakkai president Tsunesaburo Makiguchi resolutely advocating the validity of Buddhism under the surveillance of Japan's special higher police during World War II.

SHIN'ICHI then announced the Soka Gakkai's purchase of buildings that would serve as a new community center and temple facilities, and that Brazilian marble would be used in the construction of the Grand Main Temple in Japan.

"I hope that you will all become people of great fortune and ability so that you can travel all over the world and come to Japan to participate in the opening ceremonies of the Grand Main Temple as well as to attend general meetings held in Tokyo," he continued. "Please attain a state of complete freedom and happiness."

"The purpose of this faith is for each of us to become happy. I think that Soka Gakkai members have a responsibility to become living proof of this goal and be able to proclaim their unsurpassed happiness. Do you agree?"

"Yes!" the members replied, applauding heartily.

"So how do we go about achieving such a state of happiness?" Shin'ichi then asked. "We do so by carrying out our faith patiently and consistently. We need to chant abundantly. By chanting Nam-myoho-renge-kyo, the fundamental Law of the universe, we can realize happiness for ourselves and others.

"It follows that, for the sake of our own selves as well as for our families and communities, persisting courageously in faith is the way leading to an upright and prosperous life. The path of faith, however, is by no means smooth. There are steep hills to climb, and storms to endure. But whatever happens, I hope you will not be defeated. This is how we demonstrate actual proof of faith. If you allow yourself to be defeated, you'll only end up miserable. It is in the victory achieved through faith that the truth of life and absolute happiness are found.

"I hope that you will create an organization of solid unity here in Brazil so that all of you, without a single exception, can attain happiness. The journey of kosen-rufu is long. I therefore also hope that you will make your organization a realm of wonderful, enjoyable faith. I will continue to pray earnestly every day for your brave struggle and good health. Please take care of yourselves and live long, healthy lives! Thank you so much for coming today!"

Joyous applause resounded throughout the auditorium. The members clapped vigorously. Some had tears in their eyes, while others cheered. The majority of the participants were meeting Shin'ichi for the first time. They had all prayed single-mindedly for his visit to Brazil and waited eagerly for this day, this moment.

The members rose to their feet and stood on their toes, craning to see Shin'ichi exit the auditorium. They wanted to engrave his image deep in their hearts. Their applause continued without end.

THE CULTURE festival and the meeting that followed it were given coverage in local Japanese-language and other newspapers. While some of the stories were objective and accurate, more than a few were filled with errors and prejudice.

One headline blared, "A Religion Set on Conquering the World Arrives in São Paulo." The text of the article read: "About two thousand participants gathered at the municipal theater. While most of the followers were of Japanese descent, about seven hundred of them were native Brazilians. The men wore white uniforms with black shoes and neckties, while the women wore green. Together they sang the Soka Gakkai's 'Song of the New Century.' After listening to a speech from their president, their absolute leader and prophet, they marched off the stage."

The men and women who were described as if they were wearing strange uniforms in this innuendo-filled article were simply the choral groups that performed in the culture festival. Though Shin'ichi Yamamoto had not spoken at the festival, it further reported that he had given a speech, and created the impression that the audience then marched out into the streets.

The article also erroneously stated: "The religion he [President Yamamoto] founded in 1946 is regarded as an extreme right-wing group and its young male followers are organized in a militarist fashion resembling the Hitler youth."

On the morning of March 14, Hiroshi Izumida came into Shin'ichi's room carrying the article. He was trembling with rage. "Sensei!" he said. "I just had this translated. This newspaper has published a terribly unfair article about us!"

When Shin'ichi heard what the article reported, he chuckled and remarked: "Some think that the Soka Gakkai is a communist organization, and now we're being called an extreme rightist group. Mr. Makiguchi always used to say, 'Never judge something you don't know anything about.' It is certainly true that ignorance is the cause of mistaken judgments. If one doesn't really know the facts, one is likely to blindly accept unfounded rumors and propaganda, jump to conclusions and harbor groundless fears and misgivings.

"Such fears and misgivings can sometimes turn into an extremely aggressive response. It seems that this is what is happening with regard to the Brazilian secret police and the mass media's attitude toward us now. But I am confident that their viewpoint and actions will change completely once we have conveyed a correct understanding of the Soka Gakkai to them."

SHIN'ICHI added emphatically: "It's an ongoing battle."

This remark hit home for Izumida. He realized that in the depths of his mind he had assumed that after talking to the reporters in Rio de Janeiro about the Soka Gakkai everything would be all right.

I was negligent, he thought to himself. *I should have taken action to inform the local press about the Gakkai as soon as we arrived in São Paulo. Now is our chance to eradicate the ignorant criticism of the media. Every moment is crucial. The slightest complacency could cost us the opportunity to turn the situation around forever.*

Izumida said to Shin'ichi apologetically: "I was careless. Precisely because the situation is so serious here in São Paulo, I and the others should have taken the initiative to meet with journalists while you were engaged in your activities."

"Yes," Shin'ichi said. "Making various people aware of the truth is no easy matter. It requires the perseverance needed to irrigate a desert. While you are watering the sand on your right, the left dries out, and while you water to the left, the right dries out. The point is to continue watering with unswerving patience.

"It can also be compared to waves eroding a rocky shore—another action that takes time and perseverance.

"Similarly, without patience, you cannot change people's outlooks. I'll always stand in the forefront of such efforts with you."

That day, Shin'ichi had held a press conference with a United Press International reporter who had come from New York, as well as reporters from a number of local newspapers. As usual, their questions centered on the Soka Gakkai's political activities. Some of the journalists listened to Shin'ichi's remarks with skeptical sneers, while others asked blatantly hostile questions. Shin'ichi nevertheless spoke with complete sincerity and earnestness, wanting to eliminate misunderstanding and destroy prejudice.

The contents of that meeting with journalists were published in several newspapers, including the Japanese-language press, on March 15, the following day. With headlines that read: "A Philosophical Religion Aiming for Peace and Stability for Humanity" and "Tolerant of Other Religions," the articles presented Shin'ichi's words objectively and without bias.

After the press conference, Setsuko Saiki gave Shin'ichi, his wife, Mineko, and the other leaders from Japan a tour of São Paulo. One of their stops was the famous Butantan

Institute, where research on snakebite antivenins was conducted. When Shin'ichi had visited the Amami Oshima Islands in the south of Japan three years earlier, he was told of the danger faced by the locals because of the islands' large population of venomous *habu* snakes. He hoped he might learn something useful at the institute.

ON THEIR WAY back to the hotel after sightseeing in São Paulo, Shin'ichi and the others went with Setsuko Saiki to her home for a visit. Shin'ichi wanted to learn more about the lives of Setsuko and her husband, who were leading the kosen-rufu movement in South America. The Saikis lived in an apartment in a residential area near the São Paulo city center. Sipping the green tea that Setsuko had prepared, Shin'ichi asked about her and her family's life in Brazil.

At first Setsuko humorously told of her struggles to speak

Portuguese and other difficulties she and her husband faced as new immigrants, but when the topic shifted to the culture festival of the previous day, tears filled her eyes. Dabbing at them with a handkerchief, she bowed her head and said: "I apologize sincerely, Sensei. I am sure you are worn out from being constantly watched by the police, not only at the culture festival but wherever you have gone. I'd also like to thank you for the many long hours you have spent with journalists for the sake of the Brazilian members."

Setsuko, an honest and pure-hearted individual, was deeply distressed by the relentless police surveillance Shin'ichi and the rest of his party had been subjected to since their arrival in São Paulo. Time and again she had wanted to lash out at the police and declare: "President Yamamoto has done nothing wrong! The reason he has come all the way to São Paulo is to open a path to happiness and peace. Why are the police harassing such a person?"

But when she considered the matter, she realized that this had all happened because she and the other local leaders had failed to give Brazilian society a clear understanding of the Soka Gakkai, and her anger was directed right back at herself. She reproached her own ineptness and blamed herself for the entire situation. Furthermore, she felt deeply sorry and apologetic that President Yamamoto had to personally take on the media—agreeing to meet with journalists and answering a barrage of hostile questions—in order to change their perception of the Soka Gakkai.

Shin'ichi was perfectly aware of Setsuko's feelings. He said to her: "I came here to protect our Brazilian members and to lay the groundwork for kosen-rufu in this country. That is my role and my responsibility. There's absolutely no need to be worried or concerned about me."

WITH FIRM determination, Shin'ichi continued: "It would be my fortune to be killed while on the journey of kosen-rufu. Encountering persecutions and being imprisoned for the sake of the Law are sources of great pride. I came here completely prepared for such a turn of events. I'm not afraid of anything.

"My only concern is how I can protect you, the Brazilian members. All I care about is that you are able to continue doing your best without abandoning your faith, even in the face of persecution, and that all of you can advance courageously and come out triumphant. I will be happy if you are able to remain undaunted and become victors in life. I'm not in the least worried about what happens to me personally."

Setsuko felt the warmth of the sun in Shin'ichi's words. She was deeply moved by his profound compassion. Once again tears filled her eyes. But then she lifted her head resolutely and declared: "Sensei, we won't be defeated. We will definitely transform Brazil into a bountiful land of happiness that is a model for global kosen-rufu! Please wait and see."

Shin'ichi smiled and nodded at Setsuko's impassioned resolve. "Yes," he said. "That's the spirit. Thank you. Single-minded determination is the key. Buddhism has the power to move even the universe, so if the Brazilian members pray and strive in earnest, the situation here is sure to change dramatically.

"The air is cleared after heavy rains, and kites are lifted

high into the sky by strong winds. In the same way, we are strengthened by persecutions and our efforts to surmount them result in tremendous advancement for kosen-rufu. You may feel frustrated and angry by the harsh treatment of the Soka Gakkai by the authorities in your country, but depending upon the way you deal with the situation, you can create the cause for great progress and victory.

"The Daishonin states: 'Though misfortune may occur, we can transform it into a blessing' (GZ, 979). Those who struggle against persecution will win in the end. At the same time, there's no need to be impatient. The outcome will be apparent twenty or thirty years from now, or in the twenty-first century. A wonderful future lies ahead for Brazil!"

A bright smile lit up Setsuko's face.

That day, Shin'ichi ignited the flame of kosen-rufu in the heart of one woman, Setsuko Saiki. It may have been a small flame, but in the fierce winds of opposition blowing across the vast land of Brazil, it would blaze up brilliantly and spread from the heart of one member to another.

THE NEXT DAY, March 15, Shin'ichi was scheduled to leave Brazil and fly to Lima, Peru. Yasuhiro and Setsuko Saiki would accompany him. Their flight wasn't until 10:20 AM but since it was departing from Viracopos Airport, about sixty miles from central São Paulo, the group left the hotel by car at half past seven.

The roads were empty, and they arrived at the airport with plenty of time before their scheduled departure. Shin'ichi devoted the extra time to speaking with the

Saikis as well as the dozen or so members who had come to see him and his party off at the airport. Scattered throughout the lobby were people who were obviously plainclothes officers of the secret police intent on listening in on their conversations. But Shin'ichi paid no attention to them and said to Yasuhiro Saiki: "I am looking forward to the next culture festival in Brazil."

"We will do our best to work toward that goal," Yasuhiro replied. Standing next to him, his wife, Setsuko, added: "We will achieve such development that when you next visit our country, you'll be surprised at how much it has changed."

"Your determination is wonderful," Shin'ichi said. "The real driving force to change the times are the prayers of women and their activities that are deeply rooted in daily life. The power of women can be likened to the power of the earth. When the earth moves, everything is affected. Bulwarks of power are brought down and even seemingly indomitable mountains are moved. The strength of women is unlimited; nothing can surpass it. I'm counting on the women's division members."

Shin'ichi then turned to Yasuhiro and said: "The situation here in Brazil requires a concentrated effort by members to convey a correct understanding of the Soka Gakkai to Brazilian society. This cannot be achieved, however, simply by writing articles for Soka Gakkai publications. The most important thing is to use your voice and conduct dialogue with others. Life-to-life communication is crucial.

"The best way to do this is for each member to go out and make an effort to speak clearly and honestly to their fellow citizens about the correctness of Nichiren Buddhism and our organization. It is also vital to extend our network of friendship and trust as widely as possible, as this is the foundation for dialogue."

At that moment, Yasuhiro's expression became tense, and he whispered to Shin'ichi: "Sensei, there's a heavyset middle-aged man with brown hair sitting on the bench just behind you. He is well known as a high-ranking officer of the secret police."

SHIN'ICHI TURNED around and walked directly to the officer. He remembered the man, for he had seen him at the culture festival. Shin'ichi stood before him. The man's face stiffened and a wary look appeared in his eyes. The Brazilian members watched with bated breath, wondering what would happen next.

Shin'ichi greeted the police officer politely and smiled as he said: "I see you are working hard very early in the morning. Though I have been in your presence several times, I am sorry that I haven't properly introduced myself. I am Shin'ichi Yamamoto, president of the Soka Gakkai. I'm very happy to meet you."

Shin'ichi's words were immediately interpreted by a young Japanese-Brazilian police officer standing nearby. Shin'ichi then extended his hand in friendship. The officer shook it with a forced and awkward smile. As they shook hands, Shin'ichi said: "I have been eager to meet with someone from the police force and discuss the Soka Gakkai's views and our activities, as well as to hear your thoughts and opinions. This is the perfect opportunity. If it's all right with you, maybe we could have a cup of coffee in that restaurant there and talk a little."

The officer, perhaps because he also wanted to speak with Shin'ichi, rose silently.

Only courageous action can bring about significant change.

A discussion ensued between Shini'ichi and the officer in the restaurant, with the aid of an interpreter. Shin'ichi came straight to the point and said: "I think that after seeing our culture festival and the meeting following it, you must have a good understanding of what we are about. The Soka Gakkai has absolutely no intention of upsetting the social order. Our desire is to realize social prosperity and the happiness of all people.

"It is also the aim of our members to become trusted individuals and to make positive contributions to society as good citizens. The Soka Gakkai is by no means a dangerous organization, as has been reported by certain sectors of the media."

Shin'ichi then went on to explain why the Soka Gakkai had become involved in politics in Japan and that it had no ambition to engage in political activities in any other nation. He also elucidated the goals of the organization and talked about Nichiren Buddhism from various angles. He was determined not to waste this opportunity to change the attitude of Brazil's secret police toward the Soka Gakkai.

AS THE OFFICER listened to Shin'ichi Yamamoto, his stern expression gradually softened. Shin'ichi continued: "If you have any questions about the Soka Gakkai, or anything you'd like to say, please feel free. We would very much appreciate hearing your honest opinion."

The officer replied quite amicably: "Having observed

your various activities during your visit, I am convinced that the Soka Gakkai is not a dangerous organization that seeks to disrupt Brazilian society. We are relieved to have discovered this, and in fact, we have great hopes for your movement. A large number of people, however, do have mistaken ideas about the Soka Gakkai, and many of them feel very strongly in their opposition toward you. For some reason, it seems that many such people are Brazilians of Japanese descent.

"Gaining a widespread understanding of the religion practiced by the Soka Gakkai in Brazil will be no easy feat. Not only does your religion have a profound influence on the inner workings of the life of the individual, but it also has a powerful social influence. There has never been a religion like this in Brazil before. As a result, my advice to you is to be prepared to face many ordeals."

"Thank you very much," Shin'ichi said. "I will take your advice to heart. I am very encouraged to have earned the understanding of a person such as you. Please warmly look after the Brazilian Soka Gakkai members!"

"I will," he replied. "You can count on me."

Shin'ichi extended his hand and the police officer shook it firmly.

"Meeting you has been one of the most meaningful exchanges of my trip," Shin'ichi added. The officer smiled.

Noticing that it was about time to depart, Shin'ichi said: "Please excuse me, but I must go now. I'm looking forward to meeting you again." After bidding the officer farewell, he shook hands with each of the members who had come to see him and his party off and then headed toward the departure gate.

As he neared the gate, Shin'ichi turned around once

more and waved as he called out to the members: "Do your best! Achieve victory! You have my full support!"

Mr. and Mrs. Saiki were deeply moved by his whole-hearted efforts to encourage the members until the very last moment.

LET US TAKE a brief look at the progress of Brazilian kosen-rufu in the years following Shin'ichi Yamamoto's 1966 visit. Though that visit had been a ray of hope in the darkness, the situation remained bleak for some time.

Yasuhiro said to Setsuko at the time: "Let's work hard to promote understanding and recognition of the Soka Gakkai in Brazilian society."

"Yes," Setsuko replied. "We must make it possible for Sensei to visit again free from police surveillance."

Setsuko's determination was particularly firm; she was resolved to transform Brazil into a country that understood and praised the efforts of President Yamamoto and the Soka Gakkai more than any other country in the world. She chanted with tremendous commitment day after day to make that happen. Seeking to convey her thoughts to other women's division members and to launch a wave of chanting Nam-myoho-renge-kyo and Buddhist dialogue, she also poured her energy into visiting members in their homes.

Almost daily, she would travel some twenty to thirty miles to meet with members, clasping their addresses in her hand and asking directions along the way in her halting Portuguese. There were times when she missed the last train and had to walk home, lonely and frightened, along the railway tracks through the dark night. One day, the bus she was riding on was unable to complete its route because of torrential rains and she was forced to wade for hours through knee-deep floodwaters to get home.

But Setsuko's valiant efforts gradually started to bear fruit. One after another, women's division members began to appear who shared Setsuko's spirit and wished to dedicate their lives to bringing happiness to their fellow Brazilians. Two years after Shin'ichi's visit, in June 1968, the women's division held its first general meeting in São Paulo. These courageous champions of peace, shining as bright as the sun, boldly set forth into the future.

In addition, in an effort to put into practice the Buddhist principle that Buddhism is manifested in society, the Fife and Drum Corps in each region began participating in local parades and members started making active contributions to their communities. Consequently, with each passing year, trust and recognition of the Soka Gakkai grew, and in 1972, the São Paulo City Council presented the organization with its Anchieta Medal. Membership continued to expand and eventually community centers were built in Rio de Janeiro and Londrina.

At the same time, Shin'ichi did everything he could to support the members in Brazil. In response to their requests, he dispatched top leaders Izumida and Kazumasa Morikawa to the South American country to offer support and encouragement. He also sent a young men's division national leader named Katsunari Tabuchi, who would later become the SGI-Brazil general director, to the position of South America guidance leader to support Saiki.

S HIN'ICHI eagerly looked forward to his next opportunity to visit Brazil. Finally, such a trip was scheduled
as part of a visit to North and South America in March
1974. The Brazilian members decided to hold a culture
festival to coincide with President Yamamoto's visit, and
full-fledged preparations began from the start of 1974.

The members were excited to think that they would be
able to hold another culture festival with President Yamamoto in attendance, and they were determined to make
the event a total success in every way. They hadn't forgot-
ten the bitterness and anger they felt during the previous
culture festival held under strict police surveillance at the
municipal theater in São Paulo in 1966. In the eight years
since, they were looking forward to the day when they
could once again invite President Yamamoto to a culture
festival.

The festival was scheduled to be held over two days,
March 16 and 17, at the São Paulo Anhembi Conference
Center, a large public auditorium. It was planned in the
greatest detail, and the participants gave their utmost to
the preparations and rehearsals.

For Shin'ichi as well, the trip to Brazil was a long-
cherished dream. His heart leapt at the thought of the magnificent sight of his beloved fellow members singing and
dancing on stage, their lives flowing with happiness.

Shin'ichi's departure from Japan was set for the evening
of March 7. After visiting San Francisco and Miami, he
would go to Brazil on March 13, where he would attend
the culture festival in São Paulo and participate in leaders'
conferences and other events.

It was taking some time, however, for Shin'ichi and his

party to be issued the visas they needed to enter Brazil. When the Soka Gakkai Headquarters employee responsible for organizing the visas went to the Brazilian Consulate General in Yokohama, where the applications had been made, he was told that they were delayed because of holidays related to the carnival in Rio.

As the day of departure approached, the Soka Gakkai Headquarters made a second request to the consulate, only to be told this time that preparations for the inauguration of new President Ernest Geisel in March were impeding all government business.

Shin'ichi realized that something was amiss. He suspected that, just as had happened eight years before, false information about the Gakkai had intentionally been disseminated and was raising concern about the organization within the Brazilian government.

SHIN'ICHI CHANTED in earnest each day, waiting for his visa to Brazil, but it still hadn't been issued the day before his departure. After discussing the matter at length, the decision was made among the top leaders at the Soka Gakkai Headquarters that President Yamamoto would leave Japan as scheduled and reapply for a visa at the Brazilian Consulate General in the United States.

On March 7, Shin'ichi departed Japan and headed for San Francisco, where he energetically participated in various events, including a visit to the University of California at Berkeley and the opening ceremony of the new Soka Gakkai San Francisco Community Center.

Despite his busy schedule, however, he could not stop thinking about Brazil. Every day, he would repeatedly ask one of the leaders accompanying him about his visa. When he thought of how dejected and disheartened the Brazilian members would be if his visit wasn't realized, he was beside himself with worry.

Saiki was informed that Shin'ichi and his party had left Japan without having received visas to visit Brazil, and Shin'ichi kept in constant contact with the Brazilian leaders while he was in San Francisco. Whenever the phone rang at the Soka Gakkai's South America Headquarters in Brazil, Saiki picked up the receiver with the hope that it was good news about the visas, but each time he hung up disappointed.

On his end, Saiki had also been meeting with government representatives to try to find out why the visas were not being issued. It eventually became clear that certain Japanese Brazilians had told the government that there were dangerous elements within Shin'ichi's traveling party, and the government was listening to these views. It was exactly the same thing that had happened eight years earlier.

Saiki was dumbfounded. He thought that he and the other Brazilian members had done their absolute best to turn the situation around, and it seemed that the attitude toward the Soka Gakkai had changed remarkably. But in fact that change was only superficial. Clandestine efforts to do away with the organization in Brazil were actually as strong as ever.

Saiki was made keenly aware of just how immense were the obstacles the Gakkai faced in gaining acceptance in Brazilian society, but he wouldn't give up. He knew that there were still things he could and must do, and he devoted himself to exploring every possibility.

ON MARCH 10, Shin'ichi flew from San Francisco to Los Angeles. At the request of top leaders of the US organization, he was going to attend an executive leaders conference and other meetings at the Malibu Training Center on the outskirts of Los Angeles. The skies over the coastal city were clear and beautiful, and the bright California sunlight poured down. But Shin'ichi, who had not yet received his visa for Brazil, felt as if his heart was blanketed by dark clouds.

Shin'ichi wanted desperately to fly to Brazil and personally thank each member for their efforts and praise them for their struggles. He couldn't get their familiar faces out of his mind. On March 12, however, the day before he was scheduled to arrive in São Paulo, his visa still hadn't come through. That morning, Shin'ichi was finally forced to give up his plans to visit the South American country. He decided instead to make his first trip to Panama, which had not been on his original itinerary.

Meanwhile, Yasuhiro Saiki and several other Brazilian leaders were gathered in the office of a community center in São Paulo waiting for news from Los Angeles. Because of the time difference, it was already the evening of the 12th in São Paulo.

Saiki had made every effort possible in order to realize President Yamamoto's visit, including speaking with officials at the Brazilian foreign ministry. But it was all to no avail. When he phoned Los Angeles late in the evening the previous day, he was informed that it seemed unlikely Shin'ichi would be able to visit Brazil.

Placing his last hopes on the final confirmation call on the 12th, Saiki had been sitting at his desk in the community center waiting for the phone to ring since morning. From the afternoon, other leaders began to arrive at the center. They all waited with hope and anticipation. Each moment seemed an agonizing eternity.

Then, just after five o'clock that evening, the telephone on Saiki's desk rang. Everyone listened in closely.

"Hello, Saiki speaking," he said into the phone. The voice of Kaoru Tahara, the secretary general of the Soka Gakkai International Headquarters echoed through the receiver. Saiki was familiar with Tahara's voice from their many conversations about the visa matter, but Tahara spoke with unexpected formality: "I regret to inform you that since we haven't received the necessary visas, President Yamamoto's trip to Brazil has been canceled."

Although Saiki had prepared himself for such news, when he heard the official announcement of the trip's cancellation, he felt crushed.

TAHARA briskly relayed Shin'ichi's instructions: "Please go ahead with the culture festival and other planned events under your leadership, Mr. Saiki. In addition, please go to the University of São Paulo, which President Yamamoto was scheduled to visit, explain the situation and offer our sincere apologies. As for the guests attending the culture festival..."

Tahara continued speaking, his tone businesslike. Saiki was grateful for this, though, because it helped him control his overwhelming disappointment.

"These are President Yamamoto's wishes," Tahara concluded.

Just then, his voice was replaced by another over the

phone lines. "I hope you're all right. You must be strong!" It was Shin'ichi Yamamoto.

Saiki responded energetically, trying to rouse his own courage: "I'm fine!"

"I'm sure this is difficult for you and I can imagine how disappointed and frustrated you must feel, but this is all part of the workings of the Buddha's wisdom. No doubt it has profound significance. There are times when a present victory actually plants the seed for future failure or defeat, as well as times when a present defeat creates the cause for an enduring future victory. Now is the time for the Brazilian members to rise up and use this challenge as the starting point for dramatic advancement that will lead to tremendous new growth and development. It is your firm resolve based on faith that will enable you to achieve this.

"In the long run, those who have suffered, who have endured the greatest hardship, always become strong. That is a fundamental tenet of Nichiren Buddhism. Though I am not able to visit you now, I will definitely make it there to encourage all of you at some point."

"I understand," Saiki replied, his voice choked with emotion. He was not one to display his feelings in front of others, but in spite of himself, his eyes filled with tears, and the more he tried to hold them back the more profusely they flowed.

"Listen to me," Shin'ichi said. "You mustn't show the members your disappointment but encourage them brightly and cheerfully with all your heart. And please give my very best regards to each of them." He then stated emphatically a number of times: "I'm counting on you! Do your best!" before finishing his call.

Saiki stood there for a while in a kind of a daze, holding the receiver in his hand.

"President Yamamoto isn't coming, is he?" Setsuko asked, calling Saiki back to reality. He replaced the receiver and announced to those present: "President Yamamoto's trip has been canceled."

NO ONE said a word. Then someone started crying. Some leaders covered their faces with their hands and sobbed. Yasuhiro Saiki wiped his tears away with a handkerchief and, summoning up his inner strength, said: "It starts now. Our struggle begins from today!" He was speaking to himself as much as to the others.

Setsuko's usually bright eyes were red and swollen from trying to quell her emotions. Unable to control herself any longer, she ran outside and let her tears fall freely as she gazed up at the evening sky. "How foolish we've been!" she thought. "We simply imagined that because we have worked so hard to gain understanding and acceptance of the Soka Gakkai in Brazilian society, we must have succeeded. But in fact, the moment that we began to feel satisfied with our efforts was the moment our progress ceased. We actually let our guard down.

"I will never forget this bitter disappointment. I will not be defeated! I will not give up!

"We will definitely welcome President Yamamoto to Brazil again! Since the government wouldn't issue him a visa this time, we will see to it that next time he is invited by the president of Brazil himself."

The Brazil culture festival took place on March 16 and 17. Before the performance on the 16th, a guidance meet-

ing was held for all the participants at the Anhembi Conference Center, the festival's venue. During that meeting,
Saiki made the announcement that President Yamamoto's
trip to Brazil had been canceled.

Upon hearing the news, the performers gasped. They
had all given so much to their rehearsals in the hope that
they could perform for President Yamamoto. At first there
was silence, but then some of the performers began to
weep audibly. Tears even streamed down the faces of gallant young men's division members, who kept their focus
on the ceiling trying to conceal their feelings.

Saiki, normally calm and mild-mannered, addressed the
members with unusual vigor: "I am sure that of anyone,
President Yamamoto is the most disappointed and saddened at not being able to make this visit to Brazil. If he
were to see our downcast faces, it would only cause him
more pain. We are President Yamamoto's disciples, aren't
we? What we need to do right now is make our culture
festival a tremendous success! Many guests will be attending, and this is our opportunity to demonstrate to them
the greatness of the Soka Gakkai and our mentor, President Yamamoto, who has supported and encouraged us
so much! This is a crucial moment! Let us rouse great
courage and do our very best!"

SAIKI then relayed President Yamamoto's message to
the participants. Shin'ichi had written it with the
spirit of embracing each and every member.

"Even if we cannot meet in person," the message read,
"the image of you performing today pulses vibrantly in my
heart. I hope that you will enjoy ever-increasing good

health and lead lives filled with such joy that you could declare your families to be the most fortunate of all in Brazil, a land that is sure to flow with happiness. Please continue to courageously and cheerfully advance kosen-rufu in your beloved country, which has infinite future potential.

"Ultimate victory or defeat won't be determined solely by the outcome of this present struggle. Winning is an eternal process. I promise that I will visit you in the future. That is an absolute promise."

Fresh resolve shone in the tear-filled eyes of the members.

On March 16, Shin'ichi prayed earnestly from the United States for the success of the culture festival in São Paulo. When he recalled how this was the day on which, sixteen years earlier, the ceremony of his mentor Josei Toda entrusting the entire future of kosen-rufu to him and the other members of the youth division had taken place, he was overcome with deep emotion. March 16 was a day when disciples vowed to stand up and assume full responsibility for realizing kosen-rufu in their mentor's stead. Shin'ichi was certain that in Brazil as well, this day would be a solemn ceremony of Brazilian youth rising up and taking on the mission of propagating Buddhism.

Before the culture festival began, Saiki announced to all in attendance that President Yamamoto's trip to Brazil had been canceled. A restless murmur swept through the auditorium. Even the performers waiting on standby backstage could sense the audience's disappointment. But a sunlike passion burned in the hearts of the Brazilian members, drying their tears and filling them with strong determination. They knew that nothing would come of feeling sorry for themselves. They had no choice but to make an even greater effort from now on.

The culture festival began.

A stirring gymnastics performance by the young men's division members communicated the pioneering spirit that was characteristic of Brazil's history. In addition, there were energetic folk dances from Argentina, Peru and other South American nations, as well as graceful dances evoking images of cherry blossoms and butterflies. The festival was a celebration of the human spirit, an expression of life's pure joy.

The members poured their whole hearts into their performances, determined to convey the real image of the Soka Gakkai to Brazilian society. They each felt that theirs was the leading role, that they were personally responsible for the festival's success. No one considered themselves to be a mere spectator or bit player. This spirit was the key to their victory.

MUSIC PLAYED while the stage was reset for the culture festival's finale. All the performers then made their entrance dancing to the beat of the samba. Once they were on stage, the music shifted to a well-loved song of the Brazilian members, "Juntos com Sensei" (Together with Sensei). At that moment, the three thousand–plus audience rose to their feet and began clapping in time and singing.

Placing their arms around each other's shoulders, everyone swayed side to side, sending ripples of joy throughout the hall.

> *Let's welcome, let's welcome*
> *Sensei!*
> *Let's build the future*
> *Together with Sensei!*

The performers gazed up at a seat in the center of the first balcony. No one was sitting there, but it was filled with flowers. It was the seat that had been reserved for President Yamamoto. Although he wasn't there in person, he was present in the heart of each member, smiling, nodding and waving to them.

The music ended. Then one of the performers moved toward the front of the stage and began calling out a cheer. The audience joined in, and their voices echoed throughout the building.

> *É pique, é pique, é pique, pique, pique!*
> *É hora, é hora, é hora, hora, hora!*
> *Rá! Tchim! Bum! Sensei!*

It was a traditional Brazilian victory chant. Everyone shouted as loudly as they could, as if they hoped their voices, infused with fresh determination to realize kosen-rufu, would reach President Yamamoto.

The culture festival was held three times during the two days of March 16 and 17. Those who came to view it were deeply moved by the performances, and overall the event was a great success. The guests were unstinting in their praise, saying repeatedly how wonderful they thought the festival was. One guest, impressed by the performers' radiance and their solid unity, remarked: "I have profound respect for the Soka Gakkai and its leader for raising such fine young people as I witnessed here today."

On the first day of the festival, congratulatory messages arrived from Soka Gakkai members in the United States, France, the United Kingdom, Hong Kong, Australia, Singapore, Ghana and other countries. More than seven hundred came from Japan alone, sent as encouragement by Japanese members who had learned from the *Seikyo Shimbun* that President Yamamoto's trip to Brazil had been canceled.

The eyes of members around the world were on Brazil. Everyone was praying for the Brazilian organization's dynamic growth.

THE ORGANIZATION in Brazil was spreading its mighty wings and resolutely taking flight into the vast skies of a hope-filled future.

The Brazilian members realized that while President Yamamoto had been denied a visa to enter their country because of the ignorance and prejudice of the military government, the fault actually lay with them for failing to change the government's outlook. They thus stopped accepting the situation as a problem of Brazilian society and instead began viewing it as their own personal challenge and making steady efforts to resolve it.

Nichiren Daishonin writes, "If you think the Law is outside yourself, you are embracing not the Mystic Law but an inferior teaching" (WND, 3). Buddhism teaches that all phenomena in the universe are contained within a single moment of life. Therefore, a great human revolution achieved by just one person can result in the transformation of the destiny of an entire nation and indeed of all humanity. From a certain perspective, then, it can be said that the Buddhist way of life is to regard the cause of all things as existing within our own lives.

The members in Brazil were painfully aware that their efforts and actions had been insufficient to win the broad support and trust of society. They concluded that the more formidable the resistance they faced, the more efforts they would have to make. And if that still didn't produce results, they would exert themselves three times, five times or ten times harder.

They started with earnest prayer. Setsuko Saiki took the lead in this endeavor, stirring up a powerful wave of chanting Nam-myoho-renge-kyo. She was determined to create the ideal opportunity for President Yamamoto to visit Brazil. She knew that when the time was ripe, the seed of the members' determination would come into full flower. The members also renewed their vow to make an active contribution to society as Buddhist practitioners by promoting peace and culture.

Two-and-a-half months after the culture festival in Brazil, Shin'ichi Yamamoto made his first visit to China with the aim of building a golden and eternal bridge of friendship between the people of China and Japan. Some in Brazil cited Shin'ichi's visit as evidence that the Soka Gakkai was indeed a dangerous organization with Communist ties. But the Brazilian members remained undaunted, proudly asserting to their fellow citizens that if world peace is going to be achieved, it is necessary to meet and speak with the leaders of all nations, regardless of the ideology they uphold, and that to do otherwise would be cowardly.

THE SAIKIS had firmly resolved to spend the rest of their lives in Brazil, and, in July 1974, the couple's long-cherished wish of attaining Brazilian citizenship came true. They even changed their names—Yasuhiro to Ronaldo Y. Saiki, and Setsuko to Gloria S. Saiki. From about this time, many Japanese-Brazilian members who had immigrated to Brazil began adopting new first names as a symbol of their determination to become assimilated into Brazilian society.

In September 1974, the city of São Paulo sponsored a sports and culture festival at the Pacaembu Stadium to celebrate the 152nd anniversary of Brazilian independence. At the city's request, some eight thousand Soka Gakkai Brazil members were included in the program. City officials who had attended and been impressed by the organization's culture festival in March earlier that year had suggested the members' participation.

There was only a short time between the invitation and

the actual event, so preparations were extremely rushed and arduous. Believing, however, that their efforts were for the sake of Brazilian society, the members gave their all to making the city's festival a great success.

When the day came, the audience gasped in wonder at the five thousand-person card stunt performed by Soka Gakkai members in the stands, which portrayed thirty-five images, including familiar sights of São Paulo. Their creation was more like a beautiful painting than just pictures fashioned with colorful placards. On the field below, the young men's division members performed a gymnastics routine with flags. In addition, there was a dance performance by the young women's division members as well as musical performances by the Fife and Drums Corps and Brass Band, who moved around the field in splendid formation. These performances by the Brazilian youth division members earned high praise from the public. The festival itself was televised throughout the country.

Subsequently, in April 1975, as part of the ceremonies celebrating the fifteenth anniversary of the founding of Brasília, Brazil's new capital city, the organization held its own sports and culture festival. This, too, was in response to a request from the Federal District of Brasília. It was a grand-scale event involving five thousand members, including card stunt performers. The members made the six hundred-mile journey in 137 buses from São Paulo, where the organization's headquarters was located, to the sports arena in Brasília.

The crowd of twenty thousand spectators was awestruck by the unity, passion and grace of the members' performances. Newspapers covering the event called the

Soka Gakkai "a cultural organization of which our nation can be proud."

As a result of these two sports and culture festivals, the attitude of Brazilian people toward the Soka Gakkai changed dramatically, and a strong network of trust began to spread widely throughout society.

IN AUGUST 1977, the Brazil Culture Center, which would function as the base for kosen-rufu in Brazil, was completed in São Paulo. This year also saw tremendous growth in the organization's membership. The desire of the members to welcome President Yamamoto to their country increased in tandem with the organization's development, which was being realized through the members' tireless efforts to bring happiness to their friends. Whenever the Saikis or any of the other Japanese-Brazilian members went to Japan on business or for personal reasons, they would make repeated requests for Shin'ichi to visit their country.

From August 1981, members of the women's division began gathering four times a week at the culture center under the leadership of Gloria Saiki to hold chanting sessions toward the realization of this dream. The members also took every action possible and spoke with everyone they could in an attempt to convey the Soka Gakkai's message and to expand understanding toward the organization in Brazilian society.

Eventually their efforts reached as far as the president of Brazil. In May 1982, President João Baptista de Oliveira Figueiredo sent Shin'ichi a personal letter inviting him to the South American country. The path was opened, just as everyone had determined and prayed it would be. Shin'ichi replied to the president's kind invitation and began making preparations to visit Brazil as soon as it was feasible.

In July of the following year, 1983, a thirty-eight-member delegation from Brazil comprised mostly of youth division representatives traveled to Japan to participate in a training session. In addition to scheduled visits to Tokyo, Osaka and other cities, the members were to spend three days at the Kyushu Training Center in Kirishima, Kagoshima Prefecture. This coincided with commemorative events to be held at the training center, celebrating thirty years of kosen-rufu activities in Kyushu, in which Shin'ichi was set to participate. The Brazilian members had vowed to each other that if they were to meet President Yamamoto during their time there, they would ask him to visit their country.

Shin'ichi, too, was eagerly looking forward to the arrival of these members who had come from so far away. He proposed that the delegation be given their own special name and suggested calling them the Brazil-Kirishima Group. He also composed a poem for them praising their seeking spirit:

> *Taking flight*
> *From the far distant*
> *Land of Brazil—*
> *How brightly burns*
> *Your seeking spirit!*

Several of the members from Brazil were invited to

attend a dinner with Shin'ichi on the evening of the second day of the training session. They decided that this was their chance to ask Shin'ichi to visit their homeland.

DURING THE DINNER, the Brazilian youth representatives walked over to Shin'ichi's table. Seeing them approach, Shin'ichi called out to them: "Thank you for all your efforts! You're going to Osaka tomorrow for a training session, aren't you? What time do you depart?"

"At half past nine in the morning," one of the members replied.

"I see," Shin'ichi said. "It's cool here in Kirishima even in summer because of the high altitude, but Osaka at this time of year is quite hot, so please take care of yourselves."

Shin'ichi was concerned for the health of these young people who had traveled so far from their home in the southern hemisphere, which was in the middle of winter.

More than seventeen years had passed since Shin'ichi's previous visit to Brazil. When he thought about how the members there must have felt during that time and the strong determination of these young people standing before him, he was filled with profound emotion. He looked at each of them intently, as if to engrave their faces deep in his heart.

"The sun of hope is rising over Brazil. We are entering the age of Brazil," he declared.

At that moment, Jorge Koyama, Brazil's young men's division leader, spoke up: "Sensei! Please come to Brazil!"

The other members of the group then called out: "Please!" "We're waiting for you!"

"I understand your feelings without you having to say

a word," Shin'ichi responded. "I promise I will visit you in the near future!" Hearing this, the members' faces lit up with joy.

When the activities scheduled for that day were completed, Shin'ichi invited all of the thirty-eight members who were visiting from Brazil, including the representatives who had attended the dinner, to meet with him in a room in the community center so he could talk with and encourage them personally. He wanted to create a memory that would become a lifelong inspiration for them.

The members gathered excitedly. Shin'ichi greeted them with a smile and began speaking quietly: "I am always thinking about the members in Brazil. No matter how much distance separates us, you are my family, my brothers and sisters. You are my beloved comrades in faith, whom I trust and respect deeply.

"I just now finished chanting sincerely for you to continue to be in good health and high spirits and that you will gain a great deal from this training course."

Hearing these words, tears rose in the eyes of some of the Brazilian youth.

"You mustn't cry," Shin'ichi said. "I'm definitely going to Brazil, so we are going to meet again. Lions of kosen-rufu never weep, no matter what happens."

SHIN'ICHI then said: "Since you've come all the way here to Kirishima, I'd like to play you something on the piano. I'm not very good, but this is my way of welcoming you as my family."

Shin'ichi sat down at the piano that was in the room and the youth gathered around him. It was their first chance to hear Shin'ichi play.

A powerful melody rose from the instrument as Shin'-ichi played "Atsuta Village," a song based on a poem he had composed about the village where his mentor Josei Toda was raised. Shin'ichi would occasionally look up at the members while he played, nodding his head as if engaging them in conversation. He next played "The Three Martyrs of Atsuhara," another song from a poem of his that told the story of three peasant followers of Nichiren Daishonin who died upholding their beliefs. Lastly, he played the moving "The Moon Over the Ruined Castle."

The members were deeply touched by the music, and tears streamed down the faces of those who had until then managed to hold them back. Though some of the youth didn't understand a word of Japanese, Shin'ichi's playing communicated his thoughts and feelings to them with piercing clarity.

Shin'ichi finished. The room was silent for a moment, and then the members broke out in enthusiastic applause. Looking at each of them, Shin'ichi said: "I will never forget you, noble Brazilian champions of seeking spirit. Let's meet again, next time in Brazil!"

He then shook hands with everyone, saying: "Take care!" "Do your best!" "I'll be praying for you!"

Their cheeks wet with tears, the members gripped Shin'ichi's hand firmly. On this day, at this moment, a flame of firm resolve that would never be extinguished rose up brilliantly in the lives of these youth from Brazil.

After returning home to Brazil, the members, who were filled with inspiration from their trip, told their friends in faith of their encounter with Shin'ichi: "President Yamamoto said that he would definitely come to Brazil. Let's make sure that it happens this time through our strong prayer!"

The conviction that President Yamamoto would come to see them began to shine in the hearts of all Brazilian members, becoming a source of courage and hope. A great surge of chanting Nam-myoho-renge-kyo spread throughout the country. Such focused and determined prayer is the energy that transforms society, the age and the world.

IN DECEMBER 1983, a visit by Shin'ichi Yamamoto to Brazil was at last officially scheduled for February of the following year. A grand culture festival was to be held in São Paulo on February 26 to coincide with Shin'-ichi's trip.

The members were overjoyed, but the leaders of the Brazilian organization remained cautious. They were determined not to let themselves slip into complacence. Keenly aware that kosen-rufu was an eternal struggle against devilish functions that seek to hinder the propagation of the Law, they knew that anything could happen.

And in fact, as the date of Shin'ichi's visit approached, attacks on the organization grew harsher and unanticipated problems arose. But Gloria Saiki was resolved. "I will fight!" she declared. "I will make sure Sensei's visit is realized. I will not be defeated!" She thus became directly involved in the negotiations surrounding the trip, her incredible determination overcoming one obstacle after another.

On February 11, 1984, the eighty-fourth anniversary of President Toda's birth, Shin'ichi left Japan for a tour of

North and South America. Following a brief stop in Los
Angeles, he traveled to Dallas and Miami to participate in
various activities. Just after nine o'clock in the evening on
February 18, he set off from Miami for Brazil, arriving in
Rio de Janeiro the next morning. From there he took a
domestic flight to São Paulo.

Meanwhile, SGI-Brazil General Director Ronaldo
Saiki, together with other Brazilian leaders, were waiting
anxiously on the tarmac of the São Paulo Airport for
Shin'ichi's arrival. His expression was grim and his eyes
serious behind his glasses. His brow was wrinkled in concern. He wouldn't feel at ease until he saw President Yamamoto in person.

The time seemed to pass with excruciating slowness.
Each minute felt like several hours. As Saiki waited, the
events of the last eighteen years flashed through his mind.
He recalled the culture festival in 1966, which Shin'ichi
had attended under strict police surveillance. Mortified
and angered by this treatment of President Yamamoto,
Saiki vowed at that time to turn the situation around and
be able to welcome him back to Brazil under transformed
circumstances. He remembered 1974, when the Brazilian
leaders and members were convinced that because of their
earnest prayers and struggles, President Yamamoto would
at last be able to come back to Brazil, but then his trip was
canceled at the last minute because he was denied a visa.
Saiki thought of how the members had encouraged each
other to remain strong, telling each other that it is always
darkest before the dawn. And he reminded himself of the
determined, courageous efforts they had made in order to
contribute to Brazilian society.

A SINGLE JET PLANE came into view in the cloudless sky, made its descent and landed on the tarmac. "That's it," an airline employee said to Ronaldo Saiki. When the plane came to a stop, a set of stairs was pushed up to it, and the door opened. President Yamamoto, wearing a navy blue suit, appeared in the doorway.

"Sensei!" Saiki found himself yelling excitedly. When Shin'ichi finished descending the steps, Saiki grasped his hand and shook it firmly. Saiki's face was dripping with sweat from the summer heat.

"Welcome! Thank you for coming!" the Brazilian leader said.

"Everything will be all right now. Let's advance together with the courage of lions!" Shin'ichi replied.

Shin'ichi thus embarked on his activities in Brazil, giving them every ounce of his energy as if to make up for the eighteen years he had been unable to visit. He flew to Brasília to meet with President Figueiredo as well as the Brazilian minister of foreign affairs and minister of education and culture. He also strove to lay the foundation for Japan-Brazil friendship through such efforts as donating books to the University of Brasília library.

Shin'ichi also poured his life into inspiring the members in each area he visited. On February 25, he made an appearance at the Ibrapuera Gymnasium, the state sports arena in São Paulo—where members were rehearsing for the Brazil Grand Culture Festival that would be held the following day—to encourage the participants. Shin'ichi was determined to meet with and encourage as many Brazilian members as possible. When he stepped into the arena, he was met with joyous cheers and thunderous applause. Everyone had been eagerly anticipating this encounter.

He then walked once around the arena stage, raising his arms in the air as he did so in greeting to the participants. Later, speaking into a microphone, he said with deep emotion: "I am so happy that after eighteen years I am at last able to meet with all of you, my dear friends and noble emissaries of the Buddha, on this wonderful occasion!

"I am certain that this magnificent culture festival will shine gloriously in the annals of Brazil and of kosen-rufu. One can only imagine the struggles you have faced and just how valiantly you have forged ahead in solid unity in order to arrive at this point. I would like to convey my most profound respect and appreciation to all of you. In my heart, I am embracing each and every one of you and shaking your hand.

"Nichiren Buddhism gives rise to the creation of a culture that will build a new century. I wish to declare that this teaching is the unparalleled path to realizing a world of true happiness and peace."

Shin'ichi's words penetrated deeply into the members' lives.

SHIN'ICHI'S VOICE grew stronger as he declared: "I have no doubt that Nichiren Daishonin is praising and protecting all of you who are working so hard for kosen-rufu. I, too, vow to protect and support you as long as I live."

Vigorous applause echoed throughout the arena and then the members broke out in a rousing Brazilian cheer, expressing their joy and commitment.

É pique, é pique, é pique, pique, pique!
É hora, é hora, é hora, hora, hora!

They cheered with all their might, the eyes of many red and swollen with tears. Jumping to their feet, they waved to Shin'ichi and put their arms around each other's shoulders, some weeping with emotion.

As Gloria Saiki observed this scene, tears filled her eyes and flowed down her cheeks unchecked. It was as if the floodgates of her heart had burst, unleashing a torrent of feeling that she had managed to keep a tight rein on for eighteen long years. Though it was an effort just to remain standing, she nevertheless cried out with all her being: "Sensei! Brazil has triumphed! We have fulfilled the promise we made to you!" But the crowd's excitement drowned her words.

At six o'clock in the evening on the following day, February 26, the Brazil Grand Culture Festival began with Shin'ichi in attendance. The theme of the festival was "A Paean of Peace to Our Land in the Twenty-first Century."

Members gathered joyously from all over Brazil—from Rio de Janeiro, from the capital city Brasília, and even from the remote regions of the Amazon, some twenty-five hundred miles away. President Figueiredo sent a congratulatory message, in which he praised the activities of the SGI in Brazil to promote culture, health, education and the ideals of peace throughout the country, as well as the organization's global contributions in advocating the elimination of nuclear weapons. He further expressed his earnest hopes that the SGI would achieve its lofty aims.

The culture festival opened to the exciting rhythm of

the samba. The various performances included a dance by children, the emissaries of the future; a modern dance performance by the young women's division members that communicated the joy of youth; stirring musical performances by the Fife and Drum Corps and the Brass Band; Latin folk dances; and traditional Japanese dances.

The audience enjoyed every moment.

NEXT, the auditorium went dark and a magical world unfolded as beams of light in red, yellow, blue and other colors danced through the darkness. In the stands, thousands of members performed a spectacular light show, using flashlights to create various images such as the letters "SGI" and the Brazilian national flag.

Lastly, the young men's division members performed a dynamic gymnastics routine. They moved around the arena, forming human bridges, undulating waves and a five-story human pyramid. The members in the audience watched anxiously, praying under their breaths as the second, third and fourth tier of young men rose into the air. Then a young man climbed atop the swaying fourth tier and, holding a flag in each hand, extended his arms outward. They did it! They had built a golden pyramid of victory!

A ground swell of excitement and delight swept through the audience as the grand finale commenced. The life of each performer shone with sublime brilliance.

Performers in costumes of myriad colors filled the arena, transforming it into a flower garden of humanity. Bright smiles spread across their faces and tears filled many an eye. Shin'ichi's heart flowed with emotion. Wishing to convey his profound respect and praise to them, he leaned forward in his seat, waved vigorously and called out: *"Obrigado! Obrigado!"* (Thank you) Thunderous cheers and applause resounded throughout the arena.

The strains of the samba began to play and members started singing the well-loved song, *"Saudason a Sensei"* (Welcome, Sensei). Performer and spectator alike sang and danced as one in an expression of their pride and joy.

> *La-la-la-la . . .*
> *Sensei!*
> *Welcoming you*
> *To Brazil*
> *Our dream has come true*
> *Thank you, Sensei!*
> *We offer you*
> *The flower of our sincerity.*

They sang passionately, these strongly unified champions of Soka who had endured the harsh winds of adversity and challenged their own limitations. They were a true image of the essence of human goodness and genuine peace.

They have won. My beloved comrades in faith have triumphed at last, Shin'ichi thought.

Armed with the supreme inspiration of faith and the universal power of Nam-myoho-renge-kyo, the members of SGI-Brazil had broken through the deep darkness that had shrouded them for so many years and were finally greeting the brilliant light of dawn. From that day forward, just as the sun rises higher in the sky with each passing minute and bathes the world in golden light, SGI–Brazil would go on to shine brightly as a pioneer of worldwide kosen-rufu and realize incredible advancement.

Pioneering
New Frontiers

"THE MOST NOBLE undertaking for a human being is to enlighten others."[1] These are the words of Simón Bolívar,[2] known as the great liberator of South America.

On March 15, 1966, following a forty-minute delay, Shin'ichi and his colleagues departed at eleven o'clock in the morning from São Paulo, Brazil. The next destination on their tour was Lima, Peru. It would take them five hours to fly across the South American continent.

Francisco Pizarro of Spain, who brought about the

downfall of the Inca Empire, founded Lima in 1535. Since that time, the city had served as the center of Spanish colonial rule in South America.

Just as the plane approached the Andes, an indigo blue lake came into view below: it was Lake Titicaca. Passing over snowy mountains that rose more than twenty thousand feet in height, the flight continued. The mountains rolled by like waves, one after another. Beyond the Andes came the vast expanse of the sea, and a verdant city appeared amidst a pale brown desert. That beautiful city was Lima.

Shin'ichi descended the ramp from the plane and stood on Peruvian soil for the first time. The summer sun shone brightly in the breathtaking blue sky.

Peru Chapter Leader Masayoshi Chiná, a genial man in his early forties, was at the airport to greet them, along with Seiichiro Haruki and several other Japanese leaders who had arrived in Lima the day before. The local leaders had originally been planning to have many members at the airport to welcome President Yamamoto in grand style on the occasion of his first visit to Peru. However, the leaders from Japan who arrived in Peru in advance had convinced them that since the Peruvian government was also keeping a watchful eye on the Soka Gakkai, they should avoid a great fanfare and just have Chiná go to the airport. Although the members were sorely disappointed, they all agreed, if this would allow them to welcome President Yamamoto without incident.

When Shin'ichi heard from Haruki at the airport about the previous plans for his welcome, he felt terrible.

"I am truly sorry to have let everyone's hopes down,"

he said. "To make up for that, I will do everything I can for the sake of our movement's future development in Peru, so please rest assured."

Hearing these words, Chiná was profoundly moved by Shin'ichi's humility and deep consideration.

Trust arises from the character of a person who succeeds in striking a chord in others' hearts.

PERU CHAPTER LEADER Masayoshi Chiná was born in 1924 in Okinawa. His parents emigrated to Peru shortly after his birth, and Masayoshi was raised by his grandmother who remained in Okinawa. The plan was for him to join his parents once their life in Peru became stable.

Mass emigration of the Japanese to Peru first started in 1899, with 790 contract laborers setting sail aboard the *Sakura maru*. It was the first major mass emigration of this kind by the Japanese to South America. A similar mass emigration to Brazil took place nine years later, in 1908, aboard the *Kasato maru*.

Once the emigrants arrived in Peru, however, their circumstances were truly wretched. They were treated poorly, and there were many who succumbed to endemic diseases. Some even fled from the workplaces to which they had been contracted, unable to endure the harsh labor.

A quarter-century had already passed since the first emigration by the time Chiná's parents moved to Peru, and people of Japanese descent were beginning to gain a footing in Peruvian society. Nonetheless, it was still difficult for new emigrants to secure a foundation for their existence. Thus, seventeen or eighteen years elapsed before Chiná's parents were finally in a position to send for him.

Meanwhile, Chiná had enlisted in the Japanese navy at the age of seventeen, and was constantly relocating to various bases around the country. In addition, since Peru had declared war on Japan in February 1945, Chiná and his parents had been unable to contact each other. His parents, having heard that "Okinawa fought to the last man," assumed Chiná had been killed.

After the war, Chiná moved to Miyazaki Prefecture on the Japanese island of Kyushu, where his grandmother had taken refuge, and shortly thereafter, he started a construction company. Although he was able to get his business off to a good start, he always carried in a corner of his heart the thought of his parents in Peru.

In his early thirties, Chiná was introduced to Nichiren Buddhism by an acquaintance. Having been separated from his parents in infancy, Chiná had been seriously pondering the notion of karma, and he was therefore very receptive to Buddhism.

Just around the time he considered joining the Soka Gakkai, he began listening to a radio broadcast when he learned that someone was looking for him. When he contacted this person, it turned out to be a friend of his father's who had once lived in Peru. Chiná's father had implored this friend to search for his son, saying: "My son appears to be dead, but there's also a possibility he may still be alive somewhere in Japan. Please look for him."

CHINÁ felt there was something mystic about receiving news of his parents just as he was considering practicing Buddhism. He thus joined the Soka Gakkai in March 1957.

As he applied himself in the practice, he was able to gain conviction in the power of the Gohonzon. Gradually, a desire grew in him to meet his parents and to tell them about Nichiren Buddhism. He also wanted to take care of his parents now that his grandmother, who had raised him, had died.

In due course, he made a decision to move to Peru. Selling the company he had successfully developed by himself, he left Japan in 1961.

His father was running a restaurant and hotel in Lima. The reunion of Chiná and his parents after more than thirty years took place amidst embraces and tears.

Their joy was fleeting, however; for the moment Chiná mentioned that he was a Soka Gakkai member, his parents' expression changed. No sooner had he begun to talk about the practice than they began to shout at him, their faces flushed in anger. His parents were staunch believers of another religion, and his mother, in particular, was a central leader of that religious organization in Peru.

His father stormed: "My son is supposedly dead. If you really are my son, as you claim to be, show me clear proof!"

Glaring at him, his mother said: "The Soka Gakkai? Out of the question! How dare you bring misfortune on this household, which we took such pains to build!"

Nevertheless, after much pleading, Chiná persuaded them to allow him to live and work at their restaurant. Even though he was their son, he was treated no differently than any other employee. What is more, the restaurant had been running in the red for some time, and business was stagnant.

Chiná was disheartened and thought that if things were going to turn out this way, he should never have come to Peru. But he convinced himself that if he gave up now, he could never share his practice with his parents, so he continued to work diligently.

Though the restaurant had been suffering financially, as a result of Chiná's assiduous efforts, by the end of two years, it had made a spectacular recovery. Even his father praised him highly, saying: "I was wrong. I deeply regret how I treated you. I'm proud to have a son like you."

His parents also began to show understanding for the Soka Gakkai, and both became members.

Nothing attests more eloquently to the truth of the Daishonin's Buddhism than actual proof of the power of faith shown in daily life.

CHINÁ dedicated himself to sharing Buddhism with others. Since he could not communicate very well in Spanish when he first arrived in Peru, he spoke with every Japanese person he could find. Whenever he heard of someone from Japan living in the country, he would go see them, no matter how far away they lived, and talk to them wholeheartedly about Nichiren Buddhism.

There were even times when he was so absorbed in conversation that he missed the last bus home. On such occasions, he had no recourse other than to thumb a ride from a passing car. But even this was no easy task. First of all, depending on the location, there were very few cars on the road. Even if one were to drive by, at such a late hour the driver would be wary and would not stop, no matter how much Chiná waved and shouted. More, even if someone did stop to pick him up, he could not explain where he needed to go, due to his inability to speak the language.

Every day was a succession of hardships, but before long, his efforts bore fruit and the number of people who started to practice steadily began to increase.

In February 1962, a woman named Kyoko Shiroyama, who had been visiting her parents' hometown in Okinawa, received Gohonzon and returned to Peru. She also happened to be proficient in Spanish. From that time onward, the tide of kosen-rufu in Peru was carried by Chiná and Shiroyama.

However, that path was by no means smooth. Chiná faced numerous perilous situations. In July 1962, he was returning home in a taxi in the predawn hours after a late night of activities when he came across a military checkpoint and was taken to the river's edge. There, at gunpoint, he was forced to keep his hands in the air as the interrogation began with a volley of questions: "Where were you coming from at such an hour?" "What's your occupation?"

They held him for more than four hours. Actually, at this time, a coup d'état initiated by the military was under way. As he was traveling by car in the middle of the night, Chiná had been perceived as a suspicious character.

And yet, amidst these circumstances, kosen-rufu in Peru advanced steadily.

On the occasion of Soka Gakkai Director Hiroshi Yamagiwa's guidance tour to Peru in November 1962, Peru Chapter was established. Chiná was appointed chapter leader, and Kyoko Shiroyama, chapter women's division leader. The chapter started with two districts, consisting of a total of 125 member-households.

The birth of this organization inspired everyone to renew their determination. Propagation progressed even further, resulting in a host of new members, even in the remote villages scattered among the Andes Mountains. By the time Shin'ichi Yamamoto visited Peru in March 1966, they had more than one thousand member-households.

Meanwhile, however, the government had begun to keep a watchful eye on the Soka Gakkai.

LEAVING the airport, Shin'ichi and his party headed for their hotel in Lima. From their car window, they saw rows of adobe and thatched-roof houses and, as they entered the heart of the city, a forest of tall buildings against the backdrop of the Andes.

The blue expanse of the Pacific Ocean was visible from their hotel near the Rimac River.

As soon as they had taken care of their luggage, the party gathered for a meeting. Shin'ichi received a detailed report from the Japanese leaders who had arrived in Peru in advance. They had been enthusiastically engaged in various activities, organizing a study examination, considering a new organizational lineup and conducting interviews with leadership candidates, in addition to meeting with the Minister of Justice.

As the briefing at the hotel began, one member of the advance party spoke up, his expression serious: "I would like to make a report on the conditions concerning the Soka Gakkai in Peru, based on what I've learned from our contact with relevant parties.

"In a word, the perception of the government and police with regard to the Soka Gakkai is considerably negative. As in Brazil, government officials and the mass media are concerned that the purpose of your visit, President Yamamoto, is to prepare for the initiation of a political party. Consequently, they are anxious regarding your activities.

"Someone affiliated with the police told me in these exact words: 'If there should be the slightest hint of instigation during this visit, we will have to be more vigilant about the Soka Gakkai in Peru in the future.'"

From six o'clock that evening, Shin'ichi was planning to participate in a meeting at the Metropolitan Theater. He had placed all his hopes on seeing the members there and encouraging them.

However, in that moment, the wheels of his mind turned rapidly.

He thought: *If I were to attend this meeting as scheduled, the authorities will surely interpret this as an instigation and a provocation. One can foresee that they will clamp down on the members after I leave. I cannot let such an awful thing happen to the Peruvian members. Although the members may be disappointed, viewed from the long term, it would not be wise for me to attend the meeting tonight. What is important is how we can best protect the members, how we can create conditions in which everyone can enjoy their practice with peace of mind.*

KIYOSHI JUJO ventured to speak. Addressing Shin'ichi, he said: "Considering the present circumstances, perhaps it would be best if you didn't attend the meeting tonight. The authorities will not be so concerned if the rest of us attend, but they may be provoked by your participation."

"I was just thinking the same thing," Shin'ichi replied with a nod. "I have no alternative but to entrust the meeting to all of you. While the members may be disappointed, I'm sure that one day they will understand why I had to make this choice. Although I can't attend the meeting, I will do my utmost for the sake of Peru. As long as we have a strong determination to do our best for the happiness of our fellow members, we can always find ways to take action, regardless of the circumstances!"

A firm resolve resonated in his voice.

"Incidentally, is there anyone I should meet for the sake of the future development of our organization in Peru?"

Immediately came a response from a member of the advance party: "First, we would like you to meet with some people of Japanese descent who are influential in Peruvian society."

"That sounds fine," Shin'ichi said. "In addition, let's all

share in the task of meeting with members of the mass media. In any event, it's vital that people in various spheres have a correct understanding of the Soka Gakkai."

Shin'ichi's hotel room had been transformed into the power source for the future development of kosen-rufu in Peru.

They further continued with discussions on a new organizational lineup and proposed leadership appointments. It was decided that the current Peru Chapter would become a general chapter and make a fresh departure with three chapters—Peru, Callao and Victoria. Masayoshi Chiná would be the general chapter leader. Young men's and young women's divisions were also created.

The leaders then went on to decide the agenda for that day's meeting and to confirm the schedule for various activities they would be carrying out.

As their discussion drew to a close, Shin'ichi asked: "After tonight's meeting, would it be possible for the district-level leaders and up to gather here at the hotel? At the very least, I'd like to meet personally with some representatives and offer encouragement."

A little after five o'clock in the evening, after seeing off Izumida and the others, Shin'ichi and his wife, Mineko, recited the sutra and chanted for the success of the meeting. Shin'ichi had learned from Chiná that there would be some members traveling from remote villages in the Andes and others traveling by bus for several days in order to attend. He deeply prayed that the night's event would bring hope, courage and joy to every single one of those valiant and pure-hearted members. He put his entire being into his prayer.

MEANWHILE, at the Metropolitan Theater, about seventeen hundred members from throughout Peru awaited the start of the meeting at six o'clock. It was a magnificent turnout. The participants had gathered in high spirits, eagerly anticipating the chance to meet Shin'-ichi Yamamoto.

Adorning the stage was the Soka Gakkai's theme for 1966, "Dawn," written in bold Chinese calligraphy, and just beneath it a banner proudly proclaiming, "Soka Gakkai del Peru."

Everyone's gaze turned to the stage as the leaders took their seats. "Which one is President Yamamoto?" they wondered. While the members were familiar with Shin'-ichi's face from such Soka Gakkai publications as the *Seikyo Shimbun* newspaper and the *Seikyo Graphic* magazine, most of them had never met him in person, and were therefore having some trouble identifying him.

They scanned the stage intently, but could not find anyone who bore any resemblance to President Yamamoto. As they were all wondering where he was, the start of the meeting was announced, and Soka Gakkai General Director Hiroshi Izumida took to the podium to speak.

"Good evening! I imagine you have all been anxiously awaiting President Yamamoto's visit to Peru. He arrived in Lima this afternoon in high spirits!"

The news was met with cheers and thunderous applause. The members beamed with delight and clapped vigorously.

Seeing their happy faces, Izumida was deeply pained at what he would have to say next. Nevertheless, summoning his courage, he continued: "However, due to some important business that suddenly required his attention, President Yamamoto will not be able to join us this evening."

A hush instantly fell over the audience. And then sighs of disappointment rippled through the room. The members looked openly downcast.

With every ounce of energy he could muster, Izumida declared: "The reason that President Yamamoto cannot be here with us is that he is, right at this moment, engaging in a struggle for the sake of all Peruvian members. He has asked me to convey this message to you:

> It was with great anticipation that I had been looking forward to today's meeting, but unfortunately, due to a sudden, unexpected matter requiring my attention, I will not be able to attend. However, here, on Peruvian soil, in this land that is the stage for your endeavors, I have begun an all-out struggle to open the way for your glorious future. Throughout my life, I shall support and protect all of you, the precious children of the Buddha.

THE MEMBERS' FACES were solemn as they strained to hear every last word of President Yamamoto's message read by Hiroshi Izumida:

> You and I are comrades in faith. Comrades are those who are linked by a common awareness, a common resolve. I hope that you, sharing the same awareness as I, will rise into action like lions and work for the happiness of your friends and for the betterment of

society. I would also like to ask that, in my stead, you compassionately and stoutly encourage those who are suffering.

Today's gathering marks the occasion on which you stand up as lions. I will be supporting you with my prayers. My wish is that you will do your best to make this a historic meeting, flowing with joy, enthusiasm and hope. I pray from the bottom of my heart that you will advance in life as upstanding citizens who contribute to the well-being of society, while proudly singing the Peruvian national anthem.

I will, without fail, visit Peru again. I therefore look forward to meeting you some time in the future.

This concludes the message from President Yamamoto."

Many members nodded to convey their understanding of Shin'ichi's words.

Izumida then said: "President Yamamoto has also entrusted me with prayer bead cloths to present to all of you who have traveled long distances to be here today.

"Additionally, after discussing the organization here in Peru with President Yamamoto, we have decided to establish a general chapter."

The room broke out in applause.

Izumida then set about introducing the new organizational structure and confirming the leadership appointments. This announcement brought radiance back to the members' faces.

The meeting proceeded with a number of experiences and words from Ronaldo Saiki, as well as from the leaders who had accompanied Shin'ichi from Japan.

These visiting leaders were deeply intent on encouraging the members in every possible way. They resolved: "If this meeting should turn out to be a lackluster gathering, offering no hope or joy simply because President Yamamoto could not be present, we would be wasting precious time in the lives of all these members who have traveled here with such an ardent seeking spirit. As those responsible for the success of this meeting, we absolutely cannot let that happen."

It was this intense, almost desperate desire that gradually began to move the hearts of the members. Before long, their disappointment turned to determination.

At the close of the meeting, everyone raised their voices and sang "Song of Worldwide Kosen-rufu" and, in response to a proposal by Shin'ichi, Peru's national anthem. By now, the members' cheeks were aglow, and their hearts leapt with enthusiasm at this vigorous new departure.

THAT EVENING, after reciting the sutra and chanting Nam-myoho-renge-kyo for the magnificent development of the organization in Peru, Shin'ichi immediately set out to meet with an influential Japanese Peruvian in order to promote a better understanding of the Soka Gakkai. He poured all of his energy into their ensuing dialogue. Determined to protect his beloved fellow members, Shin'ichi worked quietly and inconspicuously behind the scenes in this way to secure the foundation for the kosen-rufu movement in Peru.

Shortly after he returned to his hotel, two dozen or so representative chapter and district leaders gathered in his room.

Welcoming them warmly, Shin'ichi said: "Thank you all so much for coming. I've been looking forward to this moment and am delighted to have this opportunity to meet you."

In response, a robust, bespectacled man of Japanese descent in his fifties replied: "On the contrary, it is we who should thank you for coming to Peru. President Yamamoto, thank you from the bottom of our hearts."

The man, who spoke in a relaxed and friendly manner, had the noble bearing of a person who had surmounted a multitude of hardships. Shin'ichi asked him his name.

"My name is Vicente Seiken Kishibe. I was appointed just today as Callao Chapter leader." He then introduced the woman next to him: "This is my wife, Rosalia Harue Kishibe. She was also appointed today as Callao Chapter women's division leader. We will work hard and take responsibility for kosen-rufu in Peru."

A firm resolve resonated in his voice.

Kishibe was born in Nago, Okinawa, in 1913. Upon graduating from an agriculture and forestry school, he found employment at an agricultural experiment station. A trip to study farming practices in Argentina had brought him to South America for the first time. Enchanted with this continent, he lost interest in returning to Japan. Since his older brother was living in Lima, he settled there. For a time, he helped out at his brother's barbershop, but later the two of them started a milk delivery business together.

In June 1945, Kishibe married Rosalia, a second-generation Japanese Peruvian. Earlier that same year, in February, Peru had declared war on Japan. As a strong anti-Japanese sentiment pervaded the country, their new life as a couple began amidst an atmosphere of apprehension.

After the war, Kishibe opened a hardware store and also had a thriving business selling sewage pipes, which he imported from the United States.

IT LOOKED as though Vicente Kishibe's business was on the path to success. However, these prosperous times did not last long.

One day, in the course of a business transaction, he signed a contract without giving it much thought, neglecting to confirm the details. It turned out to be a scam that plunged him into serious financial trouble. His problems were further exacerbated by the high rate of inflation that was then sweeping the country. Things grew really grim when his business went bankrupt and he was left with enormous debts.

To make matters worse, three of his children were afflicted by illness: his eldest daughter had arthritis, his eldest son, asthma, and one of his younger sons, epilepsy. He couldn't afford to buy medicine for them, because he hardly had enough money to put food on the table each day. It pained Kishibe deeply to see his children suffering in this way, and he felt terrible about his powerlessness to do anything to help them.

In addition, acquaintances that he had helped out in the past turned their backs on him and kept their distance.

By this time, Kishibe was already in his late forties. His life in Peru, which he had managed to establish for more than twenty years, seemed to be falling apart. With no prospects for raising money to pay off his debts and reestablish himself, he was constantly tormented by nightmares.

Overcome with despair, he attempted to take his own life on two separate occasions. The first time, he threw himself off a cliff overlooking the sea on the outskirts of Lima. Although he was badly hurt, the fall did not kill him. The second time, he tried to commit suicide by jumping off a speeding bus. Again, he was unsuccessful.

In order to support their family, Kishibe's wife, Rosalia, managed to set up a beauty salon with money she borrowed from her father and younger brother. It was around this time that Kishibe was invited to Masayoshi Chiná's home by a former classmate from his junior high school in Okinawa. There, he was introduced to Nichiren Buddhism.

Kishibe was struck by Chiná's total conviction that any problem could, without fail, be resolved through the earnest practice of Buddhism. He thus decided then and there to join the Soka Gakkai and promptly filled out the application form. This was in March 1962.

When Rosalia heard about this, her face turned white with anger: "What on earth were you thinking, signing that form? You of all people should know how dangerous rash decisions can be! Haven't we been reminded of this, day in and day out?"

Their huge debt after all had arisen as a result of her husband's careless signature on some documents. Rosalia was exasperated, for obviously her husband had not learned his lesson, this time signing an application form to join some dubious religious organization.

ROSALIA had always deemed highly suspect any religion that promised people they could solve their problems through prayer. She therefore could not support her husband's decision to join the Soka Gakkai.

Kishibe, however, conscientiously applied himself to reciting the sutra and chanting. Hoping to make a fresh departure in life, he began working as an assistant in his brother-in-law's photography shop.

As he continued participating in Buddhist activities, he began to feel himself grow more hopeful and alive. He also noticed that his way of thinking was changing. Until then, Kishibe had believed he was the unluckiest person ever. However, through his practice, he gradually gained an appreciation even for his hardships. Had it not been for this bitter life experience, he realized, he would not have been able to encounter the Gohonzon; in other words, all these circumstances were simply stepping-stones, guiding him toward true happiness. This conviction that he was on the correct path gave him courage, and he threw himself into everything with fresh energy and enthusiasm.

Eventually, Kishibe started his own photography business in the suburbs of Lima. He named his shop "Siawase" (happiness), to reflect his absolute determination to become happy through the practice of Buddhism.

Although Rosalia was delighted to see her husband getting back on his feet again, she still remained cool toward his faith.

One day, Kishibe implored her to come to a meeting with him. Though still reluctant, she finally agreed to attend, merely with the intent of helping her husband keep up appearances.

At first, she maintained a distrustful attitude as she listened to the discussion, but as people started sharing their experiences, she leaned forward, wanting to hear every word. These testimonials of how people were able to overcome health, financial and family issues through their Buddhist practice were highly persuasive. The notion of changing one's karma left a particularly deep impression on Rosalia.

"Although it sounds hard to believe," she thought to herself, "perhaps we can change our family karma through this practice. Since we have no other way out of our predicament, it shouldn't do any harm to give it a try." She made a bold decision to start practicing.

Seeing their parents reciting the sutra and chanting together, the Kishibe children decided to join them. The whole family recited the sutra together—the eldest daughter fighting the pain of arthritis and the eldest son gasping for air due to his asthma as they did so.

Although their life continued to be a struggle, they now had hope.

WITH THE FORMATION of the Peru Chapter in November 1962, Vicente and Rosalia Kishibe were respectively appointed as district leader and district women's division leader. On this occasion, Vicente Kishibe made a solemn determination: "I will devote my entire life to kosen-rufu. In order to do so, it's imperative that I secure a solid financial basis."

Strangely enough, it was right around this time that Rosalia's beauty salon began to thrive. Not long after that, the roads around Kishibe's photography shop were improved, and buildings such as government offices and schools sprang up one after another. With this, his business also began to flourish. As a result, the Kishibes were able to pay back their enormous debts in a short period of time. To their added delight, before they knew it, their children also recovered from their illnesses.

Full of appreciation, Kishibe applied himself wholeheartedly to spreading the Law and working for kosen-rufu. Whenever he heard of someone suffering, he would readily go to see them, even if it took him twenty or thirty hours to get there. With warmth and compassion, he would listen to their problems, talk with them and offer encouragement. It was the greatest wish and determination of the owner of Siawase photography shop to enable every person in Peru to become happy. This inner resolve manifested itself in Kishibe's character, and he would eventually be known as someone who understood the Peruvian people's hearts better than native-born Peruvians did.

It was also due to the efforts of Mr. and Mrs. Kishibe, who were fluent in Spanish, that, in time, people other than those of Japanese descent began to practice. But as the number of non-Japanese members began to grow, this presented them with new challenges. First was the issue of how to translate and explain Buddhist terminology.

For instance, Peruvians had never been exposed to the idea of causes created in past lifetimes. Thus, when discussing the concept of karma, more often than not, their response would be: "But I don't recall creating any negative causes for which I should receive retribution." And, given the strong Catholic influence in Peru, many people tended to associate karma with the Christian notion of original sin, the hereditary stain with which all people are held to be born as descendants of Adam, who disobeyed God's command.

The Kishibes faced yet another major challenge when it came to teaching the new Peruvian members how to recite the sutra. At first, they were using mimeographed or handwritten copies of an English sutra book that Chiná had been able to obtain. However, due to phonetic differences between Spanish and English, the resulting pronunciation was incorrect. For example, since in Spanish the letter *h* is silent, the word *Hoben-pon* (the name of the chapter title) at the start of the sutra would end up being pronounced *Oben-pon*.

THE PRONUNCIATION of the English letter *z*, rarely used in Spanish, also proved difficult for the Peruvian members, and so would be pronounced more like an *s*. It was also only after much practice that they were able to master the double consonants found in Japanese that were nonexistent in Spanish. This entailed a small pause being made between the preceding syllable and double consonant.

After discussing this problem, it was decided that those already proficient in pronouncing the words in the sutra would tutor the new members individually, sitting side by side as they practiced out loud. More, in order to ensure accurate teaching, the leaders agreed to test each other on their pronunciation, and only those with an acceptable level of mastery were officially designated to take on the responsibility of teaching new members.

Peru was not the only country that had to grapple with the challenge of how best to translate Buddhist terminology and teaching the sutra to non-Japanese members. The same problems were encountered by those pioneering the way for kosen-rufu throughout the world. Nonetheless, in every country, they were able to overcome these difficulties one by one, through a process of trial and error. And it is precisely because Nichiren Buddhism established a foundation in these countries and took root in people's lives that today's great tide of kosen-rufu was created.

To what degree was the priesthood aware of such difficulties in advancing kosen-rufu? Should the priests not have expressed their utmost respect for the efforts of all our fellow members, who fought through countless hardships for the sake of kosen-rufu?

Many overseas members were angered by the condescending attitude they discerned among members of the priesthood, who knew nothing of the profundity of human life, the vastness of the world or the concept of

Buddhist compassion. The Soka Gakkai, however, had done its utmost to ensure that the members did not direct their anger toward the head temple. But members of the priesthood, taking advantage of the Gakkai's sincere desire to protect the head temple, conducted themselves with utter arrogance and gave in to idle pleasures, all the while causing Soka Gakkai members to suffer. Do they not represent the most despicable, most base model of a human being?

How deeply anguished the Daishonin must surely be to see the high priest, the supposed guardian of the orthodoxy of Nichiren Daishonin's teachings, soliciting prostitutes, and priests engaging in a variety of other immoral activities.

With a gaze filled with respect and affection, Shin'ichi thought about Chiná and the Kishibes, along with the other pioneer members who had gathered in his hotel room. Courage glistened in the eyes of the young men's division members, and radiant smiles adorned the faces of the young women's division members.

Smiling warmly at those present and speaking as if to embrace them all, Shin'ichi said: "I heard that seventeen hundred people attended the meeting today. It is a marvelous result achieved in spite of the difficult circumstances many of our members here face—it is a result that surpasses that of any such activity in Japan. I will tell our struggling chapters in Japan to go to Peru to receive guidance from you!"

Happy laughter erupted.

FULL OF ADMIRATION and appreciation for these brave pioneers of kosen-rufu in Peru, Shin'ichi continued: "We are able to grow crops because someone has cleared and cultivated the land. Those who have pioneered new frontiers are truly praiseworthy. It is such pioneers who receive the greatest benefit.

"I have been given a full and detailed report of your valiant efforts. I know, for instance, that some of you travel by bus for days to encourage friends living five hundred or six hundred miles away. Aware of the challenges you face on a daily basis, I am filled with admiration for you. I am deeply impressed. You have my most sincere respect. Seeing all of you, I am even more strongly confident that Bodhisattvas of the Earth are appearing throughout the world, in accord with predictions of the Lotus Sutra and the writings of Nichiren Daishonin."

The members felt a surge of courage as they listened intently, eyes shining, to Shin'ichi's words.

He continued: "Among leaders in the organization, there are likely to be those who exert themselves wholeheartedly, as well as those who perhaps neglect their responsibilities or try to get away with the least amount of effort. However, irrespective of what other people do, you yourself will receive benefit and good fortune in direct proportion to your hard work and efforts for the sake of kosen-rufu. This is a principle of Buddhism. Even if you manage to deceive others, you can never deceive the strict law of cause and effect taught in Nichiren Buddhism.

"Faith consists of having absolute conviction in the Mystic Law; it comes down to whether or not we can believe in this law of cause and effect, apprehend its workings in the depths of our beings and understand it in the context of our daily lives. Faith also means to dedicate ourselves to taking action for the sake of kosen-rufu.

"Consequently, we shouldn't take the view that, because others around us are irresponsible, it's all right for us to assume a casual, halfhearted attitude as well. Nor should we feel envious of others who shirk their responsibilities and devote all their time to idle amusements. That way of thinking is inconsistent with Buddhism.

"Who is it that will construct a life-state of eternal happiness in the end? Who is it that will win in life in the end? The answer is those who have dedicated their lives to the Mystic Law, kosen-rufu and the Soka Gakkai and have striven to spread the teachings of Buddhism with their entire beings. I would like every single one of you to become great victors in life.

"Today, therefore, I would like to talk with you a little about the key elements to leading such a life. The first is chanting Nam-myoho-renge-kyo. The state of our life force determines everything: our health, courage, wisdom, joy, motivation to improve our lives, as well as self-discipline. Chanting itself is the source that enables us to limitlessly tap our life force. Thus, those who base themselves on chanting Nam-myoho-renge-kyo are never deadlocked."

THE LEADERS present had been taught about the power of prayer, and each had personally experienced that power in their own lives. Shin'ichi's explanation of the significance of chanting helped further strengthen their conviction.

"At any rate," Shin'ichi continued, "the point is to continue chanting every day, no matter what, because Nam-myoho-renge-kyo is the fundamental power of the universe. Our voices when we chant in the morning and evening should be vibrant and refreshing, like the sound of mythical white horses galloping through the heavens."

A women's division leader then spoke up: "Sensei, what kind of attitude should we have when we chant to the Gohonzon?"

Smiling, Shin'ichi responded: "Of course, since we face the Gohonzon with the spirit of facing the Buddha, it's important that we conduct ourselves with a respectful and solemn attitude. Other than that, though, we should feel free to express what's in our hearts honestly and directly to the Gohonzon.

"The Gohonzon is the manifestation of the Buddha endowed with infinite compassion. We should therefore go ahead and chant about our desires, our problems and our aspirations, just as they are. When we're suffering, feeling sad or experiencing hard times, we should just go to the Gohonzon with an open heart, like an infant who throws himself into the arms of his mother and clings to her. The Gohonzon will 'listen' to our every word, so we should chant abundantly as if we are carrying on a conversation, confiding our innermost thoughts. In time, even hellish sufferings will vanish like the morning dew and seem as but a dream.

"If, for instance, we recognize that we have been in error in some way, we should offer prayers of deep apology and correct that error. Then we should make a fresh determination never to repeat the same mistake again and set forth anew.

"Also, in crucial moments where victory or defeat will

be decided, we should firmly resolve to win and chant with the power of a lion's roar or the ferocity of an *asura* demon, as if to shake the entire universe.

"And, in the evening, after a happy day, we should chant to the Gohonzon with profound appreciation.

"In the Gosho, Nichiren Daishonin cites the words: 'We awaken with the Buddha every morning and go to rest with the Buddha every night....' (GZ, 737). This means that those who continue to chant in earnest are always together with the Daishonin, the Buddha of the Latter Day of the Law. This holds true not only for this lifetime but even beyond death, with the original Buddha and all heavenly deities throughout the universe extending their protection to us. We can therefore feel completely secure from the depths of our being and need fear nothing. We should enjoy our lives with complete confidence.

"Chanting transforms suffering into joy, and joy into supreme joy. This is why it is important to single-mindedly chant Nam-myoho-renge-kyo no matter what, whether we are happy or sad, in good times or in bad. This is the direct path to happiness."

AFTER PAUSING to offer the gathered leaders something to drink, Shin'ichi continued speaking: "The first key element for leading a victorious life, therefore, is chanting Nam-myoho-renge-kyo.

"I know what I've been talking about is a little complex, but have you all been able to understand?"

Although all the leaders present were of Japanese descent, many had been born in Peru. Some of them therefore had difficulty understanding Japanese. It was out of consideration for them that Shin'ichi asked this question.

Confirming that they understood, he went on: "The second key element is studying Buddhist principles. Upon the mere mention of study, some of you may feel intimidated. But Buddhist study does not consist simply of learning facts. It means having a life philosophy as Buddhist practitioners.

"In practical terms, I would like to propose that we make steady efforts to read the writings of Nichiren Daishonin and to apply them to our lives. It need not be difficult writings, at least to begin with. For example, it could be the well-known passage, 'Those who believe in the Lotus Sutra are as if in winter, but winter always turns to spring' (WND, 536), or perhaps, 'I am...praying as earnestly as though to produce fire from damp wood, or to obtain water from parched ground' (WND, 444).

"When we have total faith in these passages and continue to strive in exact accordance with them, we will be able to see the validity of these words for ourselves and develop great conviction in the Gohonzon.

"This is the true meaning of studying the Daishonin's writings. In other words, it is practical Buddhist study that we can apply to our daily lives. If we succeed in engraving one passage in our heart, making it our own, we will naturally be able to grasp other passages of the Daishonin's writings. This is because the mastery of one phrase leads to the comprehension of all others."

Listening to Shin'ichi's guidance, each member was beginning to feel more comfortable with the idea of Buddhist study and reading the Daishonin's writings.

"The third key element I would like to present is

persevering in one's faith," Shin'ichi continued. "Our state of being at the end of our lives is all-important. No matter how much we may have exerted ourselves at any given time during our lives, it will all come to naught if we later abandon our practice and stray from the Soka Gakkai. A common Asian proverb speaks of the folly of 'plowing the field but forgetting the seed.' What this means is that unless we see things through to the end, it will all be in vain.

"Even if we build a house, all it takes is one match to reduce it to ashes. If a plane has an accident as it makes its final descent, the travelers will never reach their destination.

"What is most important is to persevere in faith, without ever giving up, until the very end. With that in mind, I would like to ask that you begin with setting your sights on ten years from now."

SHIN'ICHI spoke ardently, compelled by his intense desire to make these leaders the catalysts for the development of kosen-rufu in Peru. He put his entire being into his guidance, as if every word were the stroke of a hoe cultivating the profound depths of the members' lives.

He then listened to their reports and requests. When he learned that an increasing number of non-Japanese Peruvians were joining the organization, he suggested that they begin publishing an organ paper in Spanish. The Peruvian leaders had in fact previously launched a simple, mimeographed Spanish newsletter, entitled *Reimei,* meaning "Dawn," but the project had lost steam after only two issues.

"Producing an organ paper also requires sustained

effort," Shin'ichi said. "Once you've decided to launch a paper, half measures won't do. To ensure the publication's success, there definitely needs to be someone to assume full responsibility.

"The focus of organizational activities constantly changes—at times it will be propagation, at others, study, and so forth. As a result, even those projects deemed important at the outset can sometimes fall by the wayside. For this reason, it is necessary to have someone who will always be thinking about the specific project and taking responsibility, regardless of evolving circumstances.

"If the central figure tries to take care of everything by him- or herself, then the more diverse activities become, the greater will be the risk of the organization becoming deadlocked. By having people who will shoulder the responsibility for each of the various arenas of activity with the same commitment and resolve as the central figure, we can carry out multi-dimensional activities, and the organization will become even stronger and more solid.

"At any rate, unity is the power source for the development of kosen-rufu. It is no coincidence that you find yourselves together here at this time in Peru.

"Our ties with each other are based on our relationships from the remote past. We are connected by deep, deep bonds from previous lifetimes. Therefore, let us all unite and advance together on good terms, encouraging and supporting each other."

At this point, one of the leaders present spoke up.

"Sensei, would you please select a name for our new Spanish paper?"

"All right. How about using the same basic title as the

Japanese organ newspaper, *Seikyo*? How does *Peru Seikyo* sound? But please understand that I have proposed this name with the hope that you here in Peru will lead the way for the members in Japan."

Approving applause broke out.

The discussion then turned to other issues, including the establishment of a community center. It was an exchange that abounded with hope for the future.

IN CLOSING, Shin'ichi stated: "The fact that there are currently more than one thousand member-households practicing in Peru means that the foundations for the kosen-rufu movement here are now in place. This is a historic achievement.

"I will be sending my prayers every day for all of you in Peru to become happy without exception. Next time, let's meet in Japan."

Both consideration and friendship start from prayer. Prayer has the power to connect one human being to another.

At the conclusion of the meeting, Shin'ichi shook hands with everyone and then joined them for a group photo to commemorate the occasion. The members' faces were radiant and wreathed in smiles. A fresh new resolve shone in their eyes.

The next day, March 16, proved to be a full and hectic day for Shin'ichi and his colleagues.

Shin'ichi traveled from one place to another meeting with influential Japanese Peruvians and taking in the important historical sites of the city, while Jujo met with members of the local media. Izumida and his party, meanwhile, left Peru for Bolivia to encourage the members there.

In between appointments, Shin'ichi stopped off to see the pre-Inca ruins of Pachácamac, situated about twenty miles to the south of Lima. Wherever he went, he earnestly chanted, as if to infuse Peru—the mountains and rivers, and every last corner of this great land—with the Mystic Law.

On arriving back in Central Lima, he took a walk through the main business district. There, he came upon a public square dominated by a large central monument—some four or five stories high—crowned with an equestrian statue. It was the renowned Plaza San Martín, and the statue was that of the hero of Latin American liberation, José de San Martín, who had played an indispensable role in the movement for Peruvian independence.

San Martín was born in 1778 in Yapeyú, a town in the northeastern part of what is now Argentina. At that time, Argentina, along with Peru, Chile and other countries in the region, were Spanish colonies. In his youth, San Martín moved to Spain, the birthplace of his parents, where his father, a member of the Spanish army, had been transferred. Perhaps due to his father's influence, he also joined the military. However, when a revolution seeking independence from Spanish rule erupted in Latin America, he left the Spanish army, returning to Buenos Aires in March 1812. San Martín was then thirty-four years old. For him, South America was his birthplace, his homeland. He had thus determined to devote his life to its liberation and independence.

EVENTUALLY, San Martín led a liberation army of four thousand men (five thousand, according to some sources), whom he had personally trained, across the Andes. They fought against the Spanish army and gained control of Santiago, Chile.

He was called upon to become governor of Chile with full powers, but San Martín categorically refused and continued his campaign for freedom. He next planned an offensive against Peru, this time traveling by sea. On landing on Peruvian soil, San Martín issued a proclamation to his army: "Remember that you come, not to conquer, but to liberate a people."[3]

In July 1821, he and his forces succeeded in liberating the Peruvian center of Lima.

On July 10, San Martín entered the city, accompanied only by his aide-de-camp. When the people caught sight of him, they cried out, "Long live the general!"

"No, no," he said, plainly disconcerted. "Instead of shouting, 'Long live the general!' let us cry out, 'Long live Peruvian independence!'"

Then, on July 28, in front of a large crowd gathered in Lima's public square, San Martín solemnly proclaimed the independence of Peru.

He subsequently assumed the role of Protector of Peru, a function that gave him supreme administrative authority, both military and political. However, awaiting him was a barrage of jealousy and criticism, with people accusing him of harboring ambitions to be king. They denounced him as a despot, an emperor, a devil.

Not a single person tried to find out what was in his heart or what his true aspirations were. In a letter he wrote to a friend around this time, he confided: "Peru is free. I now see before me the end of my public life, and watch how I can leave this heavy charge in safe hands...."[4]

It was never San Martín's wish to obtain personal power. He had simply wanted to liberate Lima, the stronghold of Spanish colonial rule in South America.

Although the independence of Peru had been declared, still more battles had to be fought against the Spanish army in order to ensure its complete independence.

As San Martín had been fighting his way northward from Chile, there had been yet another hero of Latin American liberation, Simón Bolívar, who was working his way south, liberating Venezuela, Colombia and Ecuador. Sensing that he would need the support of Bolívar's army to secure Peru's independence, San Martín met with Bolívar in Guayaquil, in present-day Ecuador.

WHAT TRANSPIRED between San Martín and Bolívar during their meeting remains one of the mysteries of Latin American history. From what can be gathered, however, there appears to have been a wide discrepancy in the perspectives of these two heroes. Their ideas regarding the future political structure of the region, for instance, were radically different.

In accord with the saying, "Two great rivals cannot coexist," San Martín decided to step down, entrusting Bolívar to complete the task of liberating the South American continent. No one really understood why San Martín had made this decision, for he chose not to elaborate on the matter. However, a letter he wrote to Bolívar provides some insight: "My decision is irrevocable.... I shall leave for Chile, convinced that my presence is the only obstacle that keeps you from coming to Peru with your army. For me it would have been the height of happiness to conclude the War of Independence under the orders of a General to whom [South] America owes her liberty. Destiny has decreed otherwise, and I must resign myself to it."[5]

No doubt San Martín recognized that his mission was to pave the way for Latin America's freedom from Spanish rule by liberating Peru and declaring its independence. That task completed, he must have considered that the greatest priority was to consolidate the struggle under the command of a single leader.

In addition, San Martín's health had been deteriorating for some time. Now that an unstoppable tide toward independence had been created, he had absolutely no regrets or attachments to the power or positions he had obtained. For these reasons, he ultimately decided to entrust the final phase of Peru's liberation to Simón Bolívar, five years his junior.

On his return to Peru, San Martín attended the first session of the Congress in Peru since the proclamation of independence, in order to hand back the functions and powers that had been conferred upon him. He then immediately left Peru.

The sudden departure of this respected leader, who had made such an immense contribution to the continent's liberation, prompted a chorus of abuse and insult. People condemned him for what they saw as the height of irresponsibility in leaving them this way. This selfless, noble hero, however, held firm to his convictions, unperturbed by these attacks.

San Martín later moved from Argentina to Europe, and it was in France, in August 1850, that he died at the age of seventy-two. He lived out his days in such modest surroundings that one could hardly imagine that this was a great champion of Latin American liberation. They say, however, that his commitment to protect the weak never diminished to the end.

THERE IS the following anecdote about San Martín in his final years. One day, his granddaughter entered his room crying. In her hands she clasped a doll.

"My baby doll is broken," she said, sobbing, "and she says she's cold."

From a bureau, San Martín took out a medal attached to a yellow ribbon. Giving it to her, he said: "Put this on your doll. It will take away her chills."

The girl stopped crying, but her mother, San Martín's daughter, now turned to him with a look of concern.

"But father," she said, "that is the medal of honor you received from the Spanish government when you defeated the French army." He had helped defend Spain against Napoleon in 1808.

With a smile, he responded in a lightly chiding tone: "If they cannot even stop the tears of a child, of what value are ribbons and medals?"

It was most likely his conviction that such things were meaningless unless they helped relieve people from suffering.

Shin'ichi stood in the square for some time contemplating the equestrian statue of San Martín. As he reflected on the renowned hero's life, he felt a profound sympathy for this man who had wanted nothing other than to liberate Latin America, only to be attacked as a despot or as having ambitions to be king.

Shin'ichi, likewise, had dedicated himself for the sake of people's happiness and world peace. And yet, within Japan, spurious rumors abounded that he aimed to take control of the country and become its most powerful leader by having the Clean Government Party, whose main supporting body was the Soka Gakkai, take the reins of government.

Even here, in Latin America, the mass media was attacking Shin'ichi, portraying him as a dictator who planned to establish political parties in countries around the globe with the design of world domination.

Human beings judge things according to their own mindset. Consequently, people driven by selfish desires and personal ambition cannot recognize and accept the existence of selfless individuals. When the altruistic win applause and kudos because of their altruism, the self-serving are filled with raging resentment and jealousy and begin to denigrate them virulently.

Shin'ichi made a vow in front of this towering dignified statue: "My life, too, will no doubt be a succession of persecutions. But I will continue to fight. I will not be defeated. For my mission is to liberate humanity from the chains of karma that hold it prisoner to suffering."

SHIN'ICHI'S schedule in Peru was extremely hectic, lasting only three days and two nights. He arrived in the afternoon of March 15 and departed on the morning of March 17. During this short time, however, he not only met with and encouraged representative members but also undertook various measures aimed at consolidating the organization's future growth. And on March 16, praying sincerely for the Peruvian members' dynamic development, he presented them with a poem:

> *The spirit of valiant champions*
> *Of the Mystic Law*
> *Pulses here and now.*
> *Widely spread*
> *The golden seeds.*

March 16 exactly eight years earlier had been the day of the ceremony at which President Toda entrusted the entire responsibility of kosen-rufu to Shin'ichi and the rest of the youth division members. On that day, the torch of kosen-rufu had been transmitted to Shin'ichi and the other youth, and the golden seed of a profound mission to realize kosen-rufu had been planted in the depths of their hearts. This opened new horizons for the movement's development in Japan.

In all likelihood, Shin'ichi composed this poem for the Peruvian members with the desire to convey the significance of that March 16 ceremony, and to sow the golden seed of kosen-rufu in the lives of each one of them.

After departing from Lima the following morning, March 17, Shin'ichi headed for Miami. From there, he traveled to Los Angeles and Honolulu on his return journey to Japan, arriving back in Tokyo on March 23.

Shin'ichi's departure from Lima was subdued. To avoid provoking the Peruvian authorities and to protect the members, Shin'ichi had asked not to be seen off at the airport. Nevertheless, a passionate fighting spirit for kosen-rufu blazed in the hearts of the Peruvian members whom Shin'ichi had encouraged during his stay.

In particular, Vicente Kishibe was firmly resolved to take full responsibility for kosen-rufu in Peru. As his first initiative, he volunteered to edit the local organization's Spanish-language newspaper, *Peru Seikyo*.

He thought to himself: *Spanish is the official language of many Latin American countries. If we publish a Soka Gakkai newspaper in Spanish, kosen-rufu not only in Peru, but in all of Latin America will surely advance in leaps and bounds. Sensei has entrusted us, the Peruvian members, with an important mission. I am absolutely determined to make a success of this newspaper, which Sensei himself named!* He felt himself tremble at the gravity of this responsibility.

With great energy and enthusiasm, Kishibe threw himself into producing the publication.

Awareness of one's mission gives rise to bold action.

IN ADDITION to Vicente Kishibe, several others joined the editorial staff of *Peru Seikyo*. Together, they set to work on the newspaper every night after their other Soka Gakkai activities. None of them had any formal training as reporters or editors. They were all novices to newspaper-making and they had to learn as they went along.

Their biggest challenge was translation—the translation of faith-related guidance and Gosho lectures in particular proved to be more difficult than anticipated. In preparing articles of this nature, it was not rare for them to work through the night, battling with every word and every term.

From such arduous labor emerged the first issue of *Peru Seikyo*, a four-page typeset tabloid-sized paper, on April 20—just thirty-six days after Shin'ichi Yamamoto had made his proposal. Incidentally, this date marked the anniversary of the launch of the Japanese newspaper, *Seikyo Shimbun*, fifteen years earlier, in 1951.

Around the same time as *Peru Seikyo* got off the ground, a new community center opened amid great celebration in the city of Lima, the eighth such center established by the Soka Gakkai overseas.

With a solemn pledge in their hearts to create a new era and to transform the negative attitude toward the Soka Gakkai in Peruvian society, the members made a fresh, hopefilled departure, determined to sow the seeds of trust and friendship in society.

Kishibe would later become the general director of the Peruvian organization, opening up a new chapter in the annals of kosen-rufu in this vast continent that was the home of the ancient Incas.

Meanwhile, the members, as Buddhist practitioners, sought to become model citizens, and gave their all to contributing to society, gradually winning the profound trust of those around them. As a result, they were also able to further understanding of the Soka Gakkai and Shin'ichi Yamamoto in Peruvian society.

Consequently, when Shin'ichi returned to Peru eight years later in 1974, the city of Lima welcomed him with open arms, and conferred on him the title of Special Honorary Citizen. And on the occasion of Shin'ichi's third visit to Peru in 1984, President Fernando Beraúnde Terry conferred on him the country's highest honor, the Order of the Sun of Peru in the Grade of Grand Cross, in recognition of his contributions to global peace, culture and education.

The passionate wish and determination of Shin'ichi, and that of his fellow Peruvian members who shared his spirit, brought about a dramatic transformation in the times and society.

History was setting a new course, and the sun of hope had risen over Peru.

DURING THE MONTH of March 1966, Shin'-ichi visited the United States, Brazil and Peru. Meanwhile, during that same period, a number of other top Soka Gakkai leaders traveled in separate groups to various other cities in Central and South America to encourage the members there.

On March 4, two days before Shin'ichi left Japan, seven leaders, including Seiichiro Haruki, Katsu Kiyohara and Ittetsu Okada, visited Argentina. As soon as they landed in the capital Buenos Aires that morning, they met Argentina Chapter Leader Takeo Shiroya to discuss the structure of the local organization. After conducting a study exam for local members in the afternoon, the visiting leaders attended a chapter convention, which was held at a center belonging to the Association of Japanese in Argentina. More than a hundred members assembled for the event.

The Soka Gakkai organization in Argentina was founded in August 1963, when Soka Gakkai Vice General Director Seiichiro Haruki and Director Hiroshi Yamagiwa visited Buenos Aires. The some twenty member-households there had formed a district, with Takeo Shiroya as district leader.

Takeo was the younger brother of Kunio Shiroya, who had served as the first student division leader of the Soka Gakkai in Japan. It was at Kunio's introduction that Takeo joined the Soka Gakkai in 1943.

Having enrolled in the Japanese Naval Gunnery School toward the end of the Pacific War, Takeo was sent to Okinawa. He miraculously survived the bloody battle of Okinawa, which claimed so many lives. While he keenly sensed at that time that he had been protected through the power of faith, he remained rather passive in his Buddhist practice.

After the war, visions of going overseas began to unfold in his mind. He thought of moving to Argentina, as one of his friends had done. However, he still felt some hesitation. Having the occasion to meet President Toda at his brother's wedding in October 1953, Takeo ventured to ask this man, whom his brother seemed to respect so much, for advice regarding his future.

Upon hearing his plans, Toda said: "So, you want to go to Argentina. I think that's good. You should go. It'll be a great challenge for you as a young man."

These words served to solidify Takeo's resolve. In July of the following year, 1954, Takeo boarded a ship bound for Argentina. Once there, he started out working for a steel mill, and then in a series of other jobs, including as an employee of a launderers' union and the manager of a fish store. He eventually settled into a position as a locally-hired staff member of the Japanese Emigration Service.

Takeo was finally inspired and encouraged to practice Nichiren Buddhism seriously by a young man and fellow immigrant named Kazuya Okida, who was originally from Akita Prefecture in Japan.

For Okida, Argentina had been the land of his dreams since childhood.

DURING the strained economic times after the war, Okida and his family would often receive parcels containing such things as notebooks, pencils, biscuits and various other food items. They were sent by one of his father's friends, who apparently owned a thriving flower nursery in Argentina. Gazing at this bounty, Okida began to formulate a dream of one day going to this prosperous country of Argentina and owning a huge nursery himself. He quit high school and set about making preparations for his move.

In September 1957, at the urging of his mother, who had already started practicing Nichiren Buddhism, Okida joined the Soka Gakkai. At the time, he was in Kanagawa Prefecture studying floriculture to fulfill his dream. A year later, in September 1958, Okida left Japan.

In Argentina, his father's friend, who lived in the suburbs of Buenos Aires, gave him room and board with his family and a job at his nursery.

As he challenged his new life, Okida continued his Buddhist practice, but he felt terribly lonely, missing the companionship of fellow Soka Gakkai members. *How I wish there were some other members!* he thought. *We could talk together about Buddhism and encourage each other!*

In his search for comrades in faith, he asked every Japanese person he encountered:"Would you happen to know of anyone who is a Soka Gakkai member?"

His innocent inquiry, however, often drew an unexpectedly hostile response:"What? You're a member of the Soka Gakkai? Why, that's a violent religious organization, isn't it?" or "What do you think will happen if you proclaim yourself to be a Soka Gakkai member here in Argentina, a country where the majority of people are Catholic? Later, when you get married and have children, they'll be turned away from school!"

He was angry and vexed with himself at his inability to rebut their assertions.

Around this time, Okida remembered a letter he had received from a senior in faith encouraging him to write to Shin'ichi Yamamoto, the then Soka Gakkai general administrator, for guidance whenever he found himself in painful or trying circumstances.

But Mr. Yamamoto must surely be very busy, Okida thought. *Moreover, he probably wouldn't have the time to answer a letter from someone he's never even met!*

Nevertheless, he honestly put down on paper all that was in his heart and sent a letter off to Shin'ichi at the Soka Gakkai Headquarters.

A short while later, he received a response from Shin'ichi, which stated:"Thank you for your letter. I am firmly convinced that the presence of Soka Gakkai members who embrace the Gohonzon, boldly practicing Buddhism in various countries outside Japan signals a new dawn for our world.

"I am praying that you, as an emissary of the Buddha, will exert yourself wholeheartedly in your present workplace and circumstances, and win in society. The benefit and power of the Gohonzon encompass the entire universe. Thus they will manifest themselves no matter where you may be.

"I am praying that you will strive energetically in all your endeavors and live your life fully, while summoning forth strong faith and being confident of the protection of the Buddhist gods. Please advance in life undaunted, filled with hope, courage and conviction."

KAZUYA OKIDA was deeply moved by Shin'ichi's letter.

Mr. Yamamoto sent me a reply. I'm so touched and humbled by his kindness. In order to reply to his expectations, I will win at all costs! he vowed in his heart.

Okida received yet another letter of encouragement from Shin'ichi on April 22, shortly before the latter's inauguration as third Soka Gakkai president.

The welfare of this young man who had traveled all alone to Argentina was constantly on Shin'ichi's mind.

The sublime and noble work of worldwide kosen-rufu begins from a single individual living in each particular country. It is therefore of utmost importance that we encourage and support such people with all of our energy and being.

Okida treasured these letters from Shin'ichi. He read them over and over again, renewing and strengthening his determination as he did so. And he threw himself heart and soul into introducing others to the Daishonin's teachings. But even after two years from his arrival, no one had begun practicing Buddhism.

However, through communications with the overseas

Department at the Soka Gakkai Headquarters, Okida learned of three other members practicing in Argentina. He immediately set out to visit them.

He met Takeo Shiroya for the first time in February 1961. Okida was excited at the prospect of meeting this longtime member, only to find that Shiroya appeared to have little or no awareness of his mission as a Soka Gakkai member.

"Mr. Shiroya," Okida appealed, "since the power of the Gohonzon is absolute, let us at least start by doing the *goza,* our morning recitation of the sutra."

"Since you are so insistent," Shiroya replied, "I'll give the sutra a try, but just so you know, we don't have any *goza* here."

Goza, the Japanese term for the five-prayer format of our morning recitation of the sutra, is a homonym for the Japanese word for straw mats. Shiroya had confused the two words, betraying his total lack of familiarity with the Buddhist practice.

With Okida's continued support, however, Shiroya gradually deepened his faith and developed a sense of mission.

Okida also exerted himself fully in his work. He keenly felt how vital it was for him to show actual proof of victory in society in order to contribute to kosen-rufu.

He built a greenhouse and started his own flower nursery. In the beginning, he could not make ends meet without continuing to work at other nurseries as well. Nonetheless, during this period, he strove harder than anyone to research and devise the best methods for growing flowers.

Five years after moving to Argentina, he had increased

the number of greenhouses he owned to three. His efforts also led to an amazing achievement—a carnation he had developed through his research took first prize at a flower show, and his success was reported widely in the local papers. In addition, he was called upon to head horticultural research in the local Flower Growers Association. By the following year, he had doubled the number of his greenhouses to six.

OKIDA had begun to show splendid actual proof of his Buddhist practice within Argentine society. This served to dramatically change people's attitude toward the Soka Gakkai. Now, when he spoke of Buddhism, everyone would listen.

Shiroya, for his part, was also making remarkable strides in his practice. He began to introduce one person after another to Buddhism, including his coworkers and those whom he had met aboard the ship on his way to Argentina. He had developed into a champion of kosen-rufu.

Then, when the first district was formed in August 1963, Shiroya became district leader, and with the formation of a chapter the following year, he assumed the responsibility of chapter leader.

By nature, Shiroya was considerate and caring of others, and thus won the trust of his fellow members. Together with Okida, they were able to create a harmonious and joyful organization.

In 1965, a young men's division was established in the Argentine chapter and Okida was appointed its leader.

Shortly thereafter, through the introduction of a leader in Japan, he married a young woman named Mitsuko

Akaiwa, who had been working as a staff member at the Soka Gakkai Headquarters in Tokyo.

While Mitsuko cherished the desire to work for kosen-rufu overseas, she was unprepared for the conditions of her new life in Argentina. Okida lived in a rural area about nineteen miles outside of Buenos Aires, in a house without electricity. What is more, Mitsuko had to help with the farm work, something in which she had absolutely no experience.

Prior to her departure from Japan, Mitsuko had been appointed as the young women's division leader for Argentina. However, as she set out for her activities, she found herself surrounded by overgrown prairies as far as the eye could see. There was hardly any public transportation, with buses running few and far between, so Mitsuko had no other way of getting around than riding with her husband on the back of his moped.

All this was vastly different from what she had originally envisioned of life overseas. She had pictured living in a big modern city, like those found in Europe or the United States. In contrast, her life in Argentina consisted of an aching body from unaccustomed farm work, a daily existence without electricity and a language she couldn't understand.

Gazing at the large red sun sinking beyond the horizon of the prairie, Mitsuko wiped the tears from her eyes. Every time she felt disheartened, she would recall the encouragement she received before she left Japan.

She reminded herself: *President Yamamoto said that things may be tough at times, but that chanting Nam-myoho-renge-kyo is the key. According to the teachings of Buddhism, the place I am right now is the Land of Eternally Tranquil Light. I came here for the sake of kosen-rufu. No matter what, I cannot let myself be defeated!*

MITSUKO applied herself to her Soka Gakkai activities with serious determination. Having been a young women's division leader back in Tokyo, she found herself frustrated and impatient at the seemingly slow, relaxed pace of activities in Argentina. More, from her point of view, the members here were extremely casual about time, failing to grasp the importance of punctuality, and deplorably lacking in the Gakkai spirit to challenge any and all obstacles.

But the more zealously she tried to rouse the members, the more she alienated them. Finally one day, a member admitted to her: "I know you're very sincere, but I find your approach utterly unacceptable."

Mitsuko was deeply shocked. Wondering what she could be doing wrong, she chanted in earnest. As she did so, she came to a realization: *I've been trying frantically to pattern the activities here after those back in Japan. I have been nothing but self-centered!*

What I need to do is focus on the conditions here in Argentina. I need to concentrate on how we can enable each member to overcome their problems, and how we can go about creating an organization that wins everyone's wholehearted support and makes it possible for them to participate joyfully in activities.

When leaders are self-centered or arrogant, the organization suffers as a result.

From that moment onward, Mitsuko strove sincerely to offer careful, attentive and thorough personal guidance.

Actions necessary to achieve kosen-rufu may be likened to waves gradually eroding a rock. Steady, tenacious efforts to repeatedly engage in dialogue and offer encouragement are the primary force for transforming all circumstances.

Kazuya and Mitsuko Okida united their youthful energy behind Takeo Shiroya, and as a result the Argentine organization grew to encompass more than 120 member-households.

It was at this point in their development that they were able to welcome Seiichiro Haruki and other leaders from Japan on March 4, 1966. At the meeting held in Buenos Aires that evening, they announced the names of those who had passed the study exam, along with the new organizational lineup and corresponding leadership appointments. The highlight of the new organizational structure was the women's division. Until this time, Argentina Chapter did not have any women's division leaders, but that night, Yoshie Kobori, a woman in her late forties, was appointed chapter women's division leader.

Although she had been practicing for only a year or so, she had already experienced the immense power of faith and shown actual proof through her practice, including her child's recovery from asthma.

Mitsuko Okida was appointed chapter vice women's division leader, a position she took on in addition to her existing responsibilities as young women's division leader.

SEIICHIRO HARUKI stepped up to the podium to offer words of encouragement on behalf of all the leaders visiting from Japan: "While President Yamamoto was unable to come to Argentina this time, he has asked me to convey the following message to you:

> My dear fellow Argentine members, every single day I am chanting in earnest for your happiness and for the prosperity of your families. Some day soon, I will, without fail, visit Argentina. While Japan and Argentina may seem a world apart, on opposite ends of the earth, the hearts of those who live their lives for kosen-rufu are one with mine. You are always in my heart, just as I am probably in yours.
>
> As inseparable comrades in faith, let us joyfully and proudly fulfill our mission in this lifetime, advancing in harmonious unity. I am looking forward immensely to the day we shall meet.

"This concludes the message from President Yamamoto."

Many of the members had tears in their eyes when he

finished. Being yet few in number, most of these Argentine members had been waging lonely, solitary struggles for kosen-rufu, enduring various hardships, spurred on and encouraged only by the thought of President Yamamoto.

Continuing his speech, Haruki declared: "Today marks a fresh new departure for our organization in Argentina. To live means to create history. I call on each of you to create a new history of your own personal happiness and of the development of kosen-rufu in Argentina!"

The members applauded vigorously in an expression of their deep commitment, as if to illuminate the darkness with the light of the human spirit.

Around noon on March 5, the day before his departure on a trip to North and South America, Shin'ichi received a phone call at the Soka Gakkai Headquarters from Seiichiro Haruki, giving him a detailed report on the meeting in Argentina.

On the following evening, March 6, Shin'ichi left Japan, traveling first to Los Angeles and New York before arriving in Brazil on March 10.

The Argentine leaders, meanwhile, had gathered together after their March 4 convention and decided that Chapter Leader Takeo Shiroya, Chapter Women's Division Leader Yoshie Kobori and Young Men's Division Leader Kazuya Okida would go to Brazil to see President Yamamoto during his visit there.

Shiroya and Kobori left first, arriving in São Paulo on the 12th. They were able to participate in the Brazil representative leaders meeting attended by Shin'ichi.

Having previously been informed of their plans, Shin'-ichi had prepared a gift of prayer beads to encourage

Kobori, who had just been appointed women's division leader.

The attitude of a true Buddhist leader is to treat fellow members who are striving earnestly to fulfill their mission with the same respect one would show a Buddha.

When the representative leaders meeting was finished, Shin'ichi called out: "Is Ms. Kobori of Argentina present?"

YOSHIE KOBORI was taken by surprise, for she had never expected President Yamamoto to suddenly call out her name.

"Thank you so much for coming all this way," Shin'ichi said as he handed her the prayer beads. "I am counting on you to take good care of the women's division member in Argentina.

"A leader must be not only a person of courage, with the strength to stand alone, but also a person of harmony, who can get along and advance side by side with everyone.

"I know I am entrusting you with a heavy responsibility, and I very much appreciate your efforts."

Kobori was deeply moved by the earnestness and sincerity of Shin'ichi's words.

Shin'ichi then turned to offer words of encouragement to Takeo Shiroya, and exchanged firm handshakes with these two leaders. Having been detained by his work, Kazuya Okida arrived in São Paulo the next day, March 13.

Together with Shiroya and Kobori, he attended the culture festival put on by the Brazilian members at the Municipal Theater that evening. Afterward, the three of them went to Shin'ichi's hotel to await his arrival. Okida waited by the entrance, while Shiroya and Kobori waited in the lobby area.

Shin'ichi arrived in the company of Brazil Chapter Leader Yasuhiro Saiki and others, and headed toward the elevators. Okida hurriedly ran toward them and called out to Shin'ichi: "Sensei, I am Okida from Argentina!"

A smile broke out on Shin'ichi's face. "Thank you so much for coming. Let's meet in my room and talk."

Okida stepped into the elevator with Shin'ichi.

All this had happened so quickly that by the time Shiroya and Kobori reached the elevator, the doors had closed, and it had started going up. As they had already had the opportunity to receive encouragement from Shin'ichi the day before, they decided to wait for Okida in the lobby.

Shin'ichi could not contain his joy at seeing before him this highspirited young man, whom he had continuously encouraged through his letters.

"I cannot tell you how much I have been looking forward to meeting you," Shin'ichi said as they entered his room. "I'm really impressed with how hard you have been working!

"Through the efforts of a solitary youth who moved to Argentina, an organization for kosen-rufu was created, and one hundred, then two hundred, people have set forth on the path to hope and happiness. There is nothing that can surpass this accomplishment. There is no way of life more wonderful, more meaningful."

"Yes, I agree," Okida responded. "I feel the same way."

Shin'ichi nodded and continued: "Life is short. How and for what purpose we use that life will determine its value."

S HIN'ICHI gazed intently at Kazuya Okida as he said with emphasis: "My hope is that you will dedicate your life to kosen-rufu in Argentina. I also hope that in my stead, you will work for the happiness and welfare of the people there."

"I will!" Okida replied, in a voice brimming with resolve.

At this point, Mineko, who had accompanied her husband, Shin'ichi, to Brazil, served some Japanese stir-fried noodles.

"I thought you may not have the chance to eat this often in Argentina. Please, have some," she said.

At Mineko and Shin'ichi's insistence, Okida dug into the noodles, savoring the well-remembered flavor of back home. As he ate, he was also deeply moved by the warmth and consideration shown to him by President Yamamoto and his wife.

That day, Okida firmly resolved: *I've decided what to do with my life. I am going to dedicate myself to kosen-rufu alongside President Yamamoto. And some day, I will definitely invite him to come and visit us in Argentina!*

A short time after returning from his trip to Brazil, Okida sold his thriving flower nursery and ventured into the retail end of the business. He felt that if he were to give himself fully to supporting the members, it would be better not to live on the outskirts of Buenos Aires but move closer to the city center where it would be easier to maintain contact with everyone. This is what prompted his sudden decision.

Starting as an apprentice, he eventually went into business for himself, as a consignment sales dealer. Each day brought its own share of challenges and obstacles. However, his past experience as a flower grower served him well, to the point where he became one of the top two dealers in the flower industry in the city.

Okida traveled extensively throughout Argentina, busily engaging in activities for kosen-rufu. The following year, 1967, Argentina General Chapter was established, to which Okida was later named general chapter leader and his wife, Mitsuko, general chapter women's division leader.

But it would not be until 1993, twenty-seven years after Okida's encounter with Shin'ichi, that they would realize their long-cherished dream of welcoming Shin'ichi to Argentina.

During those long years, Shin'ichi worked hard to deepen the ties of friendship between Japan and Argentina and to promote educational and cultural exchange by meeting with university officials, artists and Argentine ambassadors to Japan. He also met with Argentine President Raúl Alfonsín on his visit to Japan in 1986.

The Argentine members did their utmost. Through their energetic efforts, they began to win broad understanding for Nichiren Buddhism as well as praise and recognition for the Soka Gakkai's movement for peace and education in society. As a result, in 1990, the Argentine government awarded Shin'ichi Yamamoto in Japan one of its highest honors, the Order of Merit of May in the Grade of Grand Cross. Numerous universities followed suit, conferring a succession of distinctions upon Shin'ichi.

The seeds of social contribution painstakingly planted by these pioneer members had taken root and blossomed into beautiful, fragrant flowers of trust all across the vast plains of Argentina.

AFTER CONCLUDING their itinerary in Argentina, Haruki and his party set out on March 5 for Paraguay, where the Soka Gakkai had also established a chapter and some one hundred member-households were practicing.

Once there, the leaders from Japan split up into two groups, with Haruki and Ittetsu Okada heading for Asunción, the nation's capital, and five other leaders, including Katsu Kiyohara, proceeding to Colonia Federico Chávez, a settlement of Japanese immigrants. Meeting and encouraging the members in Colonia Federico Chávez during this trip was considered particularly crucial for the future dynamic development of kosen-rufu in Paraguay.

In contrast to Argentina, where the kosen-rufu movement had been initiated by people of Japanese descent living in and around the capital, Buenos Aires, the spread of Nichiren Buddhism in Paraguay had been achieved through the efforts of the Japanese immigrants who had taken up residence in Colonia Federico Chávez and other similar settlements.

When Brazil began to restrict immigration in 1934, Paraguay afforded another option, with the first Japanese settlers arriving in 1936. Later, when the Pacific War began, Paraguay severed its diplomatic ties with Japan, a move that put a halt to immigration. However, when relations between the two countries were restored after the war, immigration programs were reestablished, resuming in May 1954.

The new arrivals from Japan made their way to various settlements that lay to the northeast of Encarnación, a city in southern Paraguay near the border with Argentina. These included Colonia Federico Chávez and the neighboring settlement of Colonia Fram, which were some ten miles from Encarnación, and Colonia Pirapó, which was thirty-seven miles from there.

The immigrants started their new lives by cutting down trees from the uncultivated plots of land they had been allotted, using the timber to build their own houses by hand. At night, when they retired inside these humble shedlike homes that they had worked so hard to complete, they were relentlessly attacked by insects drawn to the lamplight. Not only were the settlers tormented by armies of mosquitoes and gnats but also maggots and sand fleas. There were even times when they could hear the distant howl of pumas and the screeching of monkeys coming from the pitchblack jungle. Fighting back their feelings of helplessness and fear, they began their new life.

Among these settlers was a Soka Gakkai member—the future leader of Paraguay Chapter, Shinshichi Miyaji, who emigrated in 1957. He was later joined by Tetsuya and Tomiyo Adachi, who settled in Fram in 1959, and Kunihiro and Haru Yamaki, who arrived in Pirapó in 1960. These members took the lead in launching Soka Gakkai activities in their respective communities.

To encounter fellow members in these settlements was a joy beyond all description.

TETSUYA ADACHI, for one, was overjoyed to learn a year after he moved to the settlement that among the new settlers there was someone chanting Nam-myoho-renge-kyo morning and evening.

As soon as he heard the news, he went to each of the newcomers' homes inquiring if any of them were Soka Gakkai members. It wasn't until his eighth try, however, that he finally received an affirmative response.

Excitedly, Fumiaki Okamura said: "Yes, I am! Are you a member, too?"

They embraced each other warmly, and exchanged a firm and solid handshake.

Unlike in the cities, doing Soka Gakkai activities in these settlements was often fraught with danger.

In Colonia Pirapó, Haru Yamaki set out enthusiastically one day to do activities along with some of the other settlers. Exhausted from walking, they had stopped to take a rest in the shade when they heard a rattling sound coming from somewhere.

"I wonder what that could be," Haru said, peering into the bushes.

"Be careful!" one of her companions cried out. "It's a rattlesnake!"

"But I thought rattlesnakes made more of a low, buzzing sound."

"Yes, but sometimes they sound like this!"

It was not unusual to see rattlesnakes in the settlements. They fell from trees that were being cleared or lay coiled in the middle of the road. When someone was bitten, it caused a great commotion.

The settlers faced other hardships as well. If it started to rain on their way to activities, the red earth would turn to mud and stick to their shoes, making it slippery and difficult to walk. But the members would take off their shoes and walk barefoot if they had to.

The lives of these immigrants were far from stable. Seeds and saplings that they planted would get washed away by the rain, or destroyed by frost or hail. At times, their crops would be ravaged by hordes of locusts. Without the income from their crops, it was not long before they depleted what financial resources they had brought with them from Japan.

For the members living in these conditions, their faith provided them with the strength to rise to every challenge, and served as a source of courage to overcome their hardships. They therefore applied themselves wholeheartedly to their Buddhist practice and manifested numerous benefits in their lives.

There were those who, bringing all of their skill and ingenuity to the fore, were able to reap a bountiful harvest, while others managed to escape unharmed from natural disasters. It was just such actual proof that spread an understanding and appreciation of Nichiren Buddhism among the people living in the settlements.

In addition, there were some settlers who, moved by the peaceful countenance of those Soka Gakkai members who died, expressed a desire to take up faith.

THE EFFORTS of the Paraguayan members bore fruit, with increasing numbers of people joining the Soka Gakkai. Eventually, the first district was created in August 1961. Two years later, in August 1963, a chapter was established.

Bound for Colonia Federico Chávez, Kiyohara and four

other leaders from Japan arrived at Posadas Airport after a more than four-hour flight from Buenos Aires. Posadas was actually part of Argentina, but Paraguay lay just across the Paraná River that ran through this border city.

Ten Paraguayan members, including Chapter Leader Shinshichi Miyaji, had come to greet them at the airport. Among them was Ikuo Tanigawa, a group leader who had traveled for four days, covering a distance of more than one hundred miles from Colonia Yguazú, close to the Brazilian border. The Japanese leaders felt inspired and revitalized by the passionate seeking spirit of these members.

From the airport, they drove to the wharf where they boarded a small motorboat to carry them across the river. Twenty minutes later, they reached Encarnación, Paraguay. Once there, they held a meeting to discuss their plans.

As they spoke, one young man addressed Kiyohara. "If I may make a request," he ventured, "there are actually forty or so member-households in a settlement called Colonia Pirapó, approximately thirty-seven miles away from here. They were planning on taking a truck to attend tonight's guidance meeting at the home of Miyaji, their chapter leader, but due to the recent torrential rains, they have been unable to leave for fear of having an accident on the muddy roads.

"It should be possible to reach their settlement by jeep. I was wondering if anyone could go."

It was immediately decided to send Fumiko Haruki, the vice women's division leader, and a young men's division leader.

Around three o'clock in the afternoon, Kiyohara and

the others headed to Colonia Federico Chávez in a micro-bus, while the Haruki team left for Colonia Pirapó by jeep. The microbus slipped repeatedly, its wheels losing traction on the muddy roads. At one point en route, Kiyohara and her companions even had to get out and push.

It was already evening by the time they reached the home of Miyaji, the chapter leader. In the surrounding area stretched farmlands and forests, speckled with simple, modest houses.

Kiyohara could not help but feel profound wonder at the thought that even here, fellow members were earnestly engaging in Soka Gakkai activities. *This must be what is meant by the principle of emerging from the earth that appears in the Daishonin's writings,* she thought. *The time for kosen-rufu has truly arrived.*

MEANWHILE, Fumiko Haruki and the others continued to travel along the treacherous roads as they headed for Colonia Pirapó. Unable to go at much speed, it was after nine o'clock in the evening when they finally reached their destination.

To their surprise, however, they found that the Pirapó members, unaware of the change in plans and that leaders were coming to see them, had decided to take the risk and had left for Miyaji's house in Colonia Federico Chávez. Haruki's group quickly turned back, but by the time they reached Chávez, it was past one o'clock in the morning

The guidance meeting at Miyaji's home began at half past seven in the evening, with more than one hundred people crammed inside. It was a meeting held by lamp-light. Here, the members were invited to ask questions.

Every question bore the imprint of anguish and inner turmoil. Some members, struggling with failing crops and mounting debts, were desperately seeking a way out of their predicament. Others spoke of dealing with illness, their voices filled with deep suffering.

Kiyohara and the other leaders poured their entire beings into responding to each question, wholeheartedly affirming the beneficial power of the Gohonzon and declaring their great conviction in faith. They sought to conquer the members' wavering spirit with the force of their conviction.

An elderly woman holding a boy of about three asked a question. "This is my grandson who was born blind. If I practice this faith in earnest, will he see one day?"

This woman and her family had been actively making efforts to spread Nichiren Daishonin's teachings and share the greatness of Buddhism with the people in their community. But when the boy was born sightless, their neighbors heaped criticism on them, questioning why this should happen to Soka Gakkai members.

Every day was torture for the family. Moreover, there were no major hospitals nearby, which meant the boy couldn't even be examined by a doctor. Feeling overcome with despair, the elderly woman had asked her question.

A hush fell the room as the members awaited Kiyohara's response.

"There is one certainty," Kiyohara said with total confidence. "That is, those who continue to strive sincerely in faith can become happy without fail.

"Please raise this child so that he will uphold faith throughout his life. No child born into the practice is without a mission. If he awakens to his own unique mission, he will absolutely be able to lead the greatest of lives."

These words pierced through the darkness that had been shrouding the hearts of the members of this family who, feeling small in the eyes of their community, had begun harboring some doubt in the practice.

AFTER RECEIVING this guidance from Kiyohara, the elderly woman came to regard her blind grandson as her family's treasure. The family became strongly united as each member prayed for the child's happiness and exerted themselves fully in their practice.

Next, a man asked Kiyohara almost beseechingly: "Do you think that President Yamamoto will come to Paraguay some day?"

"If you continue to chant in earnest," Kiyohara replied, "he will definitely come. I will also convey your wishes to him immediately. Please do your very best, taking action with the goal of welcoming Sensei!"

The question-and-answer session continued late into the evening.

That night, the members who came from other settlements stayed at the homes of Miyaji and other members living in the vicinity. The next morning, after everyone recited the sutra and chanted together, personal guidance sessions took place, and then a study exam was conducted.

The delegation from Japan was deeply moved to learn that, due to the limited number of available copies of Soka Gakkai publications such as *The Daibyakurenge* study journal and *Seikyo Shimbun* newspaper, the members had copied by hand the various articles, including lectures on the Gosho, and were studying them wholeheartedly. More, despite these less than favorable circumstances, they were gaining a firm understanding of the Daishonin's teachings. This convinced the Japanese leaders all the more that no matter what the situation, as long as one had a seeking spirit, it was possible to engage in Buddhist study.

Kiyohara and the others left Colonia Federico Chávez a little after four o'clock in the afternoon on March 6. As the microbus lurched along the densely treelined road, they thought to themselves: *If I were living in this environment, all by myself, would I really be able to sustain my practice? Although I offered guidance to the members, it's actually I who should be learning from them.*

Faith is not determined by status or organizational position, but rather by the initiatives we have taken, and what we have actually accomplished, for the sake of kosen-rufu. Furthermore, regardless of where we are in the world, the place where we are right now is the place where we carry out our activities for kosen-rufu; it is the ideal training ground for our Buddhist practice. At the same time, it becomes the Land of Eternally Tranquil Light.

The prayers of Shin'ichi and the members would be realized in 1993, when he would at last visit Paraguay. It would be a moving encounter that would shine eternally, like a beautiful work of art.

During this visit, Shin'ichi would meet with President Andrés Rodríguez and Minister of Foreign Affairs Alexis F. Vaesken, among others. Additionally, in recognition of his contributions to world peace, Shin'ichi would be awarded the National Order of Merit in the Grade of Grand Cross by the Paraguayan government.

MEANWHILE, on the morning of March 16, five of the leaders from Japan, including General Director Hiroshi Izumida and General Administrator Seiichiro Haruki, parted ways with Shin'ichi Yamamoto in the Peruvian capital of Lima, and headed for Bolivia. It was a little after half past twelve in the afternoon when they arrived in La Paz, Bolivia's administrative capital.

La Paz is considered to be the highest capital city in the world, situated on a plateau twelve thousand feet above sea level—an altitude comparable to that of Mount Fuji in Japan.

Awaiting the arrival of the Japanese delegation were two residents of the city, Masae Takehara, a young women's division member, and her younger brother, Katsumi. Masae, a live-in tutor for a Japanese-Bolivian family, was twenty-one years old, while Katsumi, an employee at a hardware store, was nineteen.

Although there existed a Soka Gakkai chapter consisting of close to one hundred member-households in Bolivia, most of them lived in Colonia San Juan de Yapacani and other immigrant settlements close to Santa Cruz. Only four or five members resided in La Paz. It was this youthful brother and sister team that had been leading the activities for kosen-rufu in this city.

In accord with Shin'ichi's guidance to encourage and raise each member they encountered, Izumida and the others invited the siblings to their hotel and, after reciting the sutra and chanting with them, offered them sincere encouragement.

Masae and Katsumi had emigrated to Bolivia from Japan with their family five years earlier. The other family members were living in Colonia San Juan de Yapacani.

Aside from Seiichiro Haruki, it was the first time for these leaders to visit La Paz, and they were unprepared for the low atmospheric pressure and thin air common at high altitudes. Their ears rang and they suffered palpitations or dizziness whenever they climbed stairs or ran even a short distance.

Through this experience, Izumida had a realization. *The world is so vast,* he thought. *Places like this exist, too. It would be a mistake to view the rest of the world from the criteria of Japan.*

The following day, March 17, the Japanese leaders took a morning flight from La Paz to Santa Cruz, with a connection in Cochabamba. When they arrived in Santa Cruz, a Fife and Drum Corps of a dozen or so people clad in red uniforms was performing a song in the airport terminal building.

"That's quite a welcome," Izumida remarked. "Is the president or someone of such stature coming?"

No sooner had Izumida uttered these words than Haruki's expression changed and he cried out: "They're playing 'Song of Indomitable Dignity'!"

Izumida listened more carefully, and then said: "You're right. So it's a Soka Gakkai Fife and Drum Corps playing to welcome us. They really ought to be more considerate of their surroundings."

At that moment, Taro Kawaura, the leader of Bolivia Chapter, came running over to them.

WITH HIS EYES shining behind his glasses, and in an accent betraying his Nagasaki origins, Taro Kawaura proudly declared: "General Director, we have been awaiting your arrival. We wanted to welcome you in grand style today, with a performance by the Fife and Drum Corps."

Although Izumida appreciated the sentiments of the members, he felt he should caution Kawaura, who was the leader of the organization in Bolivia.

"I appreciate your desire to welcome us," Izumida said. "But such a display will only alarm others and cause them to frown upon us. Particularly since a number of Latin American countries are currently keeping a close eye on the Soka Gakkai, it would be best to avoid showy demonstrations that might attract attention."

This thought had clearly never entered Kawaura's mind, for he just stood there for a moment looking somewhat perplexed. After considering Izumida's point a while, he abashedly said: "You're absolutely right."

Originally from Isahaya in Nagasaki Prefecture, Kawaura had emigrated to Bolivia in 1961. While in Japan, he had served as a group leader in the Soka Gakkai's Nagasaki Chapter. Aboard the ship to Bolivia, there were thirty-eight Soka Gakkai members, comprising seven households. The Takehara family had also emigrated on the same ship.

Bolivia can be roughly organized into three geographically distinct regions: the plateaus of the Andes mountain range in the west, toward the Peru and Chile borders (of which La Paz is a representative city); the plains to the east, close to Brazil; and the valleys situated in between.

The San Juan de Yapacani settlement, where Kawaura lived, was located in the eastern plains area, about eighty miles northwest of Santa Cruz, the second largest city in

Bolivia. The members there had united behind Kawaura and had initiated propagation efforts within their community.

In Bolivia as well, the settlers had begun their lives by clearing trees and building their homes. Despite their hardships, however, these members, linked by the deep bonds of comrades in faith, were cheerful and vibrant. Some of them had put up large signs outside their homes, on which they had written "Soka Gakkai member," followed by their name. Their hearts were ablaze with the pride of being Soka Gakkai members and the passionate spirit to work for kosen-rufu.

Prior to the settlement of Colonia San Juan de Yapacani, Japanese emigrants to Bolivia settled Colonia Okinawa in an area located about sixty miles northeast of Santa Cruz. Emigration from Okinawa began in August 1954 with the implementation of the ten-year emigration project. In the first area settled by the immigrants, however, many had lost their lives when a fever of undetermined cause broke out.

THE IMMIGRANTS from Okinawa were not only afflicted by a fever, but also suffered considerable loss when the river running through their first settlement flooded. They thus had no other recourse but to move elsewhere.

The flame of kosen-rufu was lit in Colonia Okinawa with the arrival of Shutetsu Nakamura and his family in 1961. The following year, several member-households also immigrated there.

It was Taro Kawaura who continued to encourage these

members throughout the years. In order to reach Colonia Okinawa from his home in Colonia San Juan de Yapacani, Kawaura had the choice of either traveling by bus, which ran only once or twice a day, or hitching a ride on a truck. He would first go to the town of Montello, about forty-five miles away. From there, he would catch another bus or ride, and travel an additional thirty miles to the Okinawa settlement.

If the roads were muddy from the rain, however, he could only go part way by bus or truck, and so it was not unusual for him to walk for hours through the mountain pass. Moreover, even within the same settlement, the members' houses were twenty or twenty-five miles apart. If he did not have a horse and cart at his disposal, he had to go on foot.

On the occasions when he went to Colonia Okinawa, Kawaura expected to be gone for a few days. He would therefore make the necessary arrangements at work and pack a change of clothes before setting out.

His efforts eventually paid off with the gradual development of capable people and the further spread of Nichiren Buddhism in the area. Then, at the time of Soka Gakkai Director Hiroshi Yamagiwa's visit to Bolivia in November 1962, a chapter was created, comprised of San Juan and Okinawa districts and consisting of fifty member-households. Kawaura was appointed chapter leader, and his wife, Miki, the chapter women's division leader.

Yamagiwa visited Bolivia again in August 1963, this time accompanied by Seiichiro Haruki. The members, brimming with strong seeking spirit, absorbed every ounce of the leaders' guidance, just as parched land soaks up water. With this visit, a fresh start was made in the next phase of the Bolivian organization's development.

In traveling to an activity, there were times when the members would cover six to twelve miles by foot along the mountain roads at night. Stuffing a rolled-up rag into the hollow stem of a papaya plant, about three feet in length, they would soak the end with kerosene and set it aflame. Using this as a torch, they would make their way, all the while staying alert to any sign of venomous snakes.

Going to visit members after a downpour, they would wade through the flooded roads on horseback, sometimes

toppling over into the water together with their horse. When this happened, even if it meant that they became completely drenched, they struggled to keep their hands in the air so that the *Seikyo Shimbun* newspaper, which they had brought to share with their fellow members, would stay dry. Then, in high spirits, they would continue on to their destination like valiant champions.

AFTER ARRIVING at the airport in Santa Cruz, Izumida and his party headed for the San Juan de Yapacani settlement, a three-and-a-half-hour drive by car.

A Bolivia Chapter meeting and various other events in association with their visit were scheduled to be held at the home of Taro Kawaura. As with all the other families in the area, the Kawauras had built their own home. The house itself, which had an exposed beam ceiling and wooden floors, was quite spacious, measuring some 750–860 square feet in size. From the outset, they had hoped to use their home as a meeting place, and thus had built a relatively large house.

When the leaders from Japan arrived, one hundred members had already gathered. The chapter meeting began at five o'clock in the evening, with almost all present either Japanese or of Japanese descent. Everyone, their faces beaming, joyously sang a rousing Gakkai song. This was followed by experiences, words from the Bolivia Chapter leader and women's division leader, and encouragement from the visiting leaders.

The party from the Soka Gakkai Headquarters felt reinvigorated at the sight of the members, who listened intently to their guidance, nodding at their every word, at times with tears in their eyes.

After the meeting, a study exam was conducted for some of the participants, while concurrently in another corner of the room a planning meeting was held to discuss the organization's structure and development. When the exam was finished, the new organizational lineup and corresponding leadership appointments were announced. Two additional districts were added to Bolivia Chapter, bringing the total number to four. Chapter young men's and young women's division leaders were also appointed for the first time.

When the scheduled events finished, the meeting evolved into an informal discussion, centering on the visiting leaders. Since those Bolivian members who had traveled from afar had been offered night lodging in the nearby homes of fellow members, they did not have to worry about the time. Hoping to take this opportunity to ask about the problems they were struggling with in their daily lives, the members were very serious. There was no end to the number who sought guidance. The Japanese leaders earnestly exerted themselves in giving guidance, striving with all their might to infuse the members with the strength to overcome their hardships in life, and inspire them with hope, courage and conviction.

Only by applying every ounce of our being, with a passion capable of melting even steel, can we move people's hearts. Indeed, the strength of the Soka Gakkai lies in the fact that its leaders have poured their entire beings into meeting face-to-face with each person, and offering them guidance, encouragement and inspiration.

It was almost daybreak by the time the leaders from Japan were finally able to lie down and get some sleep under the mosquito nets.

This visit by Izumida and the other leaders planted the

seed of hope in the hearts of the Bolivian members, and set in motion the dynamic and monumental advance of subsequent years.

ON THE MORNING of March 15, Kiyohara and Okada left São Paulo for the Dominican Republic.

The Dominican Republic is located on Hispaniola, an island of the West Indies in the Caribbean. Of all the Japanese who had emigrated to Latin and Central America after World War II, those who settled in this island country suffered the most appalling hardships. The Japanese government launched an emigration program to the Dominican Republic in 1956. People were particularly attracted by the extremely favorable conditions that were publicized: each emigrant would receive a free parcel of 44.5 acres of land, a house, and a subsidy of sixty cents per day (in US currency) per adult until he or she could become self-sufficient.

A subsidy of sixty cents a day meant a monthly income of eighteen dollars. With the exchange rate at that time being 360 yen to the dollar amounted to 6,480 yen. Considering that the starting salary of elementary school teachers at that time was around seven thousand to eight thousand yen, one could say this was quite a handsome subsidy. Also, with 44.5 acres, these emigrants would be owners of a considerable estate by Japanese standards.

The Dominican Republic was further promoted as a Caribbean paradise, with its favorable climate, rich soil and well-developed transport infrastructure. However, upon their arrival, the immigrants discovered that the actual conditions were dreadful, and not at all as they had been promised. Irrigation systems had not been constructed, and the supposedly fertile farmland was nothing but rock and stone, making it impossible to cultivate crops. Moreover, the high concentration of salt gave the soil the appearance of desert sand. The immigrants were shocked and at a complete loss.

The Japanese government, however, had been aware from the outset of this horrific situation and the fact that the conditions it had advertised were not being met. For instance, knowing that the settlement area of Dajabón had a water shortage, the Japanese government had requested the installment of irrigation canals. In February 1956, the Dominican government had replied that building such a system at such short notice would not be feasible, and had thus suggested postponing emigration.

The Japanese government, rather than taking heed, turned around and said there would be no problem, because it would be sending farmers who were experienced in cultivating arid land. It then went ahead with recruiting emigrants and implementing their resettlement program in March of that year.

For this reason, emigration to the Dominican Republic was seen not as emigration, but as the dumping of unwanted citizens.

JAPANESE EMIGRATION to the Dominican Republic continued through 1959.

The land they were allotted was much smaller than they had been promised during their recruitment. Nevertheless, the immigrants earnestly worked together to clear the land in an effort to make it suitable for cultivating crops.

Also, the promised subsidies to sustain them until they were able to become self-sufficient were provided for only a limited time—anywhere from six months to a maximum of three years. Any savings the settlers may have had soon disappeared in outlays for food and other daily necessities. Many were even forced to sell possessions such as clothing and sewing machines that they had brought with them from Japan to native Dominicans in order to make ends meet. Some, having nothing left to sell, kept starvation at bay by picking bananas and oranges growing wild in the jungle.

The settlers lodged complaints with the Japan Overseas Associations League, a forerunner of the Japan International Cooperation Agency, the organization responsible for coordinating the emigration program, and various emigration promotion agencies, as well as the Japanese embassy in the Dominican Republic, but their appeals fell on deaf ears.

As the settlers protested, often tearfully, that the rock-strewn land was unsuited for farming, some irresponsible officials were even callous enough to declare: "In three years or so, the rocks will disintegrate and become fertilizer."

In October 1960, the Japanese settlers sent a petition to the Japanese foreign minister, setting forth their plight and seeking his intervention. However, even this attempt to be heard appears to have been quashed.

The first to pay attention to the woeful pleas of these settlers and to take swift action were the Soka Gakkai members of Parliament in Japan. In April 1961, a Soka Gakkai House of Councilors (Upper House) member heard the claims of a woman whose mother had moved to Neiba in the Dominican Republic: "The settlers are on the verge of starvation. For the last two years, they have been desperately campaigning for repatriation, but no one is doing anything to help them." Sensing the gravity of the situation, he immediately initiated an investigation and strongly urged the Japanese Ministry of Foreign Affairs to likewise conduct an onsite inquiry.

On May 30, that same year, he put the matter before the House of Councilors Committee on Foreign Affairs, seeking to have the government take responsibility for this issue. The government finally admitted that a third of the land allotted to the settlements in the Dominican Republic was unsuited for agriculture. Specific measures were then implemented to handle the settlers' grievances, including a government-funded repatriation program for those emigrants wishing to return to Japan.

The repatriation was carried out in several batches, starting from October of that year and continuing through the following year. Of the 249 emigrant families (a total of 1,319 people), 133 families (611 people) returned to Japan.

SOME OF THE EMIGRANTS to the Dominican Republic chose not to return to Japan, opting instead to remain there or to emigrate to other Latin American countries such as Brazil and Argentina. Many made this decision with the thought that they couldn't possibly go home now and in such humiliating defeat, no matter how trying their present circumstances were. Moreover, they had sold all of their belongings in order to emigrate to the Dominican Republic.

Among those who remained in the Caribbean country was a man named Hiroto Muraki. He had emigrated from Yamaguchi Prefecture in 1957 with his wife and four members of his wife's family. Armed with the resolve to spend the rest of their lives in the Dominican Republic, they had sold off whatever they could, including their house, farm and household goods. Muraki hadn't been able to resist the idea of owning a huge 44.5 acre piece of land, which the emigration program promised each family. This was comparable in size to his entire village back in Japan. Dreams of a better future unfolded in his mind at the prospect of being in possession of all that land.

On arriving in the Dominican Republic, Muraki and his group took up residence in a settlement called Dajabón, situated close to the country's border with Haiti and some two hundred miles northwest of the capital, Santo Domingo. However, the land he was actually allotted turned out to be a wasteland of red dirt, measuring only 8.9 acres and lying more than three miles from the settlement proper.

Muraki began to work the land, but the red earth, parched by the sun's rays, was as hard as rock. The earth seemed to repel the plow's blade as if in defiance of the settlers' presence. After much effort, he finally managed to clear and bring under cultivation about three acres—a mere third of his allotment. But the vegetable seeds he had brought with him from Japan and planted in his newly cultivated fields failed to grow, due to the heat and lack of water. It was only when he planted some locally acquired tomato seedlings that he was able to reap a meager crop.

At any rate, they did not have sufficient water. Each plot

of land was assigned a specific irrigation schedule, and on the nights he was supposed to receive his supply of water, Muraki would stay awake until it came. One day, however, the water failed to arrive at the designated time. As he walked along the waterway, he found that another farmer upstream had opened his water gates and had channeled the water for his own use. This was indeed the epitome of *gaden insui* (drawing water for one's own land), a Japanese expression meaning "self-serving" or "self-centered."

Finding themselves in a situation governed by the law of the survival of the fittest, everyone had long lost the capacity to honor promises or to be considerate of others. It saddened Muraki deeply that the hearts of his compatriots should have grown as hard and unfeeling as the barren red soil.

In fact, it was not rare to see arguments or fights break out regarding the water supply, even among siblings or relatives.

IN THE MURAKI household, they had almost used up all of the rice they had brought with them from Japan and the very real threat of starvation began to loom before them.

Muraki now had two daughters, born in the Dominican Republic in September 1957 and July 1959. Gazing upon their innocent faces as they slept, he was filled with anguish. He was desperate to find a way out of their situation. After much thought, he built a small, tin-roofed shack near his allotted parcel of land and started a grocery store. Since there were three women in his household—his wife, her mother and her younger sister—he thought they could more effectively earn an income by running a shop. Muraki would take his horse and cart to procure items such as rice, salt and soft drinks, which they would then sell in the store. In this way, they were somehow able to avoid starvation. However, since their only customers were the local people who lived close to their farm, their business was limited.

They were then dealt another blow when the elder sister of Muraki's wife, who had emigrated before them, died of complications in childbirth. If only there had been adequate medical facilities, she would not have died.

Muraki could no longer bear to continue such a life, devoid of all hope. It was around this time that the mass repatriation of Japanese immigrants began. In utter despair, he sent a letter to his mother in Japan, relaying his thoughts of returning home and asking her advice. This was especially painful for him to admit, for as he was leaving Japan, he had told his mother: "In ten years, I'll come home to show you my success!"

Some time later, he received his mother's response. The letter, written in pencil in an unsteady hand, stated that she had joined the Soka Gakkai: "The Gohonzon is powerful. If you chant Nam-myoho-renge-kyo, I'm sure you'll become happy. You must chant, too, and do your best."

Muraki's initial reaction was that a religion was not going to improve his life. However, as he reread the letter, he was deeply moved by the heartfelt words of his mother, who wished nothing other than her child's happiness. In any case, he had no other means of changing his life, so he decided to try chanting. Curiously enough, after twenty or thirty minutes of chanting, he felt lighter of heart.

Sensing that there was something to this chanting, he decided to start practicing Nichiren Buddhism. This was in 1962.

When he began reciting the sutra and chanting regularly, his mother-in-law, who had been suffering from gastrointestinal problems, also began to chant with him. However, the pain, rather than improving, became worse.

EVEN THE NEIGHBORS were saying that a member of his family had fallen ill because Muraki had gotten involved in a strange religion.

Muraki sent a letter to Japan in which he wrote: "This religion is no good. I'm going to quit."

A short while later, he received a reply from his brother, who had introduced their mother to the practice. In the letter, he explained: "This is the same as running some water through a pipe that hasn't been used in a long time. At first, all you will see is the rust and dirt flushed out before the water runs clear. Similarly, if you continue to exert yourself in faith, your circumstances will definitely improve."

Taking these words of encouragement to heart, Muraki did not abandon his practice and instead continued to chant in earnest. Then, amazingly, the gastrointestinal pain that his mother-in-law had been experiencing gradually abated. After that, the whole family started practicing Nichiren Buddhism.

One day, a distinguished-looking Dominican man came by the shop and bought a soft drink. He turned out to be the mayor of a town some twenty miles from Dajabón.

Speaking in Spanish, he asked Muraki: "Would you be interested in raising rice plant seedlings? The soil around my town has a high concentration of salt, so we can't grow them there. We therefore have to buy the seedlings elsewhere in order to produce rice. Are you interested?"

"Due to lack of water, we can't grow anything here," Muraki replied in broken Spanish. "If we had even a small supply of water, then we'd probably have no trouble growing seedlings."

"If it's just a matter of water," declared the mayor confidently, "leave it to me."

Following negotiations with the Water Board director in Dajabón, the mayor secured special water access for Muraki, supplying him with as much water as he needed. With this water, Muraki irrigated the rice paddies and planted the seeds. The warm climate made it possible to harvest seedlings several times a year. As the scope of this operation expanded, he even hired twenty local people to work for him. Because of this success, he was able to obtain a sizeable income. This was his first benefit in the early days of his Buddhist practice.

Toward the end of 1962, Muraki moved to Cotuí, a rice-growing region about 125 miles away from Dajabón, to open a grocery store.

He was resolved to succeed in his adopted homeland and show actual proof of the Daishonin's Buddhism in society. Chanting wholeheartedly, he thought about ways to develop his business. He then remembered someone who had made *okoshi,* a traditional Japanese sweet made from popped rice, and went to learn how to do so himself. He thus went into the business making and selling this confectionery. Knowing, however, that he couldn't just expect customers to come to him, he decided to go out and sell his wares by bicycle.

SINCE the residents around Muraki's town had never eaten *okoshi*, he had trouble finding customers. Muraki thus began distributing free samples, urging people: "Please try these. If you like them, please come and buy some more from my shop." This strategy proved fruitful. The sweets began to sell and went on to become a huge hit with customers. Muraki was convinced once again of the power of faith.

One day, while visiting the Japanese co-op rice mill, he heard that a young Japanese immigrant had been hospitalized for tuberculosis in Santo Domingo. Muraki was a person of great sincerity. Out of genuine concern for this young man, he decided to go to the hospital in order to introduce him to Nichiren Buddhism. As they spoke together, the young man confided that his father was a Soka Gakkai member.

His father, Kan'ichi Nakao, lived in the Constanza settlement, more than sixty miles from Cotuí. The very next day Muraki went off to visit him, taking a series of shared cabs to get there. This was his first time meeting a Soka Gakkai member. In his late fifties, Nakao sported a mustache and had a cheerful disposition. He had joined the Soka Gakkai in 1955, back in Fukuoka, and even after moving to the Dominican Republic the following year, had maintained a consistent practice of reciting the sutra and chanting Nam-myoho-renge-kyo.

This encounter between Hiroto Muraki and Kan'ichi Nakao set in motion the kosen-rufu movement in the Dominican Republic.

Since neither of them spoke much Spanish, they first resolved to share the Daishonin's Buddhism with the entire community of Japanese immigrants.

Being without a driver's license, Muraki worked hard in order to afford to hire a car with a driver, and he set off together with his wife, Isoko, several days each month to conduct propagation activities around the country.

Having faced tremendous hardships in their lives as settlers, many of these Japanese sensed the power of the Daishonin's Buddhism through hearing of Muraki's own experiences in developing a thriving business. Gradually, the number of members began to grow.

Many Japanese immigrants bemoaned their wretched

circumstances, but those who awoke to faith in the Mystic Law found their lives taking on new meaning. They thought to themselves: *We have a mission to lead the people of this country to happiness through Buddhism. In order to fulfill this mission, we must first start by winning in our own lives.... We cannot allow ourselves to be defeated, no matter what!*

Whether one is happy or unhappy is ultimately decided by one's own profound inner resolve or attitude.

In this way, thanks to the initiatives of Muraki and Nakao, around thirty member-households, constituting one-fourth of the total Japanese immigrant community of some 120 member-households, started practicing.

AFTER LEAVING São Paulo on the morning of March 15, Kiyohara and Okada arrived in the port city of San Juan in Puerto Rico, where they stayed overnight. The next morning, they traveled on to Santo Domingo, the capital of the Dominican Republic.

This was the first time that leaders from the Soka Gakkai Headquarters had come to visit this Caribbean country. Despite the poorly developed transportation system, fourteen or fifteen members, their eyes sparkling with seeking spirit, had come from settlements more than sixty miles away in order to greet them at the airport.

Once at their hotel, Kiyohara and Okada met with Hiroto Muraki and Kan'ichi Nakao and other key members who had taken the lead in activities to promote kosen-rufu in that country, in order to discuss the development of the local organization.

On the eve of their departure from São Paulo, Shin'ichi said to Kiyohara and Okada: "If the Dominican members agree, why don't we create a chapter there? They have all worked so hard, coming countless obstacles. Those who have undergone the greatest hardships have the right to the greatest happiness. The formation of a chapter signals the starting point of that goal."

When Okada shared these words with Muraki and the others, tears of emotion filled their eyes. Each of them remarked how deeply touched and moved they were by President Yamamoto's concern for them.

The Dominican members, who had in fact been hoping to have a chapter established, readily assented to the proposal. The group thus immediately began discussing the details of the new chapter. They decided it would be named Dominican Chapter, with Nakao, who was Muraki's senior both in age and in length of practice, being appointed the chapter leader, and Isoko, Muraki's wife, named the chapter women's division leader. It was also decided that the chapter should start out with three districts: Hima, Constanza and Dajabón, centering on the Japanese settlements. Muraki was appointed the leader of Hima District. Young men's and young women's divisions were also created and leaders appointed for both.

After these discussions, Kiyohara and Okada, accompanied by the local members, traveled from Santo Domingo to the Constanza settlement to attend a guidance meeting, at which they would now also celebrate the formation of Dominican Chapter. After a bumpy four-hour ride, the cars raising clouds of dust in their wake, the group reached its destination.

The meeting took place in the settlement's communal hall, a space that more resembled a food warehouse.

Nonetheless, the faces of the some sixty or seventy members who had gathered there shone with bright enthusiasm. When Ittetsu Okada announced at the beginning of the meeting the establishment of Dominican Chapter and introduced the new leaders, the members' joy knew no bounds. Everyone felt that a new era for the Dominican Republic had begun, the birth of a Soka Gakkai chapter signaling the start of a surging wellspring of kosen-rufu.

FOLLOWING the sharing of several personal experiences by the Dominican members and other presentations, a question-and-answer session was held, led by Katsu Kiyohara.

In closing, she said: "Through your united efforts and strength, please transform the Dominican Republic into a haven of happiness. Please create a magnificent history of which you can proudly declare, 'Sensei, look at what we have achieved for kosen-rufu!' and work toward welcoming President Yamamoto here some day."

Thunderous applause broke out in response to her appeal.

After the meeting, a woman rushed over to Kiyohara and clasped her hand tightly. "Thanks to your encouragement today, we now have a goal," she said. "Even if it takes years, decades, we will definitely welcome President Yamamoto to the Dominican Republic."

A commemorative photograph was then taken with all the participants.

As she spoke with the Dominician members, Kiyohara could not conceal her amazement at the purity of their faith. There was not a trace of criticism, complaint or ill feeling toward others in their words. She wondered how all these members had managed to develop such a strong and forthright practice—it was not as if any leaders from Japan had been coming to give them guidance and encouragement.

Through her conversations with them, however, she discovered that there was a woman back in Japan who had ceaselessly supported and encouraged these members from behind the scenes. Her name was Kiku Tadokoro, and she was a group leader in Shinjuku Ward in Tokyo. She had never been to the Dominican Republic, nor did she have any particularly close ties to the country. She simply happened to be in the same local organization as Kan'ichi Nakao's younger brother, and Nakao had once paid her a visit to thank her for supporting his brother in various ways. When Takokoro later learned that the elder Nakao had emigrated to the Dominican Republic, she began to chant for the success of his activities for kosen-rufu in this new frontier.

In 1964, she received a letter from Nakao, in which he reported that he had initiated Soka Gakkai activities together with Hiroto Muraki, and that new members were gradually emerging. Tadokoro wished to support in any way she could these fellow members struggling so earnestly for worldwide kosen-rufu. She immediately wrote back, sending the letter along with prayer beads, sutra books and Soka Gakkai publications such as the *Seikyo Shimbun* newspaper and *The Daibyakurenge* study journal.

To the Dominican members, these gifts were a veritable treasure. The publications, in particular, were passed around and read among them. They also copied down important or inspiring passages, especially from Nichiren Daishonin's writings or President Yamamoto's guidance, into their notebooks.

WANTING to be of assistance to the Dominican members, Kiku Tadokoro continued to send Soka Gakkai publications and other items to them. As leaders had not yet been appointed in the Dominican Republic, the members over time came to write her for advice whenever they faced a problem, even though they had never met her in person.

Tadokoro responded to each letter with great sincerity, sometimes even seeking guidance from the Soka Gakkai Headquarters if necessary. She poured her entire being into her replies, offering wholehearted words of encouragement. Sometimes, she would send more than ten letters in one month. Out of a desire to bring even a little brightness into the members' hearts, she would also enclose pressed flowers such as cherry or peach blossoms, according to the season. These letters became such a tremendous source of encouragement for the members that they naturally came to regard Takokoro as the "mother of Dominician kosen-rufu."

This was not something she started because someone had told her to do so. Nor did she expect any reward or recompense for her efforts. This was a personal initiative, motivated purely by her wish to support her fellow members and to advance worldwide kosen-rufu.

It is through the bonds created by such encouragement, like a network of underground roots connecting the heart of one friend to another, that have made it possible to lay an indestructible foundation of kosen-rufu throughout the world.

With the formation of a chapter in the Dominican Republic, this jewel of the Caribbean, a new day dawned and a hope-filled advance into the future began.

It was twenty-one years later, in 1987, that the prayers of the members to welcome Shin'ichi Yamamoto to their country were realized. It was a landmark visit, being the fortieth country to which Shin'ichi had traveled. During his stay, Shin'ichi met with President Joaquin Balaguer,[6] received the Grand Cross of the Order of Christoper Columbus, one of the nation's highest honors, and was named an honorary professor of the Autonomous University of Santo Domingo. This indeed was magnificent proof that Shin'ichi and the members had won wide trust in Dominican society.

The year 1966 saw members in various Latin American countries begin to pioneer new frontiers of kosen-rufu in earnest. Theirs was a painful, arduous struggle not unlike trying to cultivate rocky earth in order to grow crops. They may have even felt at times that all their efforts were in vain. How often they must have wept tears of frustration. Nevertheless, the members in each country admirably triumphed over all obstacles.

Now, in the twenty-first century, the glorious banner of the victory of the people flutters proudly across the vast expanse of Latin America.

NOTES

1   Translated from Spanish. J.L. Salcedo-Bastardo. *Bolívar: A Continent and Its Destiny* (Caracus: Universidad Central de Venezuela, 1972), p. 254.

2   Simón Bolívar (1783–1830).

3   Gen. Don Bartolomé Mitre. *The Emancipation of South America*, translated by William Pilling (New York: Cooper Square Publishing, Inc., 1969), p. 232.

4   Ibid., p. 271.

5   Ibid., p. 425.

6   Joaquin Balaguer (1907–2002): Former president of the Dominican Republic. He was also renowned as a poet and historian. Serving as president for a total of seven terms, until 1996, he was instrumental in establishing democracy in his country.

Ever-Victorious

SIMONE WEIL, the young French philosopher and
writer who participated in the Resistance movement
against the Nazis during World War II, wrote: "But words
are only a beginning. Action is a more powerful tool for
molding people's minds."[1] Indeed, it is action that stirs new
waves of change, that inspires people and that creates a history of victory of the people.

In March 1966, after Shin'ichi returned from his visit
to North and South America, he embarked on a whirl-
wind tour of Japan to offer encouragement and take commemorative photographs with group leaders, the people

working on the front lines of kosen-rufu. In April alone, Shin'ichi visited Osaka, Wakayama, Shizuoka, Kagawa and Ehime prefectures, and on May 3, he attended the annual Soka Gakkai Headquarters General Meeting held at the Nihon University Auditorium in Tokyo.

At that meeting, he spoke about the Seven Bells—seven consecutive seven-year periods that marked specific points in the organization's development and also served as goals toward the future realization of kosen-rufu. He called on members to advance toward the seventh of those goals with boundless confidence and joy.

Shin'ichi had first introduced the idea of the Seven Bells at the Headquarters General Meeting held on May 3, 1958, a month after the death of Toda. He had done so as Toda's disciple in order to inspire fresh advancement in the kosen-rufu movement.

The first seven-year period began with the publication of founding president Makiguchi's *The System of Value-Creating Pedagogy* on November 18, 1930, and culminated with the official inauguration of the Soka Kyoiku Gakkai (Value-Creating Education Society; forerunner of the Soka Gakkai) in the autumn of 1937. After that, there had been major events that had occurred each seven years. The third of the Seven Bells began on November 18, 1944, with the death of President Makiguchi in prison. Seven years later, in 1951, Josei Toda became the second president and the postwar advance of kosen-rufu began in earnest. Seven years after that, on April 2, 1958, President Toda died after having achieved his lifelong goal of increasing the organization's membership to 750,000 member-households.

Amid the sadness surrounding Toda's death, Shin'ichi

boldly proclaimed that the fifth of the Seven Bells would commence as a new beginning in the effort to spread the Daishonin's teachings. Then, on May 3, 1960, he became the third president of the Soka Gakkai and proposed several goals to be accomplished by 1964, the sixth anniversary of President Toda's passing. Among these were the achievement of a membership of three million member-households and the construction of the Grand Reception Hall to be donated to the head temple. In this way, Shin'-ichi set in motion a powerful wave of fresh advancement.

B Y NOVEMBER 1962, the Soka Gakkai had already reached its goal of three million member-households. And, with the completion of the Grand Reception Hall, the members were able to mark the sixth anniversary of President Toda's death in April 1964 amid excitement and joy. This was the prelude to the sixth of the Seven Bells, which would begin in 1965.

At the May 3 Headquarters General Meeting in 1966, Shin'ichi announced that the sixth seven-year period, which would culminate in 1972, was already under way. He then confirmed that the goals for that time would be the construction of the Soka Culture Center, adjacent to the Soka Gakkai Headquarters in Shinano-machi, and the Grand Main Temple, the effective sanctuary of the essential teaching. He further urged members to strive to realize even greater progress in kosen-rufu by the end of the seventh of the Seven Bells, in 1979.

Looking beyond the completion of the Seven Bells, Shin'ichi said that he hoped the period until 1990, the year of the thirty-third memorial (thirty-second anniversary) of President Toda's death, would be a time of putting the finishing touches on kosen-rufu. He further stated: "But if this plan is not realized in that time frame, it is because of the Buddha's wisdom. In that case, the final completion of kosen-rufu will be up to the present members of the young women's, young men's and student divisions, as well as my beloved young disciples, the members of the high school, junior high school and elementary school divisions.

"I hope that all of you, who possess a profound mission, will boldly advance, aiming toward President Toda's thirty-third memorial and the year 2000. I also hope that you will resolutely usher in a new series of Seven Bells in the twenty-first century!"

Shin'ichi was appealing with all his might to the representatives of the high school division in attendance at the meeting. After his speech, Shin'ichi thought: "By 2000, most of today's high school division members will be in their fifties. And the majority of the members of the junior high school and elementary school divisions will be in their forties. In many ways, they will be in the prime of their lives. If these members inherit my spirit and stand up in earnest, we are certain to achieve kosen-rufu!

"If, on the other hand, they are half-hearted and become cowardly, figurehead leaders who aren't capable of engaging in real struggle, it means that I am without good fortune. But my being able to serve Mr. Toda makes me the most fortunate person alive. There is no way that I am lacking in good fortune. I have every faith in my young disciples. I know they will stand up for kosen-rufu.

"I entrust the future to you, my young phoenixes!"

AFTER the Headquarters general meeting, Shin'ichi spent the remainder of May visiting Oita, Kumamoto, Fukuoka, Yamagata, Miyagi and Kanagawa prefectures, and then, in June, he went to Osaka, Nara, Okayama, Mie and Shizuoka.

From late July to early August, he directed the annual summer training course at the head temple, taking time out in between sessions to visit members in Iwate Prefecture. Toward the end of August, he made a brief visit to Honolulu, Hawaii, to attend a dedication ceremony for a new temple there. Once back in Japan, he went again to the head temple on September 2, before traveling to Hyogo Prefecture on the 3rd and to Kyoto on the 4th. He then made his way to Obihiro in Hokkaido on September 9, Sapporo on the 10th and Hakodate on the 11th to participate in commemorative photography sessions there.

In the midst of this tight schedule, Shin'ichi thought constantly about the future development of kosen-rufu and taking steps to lay the groundwork in that direction. One such focus was the translation of the Daishonin's writings into English.

It was the Daishonin's will and mandate that the Mystic Law spread throughout the entire world. His successor, Nikko Shonin, stated: "When the time comes to widely declare the sacred teachings of this country, the Japanese texts are sure to be translated and spread in India and China" (GZ, 1613). In other words, he was instructing that the Daishonin's writings—the sacred teachings of this country—be translated and made available across the globe.

Shin'ichi was keenly aware of the importance of an

English translation of Nichiren Daishonin's writings as the foundation for translating them into other languages. This was not only because of the large number of English speakers in the world but also because of the accessibility of the English language.

Shin'ichi spoke with the editorial staff of the *Seikyo Times,* the Soka Gakkai's English-language study journal, and suggested that they publish an English translation of the writing "Reply to Kyo'o," which had been selected as the study material for overseas members who would be attending the next summer training course at the head temple. The proposal was accepted, and the translation appeared in the July 1, 1966, issue of the journal.

Translation of frequently studied writings progressed, but the staff members in charge of this endeavor found themselves faced with one challenge after another. In order to convey the Daishonin's teachings correctly, they had to first gain an accurate interpretation of the original text. Doing so, however, was no easy task. This was because the originals, which represented the essence of Buddhism, had been written in classical Japanese. The translators would therefore often spend several days consulting members of the Soka Gakkai Study Department and referring to President Yamamoto's lectures as well as Buddhist dictionaries in order to arrive at a full and proper understanding of each passage.

IT WAS also quite difficult to find ways to express Buddhist terminology that did not exist in English. At times the staff sat quietly struggling with their dictionaries, and at other times they would bounce opinions off of one another, sometimes engaging in heated debate.

For example, in the famous writing "The True Aspect of All Phenomena," there is a passage: "Birds and crickets cry, but never shed tears. I, Nichiren, do not cry, but my tears flow ceaselessly" (WND, 386). In Japanese, the word *naku* translated here as "cry" is used to describe the sound that insects such as crickets make, but this is not a common usage in many Western languages. This can be attributed to a difference in cultural perceptions. In translating the Daishonin's writings and correctly transmitting the meaning of each passage, it was necessary to consider such cultural and linguistic differences in addition to other factors.

Translation is a painstaking endeavor that takes place away from the limelight, but it is crucial to the worldwide spread of kosen-rufu. Truly great achievements are carried out with quiet determination, without praise or acclamation.

The work of translating the Daishonin's writings steadily continued and in 1979, thirteen years after the undertaking had begun, volume one of *The Major Writings of Nichiren Daishonin* was published with some thirty-six works included, such as "The True Object of Worship"[2] and "Letter from Sado." From that time on, additional volumes were published at a pace of one every other year up through volume seven. Then, in 1999, all those translations were revised and combined in a single volume entitled *The Writings of Nichiren Daishonin*. While this volume contains only 172 of the more than four hundred works included in the Soka Gakkai's Japanese-language *Nichiren Daishonin Gosho Zenshu* (Collected Writings of Nichiren Daishonin), in actuality it amounts to about half of the Japanese edition in terms of translated pages.

Meanwhile, as part of another publication project, Shin'ichi's lectures on "On Establishing the Correct Teaching for the Peace of the Land" were published in Japanese on July 3, 1966, as the first volume of *Lectures on the Ten Major Writings of Nichiren Daishonin*. Shin'ichi had given his all to writing these lectures, aiming to widely communicate the principle of establishing lasting world peace.

On August 30 of the same year, Shin'ichi attended the first meeting of the Soka Gakkai's Gosho Lectures Compilation Committee, and a start was made on publishing lectures on all of the Daishonin's writings.

No matter how wonderful the Daishonin's teachings are, if the people of today cannot grasp their meaning, they will create no value. That is why Shin'ichi did his utmost to make the great teachings of Buddhism comprehensible to all.

THE GOSHO LECTURES Compilation Committee immediately set to work researching and compiling lectures on Nichiren's writings. In August 1968, the first volume of *Lectures on the Writings of Nichiren Daishonin* was published in Japanese. This included lectures on the writings "On Practicing the Buddha's Teachings," "On the Buddha's Prophecy," and "The Entity of the Mystic Law." Publication continued at a regular pace and by June 1999, thirty-five of the planned thirty-nine volumes had been published.

Both the English-language volume of the Daishonin's writings and the Japanese lecture series represented unprecedented bodies of work based on a correct interpretation of the Daishonin's teachings, and they stand as great accomplishments of the twentieth century.

In September 1966, Shin'ichi and his family moved from Kobayashi-cho, Ota Ward, to Shinano-machi, Shinjuku Ward. On September 12, a Gohonzon enshrining ceremony was held at their new home, which was located about five minutes from Shinano-machi Station, close to both the Soka Gakkai Headquarters and the *Seikyo Shimbun* head office. Several decades old, the house shook whenever cars drove up or down the steeply sloping street in front of it.

Shin'ichi and Mineko had wed on May 3, 1952, and their first home together was a rented house in Mita, Meguro Ward. The house belonged to the baseball player, Seiichiro Haruki, a relative of Mineko's, who offered to let them use it while he was playing for a baseball team in Osaka.

Concerned about Shin'ichi's family situation, President Toda had on one occasion advised him: "You will be traveling all around Japan for kosen-rufu, and in the future all around the world. I'm concerned about Mineko in your absence, and I think it might be a good idea to find a home close to Mineko's parents, the Harukis."

In the autumn of that year Shin'ichi and Mineko moved to an apartment in Sanno, Ota Ward. But after their sons Masahiro and Hisahiro were born, they had to move again because the apartment owner didn't permit more than one child. They subsequently took out a loan for a million yen and bought a house in Kobayashi-cho, closer to Mineko's family, and they moved in on June 19, 1955.

The house was old, however, and quite modest. In the summer it filled with mosquitoes, and in the winter a cold draft blew in through the poorly sealed doors and windows. When they bought it, there was no gate or wall separating the property from the street. The house had three rooms: two six-*tatami*-mat rooms and a four-and-a-half-mat room, in which they kept their Buddhist altar. That didn't leave much space for the numerous members who came by seeking guidance from Shin'ichi. Eventually, they added on a room for Shin'ichi's study and another for the children, and for security purposes they built a simple concrete-block wall with a gate around the premises.

S HIN'ICHI commuted to work from his home in Kobayashi-cho, riding his bicycle first to Japan National

Railways (now Japan Railways) Kamata Station and then taking the train from there. The bicycle parking area closed at night, so when he knew he wouldn't make it home in

time, he would contact Mineko and have her pick up the bicycle and wait for him at the station. These walks home, pushing the bicycle and looking up at the starry night sky together, were a wonderful opportunity for the couple to talk about their hopes for the future.

Their third son, Hirotaka, was born after they moved to Kobayashi-cho. As the boys grew and became more active, the house turned into a battle zone, with torn paper doors and scribbles on the walls. They would start racing around Shin'ichi early in the morning as he slept, and even on holidays they didn't allow him much time to rest.

This house was filled with many significant memories for Shin'ichi. It was from here that he left to attend the Headquarters General Meeting on May 3, 1960, when he was officially inaugurated as the third president of the Soka Gakkai. On that day, Shin'ichi, his father-in-law, Yoji Haruki, and Mineko rode together to the Nihon University Auditorium in Ryogoku in a taxi that Mineko's mother had called for them.

When Shin'ichi returned home that night, he found that Mineko had not prepared any traditional celebratory red bean rice. She instead remarked that there had been a funeral in the Yamamoto family that day—a comment that would remain etched deep in Shin'ichi's heart. What Mineko meant was that she had accepted that she was giving up her husband to the Soka Gakkai and kosen-rufu.

At that time, Shin'ichi also asked Mineko to take care of their children, saying: "Please raise them so that they will live out their lives sharing their destiny with the Soka Gakkai."

"I understand everything," Mineko replied. "And I

believe that this is the best life we could possibly lead."

Together, husband and wife were setting sail on the sea of kosen-rufu, and from that day on, the house in Kobayashi-cho became the base camp for the advancement of the Soka Gakkai's movement.

On October 2, 1960, Shin'ichi embarked on his first trip overseas to open a path for the realization of world peace. That journey, too, began from the Kobayashi-cho house. A large number of members gathered there that day to wave Shin'ichi off as he left by taxi for Haneda Airport. They rejoiced at the fact that they were witnessing the dawning of worldwide kosen-rufu.

After Shin'ichi became president, the number of visitors to the Kobayashi-cho house increased. It was constantly bustling with people coming for guidance or to report on Soka Gakkai activities. Many leaders of Japanese society and well-known public figures also began to drop by. The house was so unassuming, however, that many of them went right past it and looked around the neighborhood for some time before finally finding their destination.

WHEN THE LOCAL government implemented plans to widen the street running past the Yamamoto's house in Kobayashi-cho as part of its land readjustment project, Shin'ichi and his family decided to relocate. At the strong request of the Soka Gakkai Headquarters, they settled on a place in Shinano-machi. Shin'ichi knew that if they moved there, not only his personal life but that of his family would be even further restricted. But they were all prepared to make kosen-rufu their top priority.

September 12 was thus set as the day of the Gohonzon-enshrining ceremony at their new home. Shin'ichi prayed deeply with a solemn vow to contribute to the prosperity of Shinano-machi, the location of the Soka Gakkai Headquarters and now of his home. It is the responsibility and mission of Buddhist practitioners to love and serve the community in which they live, to help it flourish and to transform it into a Land of Eternally Tranquil Light.

At a little past nine o'clock in the morning on September 18, 1966, Shin'ichi was on a bullet train heading toward Osaka to attend the Kansai Culture Festival being held at the Hanshin Koshien Stadium in Nishinomiya City, Hyogo Prefecture. Rain had begun to fall in the Osaka-Kobe area from the evening two days earlier, caused by Typhoon No. 21, which was traveling northward from the southern coast of Kyushu.

The Kansai members were preparing for their culture festival with the possibility that the typhoon might move inland. They chanted furiously, creating a storm of prayer that nothing could defeat. As if in response to their prayers, from around noon on September 17, the force of the winds began to abate.

They put even more energy into their chanting, and around six o'clock on the morning of the culture festival, the typhoon suddenly weakened over the ocean southwest of Tanegashima Island. They had fortunately escaped the worst, but the low atmospheric pressure caused by the typhoon activated the seasonal autumn rains, which fell heavily, accompanied by strong winds.

In the train heading for Osaka, Shin'ichi watched as the rain struck the windows. He chanted silently for the

Kansai Culture Festival to take place without incident. This was the third time for a culture festival to be held in Kansai, but for the members there this latest festival had a special significance. Though this one was called the Kansai Culture Festival, unlike the previous festivals—which had been organized on the regional level—this was to be a major event under the direction of the Soka Gakkai Headquarters, with General Director Izumida as head of the festival steering committee.

THE KANSAI members had a burning desire to make this festival a celebration commemorating the tenth anniversary of the tradition of "ever-victorious Kansai," which had been started by Shin'ichi in 1956. Together with Shin'ichi, who was then youth division chief of the general staff, they had established a brilliant record of achievement of kosen-rufu in Kansai. Memories of that golden victory still shone vibrantly in their hearts. In a single chapter in the month of May, a bold drive to introduce others to Buddhism had resulted in an unprecedented 11,111 new member-households.

The Kansai members had also won a dramatic upset victory a few months later in July in the Osaka District House of Councilors (Upper House) elections, about which newspaper headlines blared "The Impossible Has Been Achieved!" These victories marked the beginning of Kansai's reputation as "ever-victorious."

Events had turned the following year in April, however, when, during an Upper House by-election in Osaka, the irresponsible and thoughtless violation of the election law by some Tokyo members in the final days of the campaign resulted in a loss of trust in the candidate supported by the Soka Gakkai. This led to the defeat of the candidate by a narrow margin.

The authorities, fearful of the emergence of the Soka Gakkai as a popular movement, used the election violations as a pretext for incriminating Shin'ichi as the head of the campaign, and on July 3, he was arrested on false charges. The prosecutors continued their relentless interrogation of Shin'ichi, threatening him with a raid on the Soka Gakkai Headquarters and the arrest of President Toda if he did not plead guilty.

This was nine months before the death of Toda, who was already in extremely frail health. If he were to be detained at that time, it would certainly kill him. Shin'ichi was therefore left with no choice but to accept the blame for the violations. But he was determined to prove his innocence in court.

When he was released from the Osaka Detention Center on the evening of July 17 to await trial, Shin'ichi attended a meeting at the Central Civic Hall in Nakanoshima, Osaka. Known as the Osaka Rally, it was a protest held amid pouring rain and crashing thunder to denounce the actions of the Osaka Police Department and the district prosecutor's office.

Shin'ichi called out to the gathering: "Let us strive with the conviction that the correct teaching of Buddhism will absolutely prevail!"

Hearing Shin'ichi's lion's roar, the members wept both with relief at his release and indignation at the authorities' actions, vowing in their hearts never to be defeated and to win in every challenge no matter what. This was the birth of an indomitable Kansai. Indeed, Kansai's golden history of triumph was built through Shin'ichi's life-and-death struggles.

Now, ten years after their towering victory, the Kansai members were firmly determined to make their culture festival a monumental starting point of fresh advancement together with Shin'ichi.

THE TRADITION of holding culture festivals in the Soka Gakkai can be traced back to a youth division sports meet held in 1954. Shin'ichi proposed that event. In addition to a footrace, an obstacle course and other games, the sports meet featured a marching performance by the Brass Band. From then on, these events came to be known as "Festivals of Youth." Sponsored by the youth division, they were held in every region of Japan as an expression of the youth's commitment to realizing kosen-rufu, and they soon became a Gakkai tradition.

Gradually, the festivals expanded to include not only athletic competitions, but also various cultural performances, such as parades by the Brass Band and Fife and Drum Corps, modern and traditional Japanese dance performances and card stunts. The program improved with each occasion, becoming more refined and professional.

Besides these sporting events, in October 1962, the youth division put on its first culture festival in two parts. Part one was held at the auditorium of Kyoritsu Women's University in Tokyo and part two at the Yokohama Municipal Culture Gymnasium in Kanagawa Prefecture. This was an artistic and cultural event that featured a choral performance, music, dance, theater and the showing of a film, as well as an exhibition of paintings, photographs and calligraphy.

When Shin'ichi attended the Kansai sports meet held in September of the following year, 1963, he suggested that the first Kansai Culture Festival be held at Koshien Stadium in Hyogo Prefecture. The Kansai leaders were visibly taken aback by this suggestion. Having only ever put on culture festivals in school auditoriums or theaters, they had never imagined the possibility of holding one outdoors and in a huge baseball stadium at that.

Seeing their surprise, Shin'ichi said: "Perhaps you are of the mindset that culture and art are created on the individual level and should therefore be enjoyed on a smaller, more personal scale. Of course it is individuals who generate such creativity, but I am convinced that when each person strives toward the realization of a lofty common goal, it will give rise to a truly magnificent and unprecedented form of art and creativity. Wouldn't it be wonderful if large numbers of people working together of their own accord, without the intervention of any authority, could create something that expresses the joy and splendor of being alive?

"The group calisthenics and other such events that are a part of our sports meets have already reached a high level of sophistication that could be considered art. If we were to include them in a culture festival, we would need a large space. Since our aim is to give birth to a new, humanistic culture, it is important to remain flexible in our thinking."

TAKING SHIN'ICHI'S proposal into consideration, the Kansai members completely changed their thinking and began to plan for a culture festival on a scale much grander than anything that could take place in the average hall. Thus, the first Kansai Culture Festival was held at Koshien Stadium with a program that included group calisthenics, card stunts and performances by the Brass Band and Fife and Drum Corps.

The festival was a great success. It was the start of the Soka Gakkai's tradition of holding such unique and dynamic culture festivals, which could be called celebrations of the beauty of human harmony and solidarity. The Kansai festival was indeed the font of a new culture, and it would become a model for future events of its kind.

Another culture festival was held by the Kansai members at Koshien Stadium the following year, 1964, thus making this 1966 festival the third. When the performers and organizers awoke on that September 18 morning, they immediately looked out at the sky. Seeing that it wasn't raining, they were all relieved. At about five o'clock in the morning the rain that had been falling relentlessly in the Osaka area had stopped. Filled with excitement, they rushed to the stadium.

But it began to rain again and by the time the participants gathered at the stadium at about eight o'clock in the morning, it was raining steadily on and off. Everyone was certain, however, that the weather would clear—and in fact—at nine o'clock it did.

The twenty-two thousand card stunt participants took their places in the stands. The wind was strong, and the flags of various nations flying over the bleachers were snapping briskly. Nevertheless, the faces of the youth were bright and shining, conveying their determination to make the festival a great success.

Just after eleven o'clock, the rain started up again, and this time it showed no signs of abating; rather, it fell harder as time passed. Everyone watched with concern as sheets of rain poured down from the dark gray skies. The eight thousand young women's division members of the card stunt performance took shelter under the roofed section of the stadium. After toweling off their hair and drenched clothing, they put their hands together and began to chant earnestly, praying for the rain to stop. Just then, a loud, resounding cheer arose from the young men's division members still sitting in the stands, and they began to sing Soka Gakkai songs at the top of their lungs in the rain, their arms wrapped around each other's shoulders.

THE SPECTATORS began to arrive at the stadium. Hearing the chorus of Gakkai songs by the young men's division members in the card stunt section, they also started clapping and singing along. The young men's determination not to let the rain dampen their spirits, and to go through with the culture festival no matter what, became fused with the audience's sincere wish for them not to be defeated. Their united voices became a rousing cry that reverberated throughout the stadium and into the heavens.

Meanwhile, the event staff was working hard behind the scenes. Not wanting anyone to catch cold, many of the staff members were rushing around gathering and distributing plastic sheets for everyone to use as raincoats. The card stunt performers seated in the stands, however, made no move to use the plastic to protect themselves. Instead, they began to cover their cards, which were made of cardboard. If the cards continued to get wet, the colors would run and make it impossible to do the performance.

Seats had been set up under the sheltered section of the stadium behind home plate to accommodate the more than one hundred journalists from seventy-plus news organizations—including those from overseas—in attendance. Some of the reporters sneered at the young men singing Gakkai songs in the rain. Deciding that the festival would surely be canceled because of the downpour, more than a few of them prepared to leave. But when they saw that the young men were covering their cards instead of themselves, they changed their minds and returned to their seats. It seemed that the members' high spirits had convinced these reporters that no matter how dreadful the weather, the festival would go on. No doubt they were also curious what it was that made the members so enthusiastic, even amid these adverse circumstances. The passion and resolve of the Kansai youth had surely touched their hearts.

The rain kept falling. The ground turned to mud under the relentless pounding, and raindrops splashed into puddles. Sheets of water poured down mercilessly on the bleachers. The sound of the rain beating on the metal awning filled the stadium like the roar of a wild beast. Drenched with rain, the ivy twining up the stadium's exterior wall seemed to writhe in the wind.

IN THE FESTIVAL operations room at Koshien Stadium, a discussion about whether to go ahead with the culture festival took place between Youth Division Advisor Eisuke Akizuki and Yoshihiko Ohya, a youth division vice leader and top Kansai leader, as well as other local leaders. Ohya and the others argued vehemently in favor of proceeding with the program. "No matter what, we must hold the festival," they said. "Given the baseball schedule, this is the only Sunday available to us, so postponing it is out of the question. If we cancel it, everyone's efforts so far will have been in vain."

With a look of grave concern, Akizuki said: "I understand how you feel and I, too, would like to see the festival go forward as scheduled if possible. But I'd also like you to consider the matter objectively. What will happen if we hold the festival in the midst of heavy rains and strong winds?

"The young men's division group calisthenics routine features human towers several levels high, as well as human rockets that will be propelled several meters in the air. If someone slips in the rain, we could have a major, even fatal accident. In addition, if the white dresses the young women's division members are wearing in their ballet number become covered with mud, their performance will be ruined. And if the cards for the card stunt become soaked by the rain, their colors will run and be rendered useless. The audience will become drenched, too, not to mention the children who are performing. It would be terrible if anyone caught cold."

"But isn't rising to such challenges the Gakkai spirit?" a Kansai leader asked. "We want to demonstrate the Kansai spirit. Please, Mr. Akizuki, let us go ahead with the festival!"

The Kansai leaders were insistent, but they were also well aware of the need to give the matter serious thought. At the end of the discussion, Akizuki said: "We still need to see what the weather is going to do, and the final decision will be up to President Yamamoto. But I'm afraid that if it keeps raining like this, taking everything into consideration, we will unfortunately have to cancel the festival.

"If it comes to that, we'll have to make completely new arrangements for everyone's return travel. Other sudden changes will have to be made as well. Please have the responsible parties come up with thorough contingency plans in case we do have to take that route."

AS AKIZUKI'S instructions on formulating contingency plans in the event of cancellation were relayed to the various people in charge, they all reacted incredulously, voicing their disapproval: "Why? Why are we considering canceling?" "That's out of the question!" "Who cares about the rain? We won't be defeated!" Some members even went about in the rain pleading their case with the Kansai leaders.

The young women's division members were also shocked. Kansai young women's division leader Chiyoko Hanamura went to the operations room with several other members in charge of the young women's performances, and urged Akizuki: "Please let the culture festival go ahead. None of the Kansai young women's division members will accept it being canceled due to rain." She seemed determined to stand there until Akizuki acceded to her plea.

At about that time, Shin'ichi headed from Shin-Osaka Station to the nearby Soka Gakkai Toyonaka Community Center, where he was scheduled to wait until it was time for the festival.

General Administrator Kiyoshi Jujo, who was already

in the Kansai area, met Shin'ichi at the station and briefly explained the situation to him in the car as they drove. "The rain has started falling harder since noon," he said, "but the members continue to chant fervently for it to clear up. At the stadium, the performers and event staff are urging the leaders to hold the festival irrespective of the weather conditions."

Watching the rain splatter against the car window, Shin'ichi said: "The most important thing to me is the health of the members, who are the children of the Buddha. If holding the festival in the rain means that our members will catch cold and get sick, I think we should cancel it."

Shin'ichi fell silent for a while and gathered his thoughts. Then he began to speak again: "But it's too soon to come to a final decision yet. Let's watch the weather a little longer."

When Shin'ichi arrived at the Toyonaka Community Center, he was flooded with one report after another—about the guests and journalists gathered at the stadium, about the participants praying earnestly for the festival to go on, about the weather at the stadium and the forecast and so forth. Shin'ichi analyzed all the information carefully and considered the situation.

In the meantime, the rain beat down on the roof of the community center with startling force. It seemed to be ridiculing the sincere efforts of the Kansai members.

SHIN'ICHI addressed Katsumi Asada, a Kansai leader and Soka Gakkai vice general director, who was in the room: "The rain appears only to be falling harder. The most important thing is the members' health, so I'm afraid we'd better consider postponing the festival."

Shin'ichi wanted to take no chances. He felt tremendous responsibility for the members' well-being. He was painfully aware of the incredible efforts they had made and their strong fighting spirit. Young and old, they were all his comrades in faith.

Asada began to speak his mind passionately: "Sensei, please allow us to proceed! Kansai will not be defeated by rain. In fact, the rain will actually make it an event that we will all remember for the rest of our lives. I am certain that overcoming this challenge will provide us with tremendous confidence that we can use to face every obstacle we encounter in life from now on.

"Besides, the stadium is booked solid for every Sunday and holiday far into the future, and it's pretty much the same with the other stadiums in the area. Even if we postpone the festival, we won't be able to find another venue. It will also be very difficult to remake the colored cards for the card stunt that have already gotten wet in the rain.

"Please, even if we have to shorten the festival, let's hold it today! I know I am speaking for all the Kansai members. Please, let us go ahead!" Asada spoke with his entire being.

Shin'ichi replied rationally: "To boldly attempt a risky undertaking in order to demonstrate one's mettle may seem at a glance to be an admirable display of determination, but such foolhardy behavior always has its costs. Holding the festival in the rain may indeed have some significance, but, I repeat, what concerns me most is everyone's health and safety.

"I can't permit even one of my precious, sincere fellow

Kansai members to be harmed. That is how a leader must think."

Asada was deeply touched by Shin'ichi's genuine concern for the members. At the same time, however, his desire to hold the festival hadn't diminished in the least.

Keenly aware of Asada's feelings, Shin'ichi then said: "You still want to hold the festival, don't you?"

"Absolutely!" Asada responded, without a moment's hesitation.

"In that case, how about having everyone who has gathered sing some Soka Gakkai songs and then bring the event to a close. It can be a culture festival with a one hundred thousand-member chorus singing together."

ASADA AGREED that, given the weather, perhaps Shin'ichi's suggestion of having a grand chorus of Gakkai songs sung by everyone in attendance and then bringing the event to a close might be the best recourse after all. Although he still strongly wanted President Yamamoto to see all of the performances that had been prepared, he made the heart-rending decision to accept Shin'ichi's plan.

"I understand," Asada said. "It's really unfortunate, but the rain leaves us no other choice." He then averted his gaze to the window, and all of a sudden his eyes lit up. "Sensei! The rain—the rain is stopping!"

Shin'ichi and Asada stood up together and looked outside. The rain abated and patches of blue sky began to peer out from between the clouds moving rapidly across the sky. The earnest prayers of the performers, the event staff and all of their families, as well as members throughout Kansai, had been answered.

Smiling, Shin'ichi said to Asada: "That's wonderful. It looks like we can hold the festival after all."

Asada's eyes filled with tears as he exclaimed: "Yes! Thank you!"

"But we don't know how long this break in the weather will last," Shin'ichi cautioned, "so I suggest we start the festival early. Let's decide whether the program should be abbreviated or performed in full once we are at the stadium."

Shin'ichi asked Kiyoshi Jujo to call the venue and inform the organizers that the starting time of the festival was to be moved up. He also asked him to relay a message to the members encouraging them to do their best to make their performances a wonderful demonstration of the Kansai spirit.

At 2:20 PM, the telephone at the operations room at Koshien Stadium rang. The leader who took the call from Jujo shouted into the receiver, his voice shaking with elation: "I see. The festival is on! We're going to start early! Thank you!" When the others in the room heard this, they cheered loudly.

"We did it!" "The festival is on!" Several members joined hands and jumped up and down in happiness, tears filling their eyes. Youth Division Leader Shoichi Tanida immediately made the announcement over the stadium's public address system, and a wave of excited shouts echoed throughout the stadium. The performers, event staff and spectators hugged each other and rejoiced.

A light rain was still falling, but the members' faces shone brightly.

THE STARTING TIME of the culture festival was
thus moved up one hour to half past three. On hearing this announcement, everyone began rushing around
in a mad dash to complete the preparations. In rehearsals,
it had required more than an hour for the twenty-two
thousand card stunt participants to take their assigned seats
and ready themselves. But now they had less than an hour
before the festival was to begin. If even one member were
in the wrong seat, the words and images wouldn't be properly displayed. Members hurried to their places, but no
one knew how long it would take before they could actually perform.

Shin'ichi arrived at Koshien Stadium at 2:40 PM. The
rain had let up considerably and the sun could be seen
peering through the thin layer of clouds covering the sky.

Stepping out of the car, Shin'ichi addressed the youth
division event staff standing nearby: "Thank you for all
your hard work! Please take care not to catch cold!"

He then headed for the waiting room. As he walked by, members called out energetically to him: "Thank you for enabling us to hold this culture festival!" "We won't be defeated by the rain!" "Please let us perform the entire show!" Everyone was in the highest of spirits.

Observing these young people filled with such burning resolve, Shin'ichi thought to himself: "They have all worked so hard with the determination to hold the culture festival, no matter what. It's almost stopped raining. I'll take full responsibility and give the green light for them to proceed with the original program."

Shin'ichi realized that this would be the third important Kansai event to take place amid adverse weather. The first was the combined general meeting of Osaka and Sakai chapters in April 1956. Heavy rains fell on the members that day as they renewed their vow to spread Nichiren's teachings. Their firm resolve became the catalyst for a series of brilliant victories, beginning with the achievement of 11,111 new member-households in a single month. The second was the Osaka Rally held at the Central Civic Hall in Nakanoshima, Osaka, on July 17, 1957. That was the evening Shin'ichi was released from jail after his arrest on trumped-up charges of violating the election laws.

In other words, decisively raising the banner of victory in the face of all kinds of obstacles has indisputably been a part of the proud history of kosen-rufu in Kansai.

A Japanese saying goes, "Rain is the mother and father of flowers." At times the rain can be like a gentle mother compassionately giving nourishment to blossoms, and at other times it can be like a strict father, coming down hard on young shoots. When youth stand tall without being defeated, they can bring the beautiful flower of their mission into full bloom.

AFTER ENTERING the waiting room that had been set up for him at the stadium, Shin'ichi said to the leaders accompanying him: "Let's hold the culture festival basically according to plan. I'd like you to consider, however, what to do about those performances that might be compromised by rain."

Jujo immediately communicated Shin'ichi's instructions to all the Kansai leaders. After discussing the situation, they decided to cancel the junior Fife and Drum Corps performance, fearing that the elementary school students who made up the corps would get wet and catch cold.

At three o'clock in the afternoon, Jujo appeared in the dugout by third base, which was being used as the performance operations center. He found Yoshihiko Ohya, who was in charge of coordinating the performances, and said to him: "I know we're supposed to start at half past three, but do you think everyone's ready now? We don't know when the weather is going to change again, so it would be a good idea to start as soon as possible."

"We can't begin immediately," Ohya replied. "The card stunt performers aren't in place yet."

"I see," Jujo said. "That's a problem. Well, how much longer do you think it will be?"

Unsure of how to respond, Ohya said: "Even moving as quickly as we can, we'll still need at least fifteen minutes."

Jujo looked at his watch. "You say fifteen minutes is

enough, right? It's just three o'clock now, so let's start the festival at a quarter past three. I'm counting on you!"

As soon as Ohya said it, he was completely beset by uncertainty as to whether they could really be ready in fifteen minutes, but there was no turning back. After communicating the new starting time to the various responsible parties, he chanted earnestly in his heart.

The time seemed to flash by. At a quarter past three, Shin'ichi left the waiting room and took his place in the stands. The rain had almost stopped completely. Ohya summoned his resolve and gave the signal for the festival to begin. A vigorous fanfare echoed in the sky and fireworks exploded. Red, blue and yellow balloons were released above the stadium along with a flock of doves. Clutching the microphone in his hand, Ohya announced: "Let the Soka Gakkai Kansai Culture Festival commence!"

At that moment the words, *Congratulations on the Kansai Culture Festival* appeared flawlessly in red and blue Chinese characters against a white background in the outfield bleachers. Ohya breathed a sigh of relief. Just then, the clouds parted slightly, giving way to small patches of blue sky. Faint rays of sunlight could be seen in the west.

WITH THE HEAVENS heralding the festival's great success and amid thunderous applause from the audience, the nine hundred-member Brass Band proudly made their entrance into the stadium. The field was covered with large puddles, but the young men marched boldly through the water, their trumpets blaring and their drums reverberating, as if to proclaim their high spirits for all to see. The mud splattered the legs of their white trousers, quickly staining them brown. It was a stirring opening by these musical champions of kosen-rufu, who remained undaunted even in these unfavorable conditions.

Following the Brass Band, fifteen hundred young men's division members in white uniforms came dashing out onto the field with a resounding yell, unfurling a large, blue cloth as they ran. It was a giant 120-by-150-foot replica of the young men's division flag, complete with a golden young eagle and a laurel wreath. Moved by the strong conviction of these young men taking flight into the vast skies of kosen-rufu, the audience cheered and applauded excitedly.

Next came the captivating performance of the young women's division Fife and Drum Corps, many of whom were junior high and high school members. As they began to play, the sky clouded over and a light rain started to fall again. Raindrops splashed the instruments and the glowing cheeks of the young women. "We will not be defeated by rain. We are the young women's division members of Kansai!" With such determination, they continued to march dynamically across the field, playing a beautiful melody as they moved into a flower formation.

While the Fife and Drum Corps was performing, a group of young girls was gathered in the standby area chanting for its success. They were the members of the junior Fife and Drum Corps, whose performance had been canceled out of concern for their safety.

They had been informed of the cancellation after they had changed into their white and yellow uniforms and were already waiting eagerly for the festival to begin. The leader of the Kansai Fife and Drum Corps had said to them: "Because you are all so young and little, we are concerned that you might catch cold if you perform in the rain. I'm so sorry, but I'm afraid we've had to cancel your performance this time."

Hearing this, they all broke down in tears. They had spent every day of their summer vacation practicing under the hot sun, a strong desire to perform for President Yamamoto alive in their hearts. When they were told that they couldn't participate after all their hard work, their sadness and disappointment knew no bounds.

INEKO YOSHIKURA, a young women's division leader and the person in charge of the junior Fife and Drum Corps, was painfully aware of just how disappointed the girls were. She felt like crying right along with them.

But she steeled herself and instead spoke sternly to them as they sobbed: "Children of the Soka Gakkai never cry out of self pity! You are President Yamamoto's disciples, aren't you? You are lion cubs! I am sure that Sensei doesn't like crybabies!"

The members lifted their tear-streaked faces. Yoshikura continued, chiding them gently: "Your event was canceled today because you are the precious treasures of the Soka Gakkai. We want to make sure you don't catch cold. And you're still young, so you'll have many more chances to participate in culture festivals. I am confident that all of the rehearsing you've done so far will be put to good use in the future. Of anyone, President Yamamoto is the most concerned about you, and I'm certain he knows how you're feeling right now.

"I understand how disappointed you all are, but isn't the real spirit of the Fife and Drum Corps to show Sensei that we're fine and he need not worry about us?"

After she said this, she could still hear sniffling from the group. Approaching one of the crying girls, Yoshikura knelt by her side, took out her own handkerchief and wiped the girl's tears. Grasping her shoulders, Yoshikura gave her a gentle squeeze and said: "I know you're sad, but let's cheer up! This is all part of the challenge of putting on a culture festival! You're a big girl, right?" The girl nodded her head.

Yoshikura then smiled and called out to everyone: "Your older sisters in the Fife and Drum Corps are about to begin their performance in the rain. Let's go give them our support! But before we go, let's sing a few songs with such vigor that President Yamamoto can hear us!"

When the young women's division leaders standing nearby saw the girls wiping their red eyes as they sang Gakkai songs with all their might, they became teary-eyed themselves. And when the members of the young women's division Fife and Drum Corps learned that their little sisters wouldn't be able to perform, their hearts reached out to them. They promised each other that they would do their very best for the sake of their pure-hearted successors. This determination manifested itself in a fresh, vibrant performance in the rain that yielded thunderous applause from the audience.

THE RAIN continued to fall on and off. After the Fife and Drum Corps performance, nine hundred young men's high school division members dashed out onto the field with a vigorous yell and launched into a calisthenics performance. The cards in the bleachers rotated into the words, *Take Flight into the Future!* Running at full speed in their white sweatpants, navy shirts and white hats, these teenagers were the very image of high school youth brimming with fresh adolescence.

This was the first time in the history of Soka Gakkai culture festivals that the high school division had planned and performed an event completely on its own. For that reason, high school division members across the country were looking to the Kansai performance with great expectations.

Some of the participants, unable to afford the train or bus fare, had made their way to rehearsals by bicycle, riding as much as an hour or an hour-and-a-half each way. Many of them were also preparing for college entrance examinations. The participants had been limited to first and second-year high school students, and for the second-year students, who would be taking the exams, that summer vacation was a crucial period in determining their results. But they vowed together to be victorious on all fronts, and threw themselves wholeheartedly into both their studies and rehearsals.

One day, just as the Kansai youth were starting to feel a bit worn out due to their daily rehearsals under the hot summer sun, they received a message of encouragement from a high school division member in Saitama Prefecture. Thinking of how his fellow members in Kansai were working so hard in the intense heat to make the culture festival a success, he had been compelled to write to them.

"The Kansai Culture Festival is coming up soon!" he wrote. "Please do your very best as representatives of the one hundred thousand high school division members nationwide. The Saitama members are sending you their prayers. Fight on, Kansai high school division members! Do your best! We are praying for your total victory."

When they heard this message, the Kansai youth were deeply inspired and renewed their determination. "We're representing high school division members across the country! They're all behind us! Let's make our event a great success!" With this resolve, they reached the day of the festival having challenged themselves in earnest and overcome every obstacle.

The high school students' dynamic performance unfolded on the field. Moving into groups of five, they took the shape of human fans. In the next moment, they dropped forward into a push-up position, hitting the soaked ground all at once with a dramatic muddy splash. Gasps of awe rose from the audience.

When they stood up again, the fronts of their white sweats were covered with mud. Thunderous applause exploded from the stands at this powerful demonstration of the pride of youth in taking on adversity.

WHEN THE CALISTHENICS performers merged into a formation on the field that spelled out the words *Aim High* in giant Chinese characters, the card stunt panel transformed into a scene of two phoenixes, one red and one navy, as if to celebrate the future of the high school division members. A storm of applause resounded throughout the stadium in praise of the young men's valiant efforts. This was the moment that these young phoenixes of Kansai took flight into the future.

In the months following the culture festival, the second-year students preparing for their college entrance exams picked up the pace of their studies. They would later say that it was their experience participating in the culture festival that kept them going in this lonely struggle. When they began to feel disheartened, they would recall how they had survived those days of practice under the scorching sun, saying to themselves: "I made it through that tough rehearsal period and came out totally victorious, so I can definitely make it through these entrance examinations! I won't be defeated!" And when they thought of the incredible inspiration they felt that day as they performed with their entire beings in front of President Yamamoto, they became filled with strong fighting spirit.

Seated in the stands on the day of the festival, Shin'ichi chanted in his heart for the event to take place without incident and to end in complete success. After each performance, he leaned forward and applauded enthusiastically. He then asked leaders who were sitting nearby to deliver messages to the participants on his behalf.

After a dance performance by young women's division members clad in red leotards, the cards in the bleachers began displaying a number of images one after another, changing in synchronicity with the music. Until this point, the card stunt had played a supporting role to the other performances, but now it took center stage and dazzled the spectators.

A depiction of two peacocks appeared, facing each other in profile, their tails gradually fanning out in a completely lifelike manner. The cards changed in rapid succession once more, revealing an image of four rose buds slowly opening their petals and transforming into beautiful blossoms of vibrant red and yellow. Next came a portrayal of the Grand Canyon. As the scene materialized, a life-size horse-drawn covered wagon made out of cardboard moved across the ground in front of it. White smoke representing dust drifted up from behind the wagon as it went. The cards also displayed popular Japanese cartoon characters like *Atom Boy* and *Qtaro the Ghost*.

The sophistication and precision of this event far transcended the usual level of card stunts done by the Soka Gakkai, achieving a spectacular realm of human painting or human animation. It was truly a work of art. The audience gasped in wonder and cheered without end.

THE FIRST TIME a large number of people were used to create images and words in a Soka Gakkai event was in 1958 at the Fifth National Youth Division Sports Meet, dubbed the Festival of Youth. That performance involved some eight hundred young men's division members lining up in a formation of Mount Fuji on the field of the stadium where the festival was held. From then on, such formations became a regular feature in major Gakkai events. At the sports meet held in 1960, the year Shin'ichi became president of the Soka Gakkai, the participants created a formation spelling out in Chinese characters *Celebrating Your Trip to America*, to commemorate his first overseas trip for kosen-rufu.

Gradually, these formations came to be replaced by card stunts. At both the first and second Kansai culture festivals, held at Koshien Baseball Stadium consecutively in 1963 and 1964, card stunts utilizing colored cards were set up in a section of the outfield bleachers. On these two occasions, however, the stunts only added color to the festivities, fashioning simple images or phrases, such as *Third Civilization* or *Global Kosen-rufu*.

The card stunt began to approach the level of art at the second nationwide culture festival held in November 1964 at the National Stadium in Tokyo. In addition to words like *Unity*, the thirty thousand participants in the stands depicted various pictures, including Carmen and the matador from the opera *Carmen,* two lion cubs, as well as myriad flowers in brilliant hues.

The highlight, however, was a reproduction of Shin'-ichi's brush-written calligraphy of the Japanese word for *victory* in red against a gold background. Unlike printed words with their lines of uniform thickness, the strokes of characters written with a brush can be extremely narrow in parts, making such a large-scale reproduction a difficult feat. But the members were able to do so with remarkable accuracy, transforming the bleachers of the National Stadium into a wonderful piece of art, for which they won lavish kudos.

Now, two years later, the Kansai members were determined to create a card stunt that surpassed that of the Tokyo festival. They therefore set themselves the challenge of using the entire outfield bleachers and creating moving pictures of unprecedented scale. But when they actually rehearsed in Koshien Stadium, they found that the images deviated greatly from the blueprint and were drastically misshapen. The staff members in charge were stumped.

It turned out that because the stadium's outfield seating was on a sharp curve, when they enacted a plan that had been designed for a straighter layout, the images appeared distorted. This was a problem that had not arisen at the National Stadium in Tokyo, where the seating was less curved. The staff members were forced to draw up a new plan that allowed for the style of seating at Koshien, and they started by measuring the actual positions of all the outfield seats.

ANOTHER BIG CHALLENGE was how to incorporate motion into the images, such as having the peacocks' tails fan out and the rosebuds blossom. Until now, the card stunt participants had followed flag signals to turn their cards, but this would only work for a uniform change of image; it couldn't be used for a gradual progression of successive changes. The members in charge studied animated movies and other sources for inspiration, but they still couldn't figure out a method that would make successive changes in a matter of seconds possible.

They refused to give up, however, chanting hours and racking their brains to find a solution. At last, an idea came to them. For the moving images, staff members would run along the lowest row of seats in the outfield stands holding up sticks wrapped in red cloth. The participants would turn their cards when the stick entered their field of vision. This method worked perfectly when tested out. The images changed smoothly, resulting in extremely naturalistic motion. And so it was that that they were able to produce magnificent moving pictures. Single-minded determination is indeed the mother of creativity.

The outfield bleachers, where the card stunt members were performing their beautiful works of art, were abuzz with excitement. Each participant held seventeen different colored cards, eighteen inches wide and twelve inches high, bound together like a spiral notebook. In the center of each card was an opening through which the members could see the scoreboard behind home base, where a number was flashed. Checking that number against a customized chart indicating which color to display, they prepared their card accordingly. For still images, a large white flag signaled when to hold up the next color.

As they performed, the participants cheered each other on, saying: "Are you ready? The next change is coming!"

Fumiko Kitano, a first-year high school student and member of the high school division who was visually impaired, was one of the card stunt performers. Born with poor eyesight, she had no vision in her right eye and almost none in her left. She could neither read the scoreboard nor see the white flag signal to turn her cards. But when volunteers for the card stunt were solicited at a meeting prior to the festival, she raised her hand without a moment's hesitation.

D ESPITE her disability, Fumiko Kitano had been a member of the Fife and Drum Corps since elementary school. This had given her the confidence that she could perform in the card stunt, regardless of how challenging it might be. But when rehearsals actually began, she found that she could not even see the signal flag.

Kitano was assisted by Hiroko Yamada, another card stunt participant a year younger than her, who lived in the same neighborhood and belonged to the same local Soka Gakkai organization. As they continued going to rehearsals together, Kitano's strong determination to participate no matter what made a deep impression on Yamada, demonstrating to her the great power of faith. Yamada thus resolved that together they would do a wonderful job and achieve a memorable victory for youth.

Seated next to Kitano, Yamada would quickly check the color her friend was supposed to hold up and tell it to her. This was no easy task, since it was difficult enough to turn her own card in time, but Yamada gave it her all. Kitano also worked very hard. She didn't want to cause any trouble to the other participants by holding up the wrong color or falling behind. She practiced until she knew the color of each card by touch.

Not long after the rehearsals began, both Yamada and Kitano had become so good that they never made a mistake. They were the most determined of anyone to do a great job.

A stunning canvas of images unfolded across the stands. Although the participants had no idea how their creation appeared, they nevertheless continued displaying their cards in the rain, spurred on by the cheers of the crowd.

Seated in the stands, Shin'ichi received a report about Kitano and Yamada and how they were working together in the card stunt. He felt as if he were watching the enactment of a beautiful drama of friendship. Shin'ichi sent a set of prayer beads to Kitano, praying in his heart that no matter what trials she might face in the future, she would never be defeated and that she would stick with the Soka Gakkai throughout her life and build a citadel of indestructible happiness.

After the culture festival, when Kitano received the prayer beads and a message from Shin'ichi praising her for not allowing her disability to hold her back, she was overcome with emotion. She later went on to make a wonderful contribution to society as an instructor at a school for the disabled, dedicating herself to helping others facing similar challenges.

NEXT to enter the stadium was a group of women's division members in matching *yukata* (light summer kimonos) and straw hats decorated with paper flowers, performing the traditional Japanese dance *Kushimoto Bushi* to the strains of a folk melody by the same name. From about this time, the rain began to fall more heavily, and the spectators started to cover their heads with handkerchiefs or plastic sheets. Shin'ichi looked on with concern as the women's division members enthusiastically performed various other folk dances, including the famous *Kiso Bushi*.

The harder the rain fell, the more vibrant the dancers' expressions grew. Many of them had been at the Osaka Rally nine years earlier, on the evening of July 17, 1957, following Shin'ichi's release from jail. Standing in the driving rain outside the Central Civic Hall in Nakanoshima that day, they had listened to Shin'ichi's lion's roar echoing through the speakers that had been set up outside. Kansai's ever-victorious history began at that time, as the members stood together in the torrential downpour vowing never to be defeated.

Remembering that night, the harder the rain fell on the women's division members now, the stronger their determination grew. They danced with their entire beings, moving their feet across the muddy ground. Their white socks became completely soiled. The dyes of the colorful paper flowers adorning their hats ran down their faces with the rain, washing away their makeup. But they continued to dance in high spirits, as if to say, "Look at us! We are members of the Kansai women's division!" Their fresh, bare faces shone beautifully with the light of indomitable conviction and joy.

The rain continued its relentless pounding. The stadium lights illuminated the raindrops bouncing off the huge puddles that had formed on the field. The Kansai leaders looked up into the dark skies and cried out in their hearts: "Please, no more rain! The young women's division ballet is next!"

In fact, until the last minute, they had considered canceling the ballet. There were many poses in the routine that were done on the ground, but with the field in the condition it was, the grace and beauty of the performance was sure to be compromised. The dancers nevertheless begged to be allowed to perform. "We don't care if we get muddy," they said. "How our costumes look is unimportant. We dance with our hearts."

The Kansai leaders wanted the members to be able to display their passion. They therefore prayed in earnest for the rain to stop at least for this part of the festival. But it continued to cruelly hammer the field.

SIXTEEN HUNDRED young women's division members wearing pristine white ballet costumes made their way onto the field, their pale blue scarves trailing behind them in the rain. For these young women, the downpour was of no consequence; simply having the opportunity to perform was an unsurpassed joy. They began to dance proudly to the strains of *The Emperor Waltz*, as if enacting a paean to the victory of youth.

They had all faced various challenges leading up to that day. Some spent their lunch breaks at work practicing their steps wherever they could find solitude, even on the rooftops of their office buildings. Others cut back on the cost of their lunches in order to afford the transportation fee to get to their rehearsals, which they attended joyfully each day.

The waterlogged field shone golden under the stadium lights. Moving like graceful swans, some of dancers slid to the muddy ground in half-splits. There they remained for a while as huge raindrops pelted their backs sharply. When they finally rose again, their costumes were stained brown. But they continued to dance, smiling and moving elegantly, as if nothing could faze them. A storm of applause erupted from the audience in praise of their noble spirits, which could not be defiled by rain or mud. The young women were flowing with the purity and beauty of life.

Shin'ichi felt as if he were seeing the living embodiment of the words "like the lotus flower in the water" (LS15, 222) from the "Emerging from the Earth" chapter of the Lotus Sutra. This passage likens the Bodhisattvas of the Earth, who carry out their practice without being tarnished by worldly affairs, to the lotus flower that rises from the muddy pond, unsullied and beautiful. He was certain that as long as these young women remembered the determination they had been filled with on this day and devoted themselves to their respective missions, they would bring the flower of happiness into bloom in their lives, no matter what problems or adversity they encountered.

Four months after President Toda's death, in August 1958, Shin'ichi had presented the Kansai young women's division with a poem:

> Burning
> With great hope,
> Today again
> Like regal princesses
> Dance gracefully.

He was overjoyed to see the remarkable development the Kansai young women's division members had achieved in the past eight years, exemplified now by the regal dance they performed.

THE STREAMING rain shone silver under the stadium lights. It had become a virtual torrent. The Kansai Culture Festival was approaching its climax. A vigorous cheer echoed into the dark sky and some twenty-four hundred young men's division gymnastics group members, dressed in white from head to toe, came charging out onto the field. Their performance was based on themes from President Yamamoto's novel *The Human Revolution,* specifically the chapters "Overture," "Skirmish" and "Dawn."

In preparing for the festival, the Kansai young men's division leaders had met on several occasions to devise a performance that would communicate the spirit of the Soka Gakkai and of Kansai and impart courage and hope to all. Concluding that the true ideal of a champion of kosen-rufu was found in *The Human Revolution,* they chose chapter titles from the novel as themes and built their gymnastics performance around them. They also decided to use Gakkai songs as their musical accompaniment, for they felt that those songs expressed the essence of the Gakkai spirit, and they had deep pride in them.

The Soka Gakkai spirit is a spirit of compassion that is dedicated to working for the happiness of all people and world peace. It is a spirit of challenge to resolutely stand up alone and face adversity without fear. It is a spirit of justice that refuses to tolerate iniquity.

The rain provided the young men with the perfect backdrop to convey that spirit. They dashed boldly out onto the field with the determination: "Let the rain fall! Let the wind blow! We won't be beaten!"

For one formation, they created a wave design, conveying through their movements the idea of one wave giving rise to myriad others. Then, while still in this formation, they laid down on their backs in the mud. In the next instant, they sprang energetically to their feet one by one. Their backs were now stained with mud.

The young men went on to perform a series of extremely challenging formations in quick succession. These included spinning human propellers, human pyramids with the person on top standing on his hands, human rockets thrust high into the air and human bridges. With every movement, they became more and more mud-splattered.

THE SPECTATORS were riveted by the young men's performance. As if daring the rain to stop them, the gymnasts built a four-level free-standing human tower. Their hands and arms were wet and slippery from rain, and if anyone were to fall from the structure, they were certain to be injured. They held on with intense resolve, struggling to remain in position without moving. The spectators watched with bated breath as a single youth climbed to the top of the tower and stretched his arms outward in the driving rain. He was more than twenty feet from the ground.

The youth's face and uniform were besmirched with mud. He gazed ahead with a fierce determination in his eyes. They were the eyes of a great champion, shining with a fighting spirit. Excited cheers and applause thundered from the stands in a rousing tribute to this incredible triumph.

The gymnastics performers withdrew from the field like the ebbing tide, and then the stadium went dark. Soon fireworks began streaming up into the rain-filled sky, announcing the culture festival's finale. Illuminated by a spotlight, the Brass Band played vigorously as it moved across the field. The spotlight went out and the card stunt members in the outfield bleachers used flashlights to create constellations and an image of the night view of Hawaii. Down on the field, torchbearers created ripples of flame. The waves then became sparkling whirls reflecting brilliantly off the pools of water covering the field. Koshien Stadium was thus transformed into a magical world of light.

The stadium floodlights came on again and a procession of the more than twenty thousand festival participants made their way onto the field while lively music played. One after another, the high school division calisthenics group, the young women's division dancers, the young men's division gymnastics members and the other performance groups made their entrance. The rain continued to fall, but they all proceeded boldly and proudly around the stadium, waving to the audience.

In the middle of the field, the young men's division gymnastics group formed a human tower on a metal frame. The twenty thousand participants arranged themselves around the tower in concentric rings, turning the field into a giant flower. The Brass Band began to play the Soka Gakkai's "Song of Victory" and the card stunt performers on the right side of the outfield bleachers displayed the Chinese characters for the word *victory*. Then the audience spontaneously joined in and started singing:

> *Now the time for revolution has come*
> *Upholding our indestructible philosophy,*
> *The great advance of young people*
> *Shaking the earth, driving away obstacles…*

THE PERFORMERS' costumes were muddied, but their faces sparkled with happy tears and bright smiles. The joy of their spiritual triumph that day filled them with deep emotion. Having endured tough rehearsals and challenged their limitations, they had given truly superb performances despite the difficulties presented by the rain. It was a victory of their unity.

In the weeks leading up to the festival, the participants had formed strong bonds of friendship as they encouraged and inspired one another. In addition to studying Nichiren Daishonin's writings and *The Human Revolution,* some of the performance groups read Osamu Dazai's popular novel of real friendship *Run, Melos!* in order to learn about trust, integrity and the way for young people to live.

Whenever they were discouraged or frustrated, they chanted in earnest and faced their weaknesses and egoism, triumphing over them. Everyone felt a great sense of satisfaction at the accomplishments each one had achieved. They had developed tremendously through their participation in the event and were brimming with self-confidence, pride and hope. The culture festival had truly been an opportunity for personal growth and for the victory of youth. But most of all it was a celebration of youth inheriting the indomitable Kansai spirit and creating a new record of achievement for ever-victorious Kansai.

When "Song of Victory" ended, the stands erupted in enthusiastic cheers. The faces of the young people, drenched with tears and rain, glowed with nobility and human brilliance. At 5:50 PM, about two-and-a-half hours after it had begun, the culture festival came to a close.

Shin'ichi applauded, waved vigorously to the performers and then went to greet the guests. All of them were unsparing in their praise. Teary-eyed, some conveyed to Shin'ichi how touched and inspired they were by the festival.

Years later, Jun Miki, one of the guests and a photographer who would become the president of the Japan Photography Association, remarked: "As I watched the young performers in the rain, covered in mud, my heart grew warm, and tears fell from my eyes. Those young people had a passion to achieve something. Transcending any desire for personal gain or recognition, it gave me hope in Japan's future."

The festival was a source of inspiration to people around the world. Aides of then Chinese premier Zhou Enlai, who had been instructed by him to study the Soka Gakkai, also deepened their understanding of the organization as a grassroots movement through viewing footage of the festival.

AS IF IT HAD BEEN waiting for the culture festival to end, the rain started pouring even harder. Shin'ichi thought to himself: *We were protected. I'm glad we began early. I only hope no one catches cold.*

On that day, Amagasaki City—which lies adjacent to

Nishinomiya City where Koshien Stadium is located—recorded four inches of rainfall from ten o'clock in the morning through eleven o'clock in the evening, and several parts of the city were flooded. In Osaka City, more than ten thousand homes suffered water damage.

Immediately after returning to the waiting room at the stadium, Shin'ichi asked the leaders with him to relay a message of gratitude to the event staff. He wanted to waste no time in conveying his appreciation to those who had worked so hard behind the scenes for the festival's success.

Some staff members had been standing from early in the morning at train stations and along the rainy streets, out of hearing range of the cheers in the stadium, serving as guides and directing traffic. Others had been up all night readying the stadium for the day's event. And still others had spent the entire day cleaning toilets. The incredible sense of mission of these behind-the-scenes members and the pride and enthusiasm with which they exerted themselves were an indication of the festival's profound significance and of the true greatness of the Soka Gakkai. Anyone seeking to understand the real picture of the organization would certainly focus on this point. The people behind the scenes play the most important roles.

In the car on the way from Koshien Stadium to the Kansai Headquarters, Shin'ichi said to Kansai Leader Katsumi Asada: "Today's culture festival was really wonderful. I'd give it a score of one hundred—no, 120. The Tokyo Culture Festival two years ago was very good, but Kansai made today's festival a success despite the pouring rain. They transformed these terrible conditions into a dramatic, inspiring event and they won. That is the Kansai spirit.

Ever-victorious is a distinction bestowed upon those who continually triumph over adverse circumstances. Let's make today a new beginning for ever-victorious Kansai."

"Absolutely!" Asada replied excitedly. Thinking of how happy his fellow Kansai members would be when they learned that Shin'ichi had given their performance a better-than-perfect score, tears came to his eyes.

Shin'ichi added: "As the years go by, this culture festival in the rain will shine with ever more brilliance as one of Kansai's golden achievements. Those mud-splattered costumes will become the participants' greatest treasures."

Rain pounded fiercely against the car window, but in Shin'ichi's heart the clear sky of Kansai's eternal victory stretched without limit.

AROUND THIS TIME, a serious situation in the world was weighing heavily on Shin'ichi's mind— the seemingly endless quagmire of the Vietnam War.

In a speech broadcast over Hanoi radio on July 17, 1966, President Ho Chi Minh of the Democratic Republic of Vietnam (North Vietnam) had called on the Vietnamese people to resist the expansion of the US attacks against the north. He said:

> The war may last five, ten, twenty or more years; Hanoi, Haiphong and other cities and enterprises may be destroyed; but the Vietnamese people will not be intimidated! *Nothing is more precious than independence and freedom.* Once victory is won, our people will rebuild their country and make it even more prosperous and beautiful.[3]

The United States had begun its bombing of North Vietnam with an attack on Dong Hoi in February of the previous year, 1965. This marked the full-scale, direct involvement of the United States in the war between South Vietnam and the Communist north, and since then, the situation had grown progressively more convoluted.

Vietnam was a lush and verdant land. Following its conquest by the Han Chinese [in 111 BCE], the Southeast Asian country was ruled by foreign powers for a millennium, but from the mid-tenth century CE it had regained autonomy. During the ensuing centuries, a series of dynasties, mostly centered in the north, had ruled the country. Except for short periods of foreign domination, the nation had been able to drive back invaders from its northern border and retain its independence.

From the latter half of the nineteenth century, however, Vietnam had become a colony of France. In 1940, just prior to the start of the Pacific War, Japan invaded Vietnam, and the Vietnamese people suffered miserably under dual French-Japanese domination. But when the war came to an end in August 1945, the Viet Minh (Vietnam Independence League) arose under the leadership of Ho Chi Minh and established the Provisional Government of the Democratic Republic of Vietnam in the northern capital of Hanoi.

The Viet Minh was a broad unified front formed in 1941 under the leadership of the Indochina Communist Party with the goal of Vietnamese independence. In January 1946, the Hanoi government held nationwide general elections, and in March, the first National Assembly was convened. Ho Chi Minh was elected as the nation's new president and prime minister, and the new republic took its first steps as an independent nation.

In June of that year, however, France, seeking to reestablish colonial rule, proclaimed the southern Vietnamese region of Cochin China an autonomous republic.

WHEN the Democratic Republic of Vietnam attempted to unite the country from north to south, the French responded with military force and the conflict between the two sides intensified. Finally in December 1946, Ho Chi Minh called on the Vietnamese people to put up an all-out resistance to the French forces, thus igniting the First Indochinese War. The neighboring countries of Laos and Cambodia, also part of the French colony of Indochina, became involved in the fighting, which would continue for eight years.

In June 1949, France replaced the republic of Cochin China, which had no real viability as a nation, with the Associated State of Vietnam, appointing former Vietnamese emperor Bao Dai as head of state. While the French had superior military forces, the guerilla tactics of the Viet Minh troops proved effective, and they managed to turn the tide of the conflict in their favor.

The global situation was also changing dramatically. In 1949, the Communists defeated the Nationalist Chinese in the Chinese Civil War (1945–49), and the following year, the Soviet Union and China recognized the Democratic Republic of Vietnam. This heightened concerns in the United States about the spread of communism, which resulted in the acknowledgement by the United States of the Bao Dai government and its offering of military and economic assistance to the French. But the Viet Minh did not surrender; rather, they put up a fierce resistance.

The battle at Dien Bien Phu, a vast, mountain-enclosed basin to the northwest of Hanoi where the French had a large garrison, became the decisive engagement in the eight-year-long war. In May 1954, the Viet Minh army defeated the French forces there. A peace conference was subsequently held in Geneva, Switzerland, between the nations directly involved in the conflict—France, the Democratic Republic of Vietnam (the Ho Chi Minh government in the north), the Associated State of Vietnam (the Bao Dai government in the south), Laos and Cambodia. These talks were also attended by four other nations: the United States, which supported France; the United Kingdom, which administered southern Vietnam immediately after World War II as a representative of the Allies; and the Soviet Union and the People's Republic of China, which supported the communist Democratic Republic of Vietnam.

The conference resulted in an agreement signed on July 21 in Geneva that temporarily divided Vietnam into north and south near the seventh parallel, with a demilitarized zone of no more than three miles on either side of the demarcation. The opposing military forces conceded to withdrawing to their respective sides of the seventh parallel. The agreement also called for nationwide general elections conducted under international supervision to be held two years later, in 1956.

Furthermore, all concerned parties were to respect the independence and autonomy of Vietnam, Cambodia and Laos, thus bringing an end to French colonial rule of Indochina.

THE UNITED STATES rejected the final declaration from the Geneva conference that included a provision for general elections. The Bao Dai government, which was opposed to the armistice itself, refused to sign the agreement as well. Both parties were well aware that if elections were to be held, Ho Chi Minh would win by an overwhelming majority.

Subsequently, Ngo Dinh Diem, who had served as prime minister under Bao Dai, succeeded in strengthening his position in the south. In October 1955, according to the outcome of a popular referendum, Bao Dai was ousted from power and Diem proclaimed a republic with himself as president. As a result, the division of Vietnam into north and south was consolidated.

After the Geneva agreements, the United States replaced France as sponsor of the South Vietnamese government. US President Dwight D. Eisenhower pledged American support for the Diem government and offered it military aid. The US position was based on what was called the Domino Theory, which held that when one nation fell to communism, its neighbors would quickly follow like dominoes toppling over in a row, and soon communism would spread around the globe. Believing this to have been the case with the Soviet Union, China and North Vietnam, the US government was determined to arrest this trend in South Vietnam.

But the US-backed Diem soon turned into a dictator. Appointing family and relatives to the leading posts in the government, he quickly established a personal dynasty. Anyone opposing him was accused of being a communist and persecuted mercilessly. Such cruel treatment was directed not only at the Viet Minh, but at any member of the general populace suspected of communist sympathies. Countless Vietnamese were imprisoned and tortured to death. Being a member of Vietnam's Catholic minority, Diem also favored his fellow Catholics while cracking down heavily on Buddhist monks and laity.

Furthermore, President Diem refused to participate in national elections in 1956 for a unified government as articulated by the Geneva agreements. Feeling betrayed, North Vietnam began to take independent steps for the country's liberation. In December 1960, the National Liberation Front was established under the command of the Central Office of South Vietnam of the Vietnam Workers' Party (which had changed its name from the Indochina Communist Party in 1951). The NLF was a broad-based, unified front of South Vietnamese groups opposing the United States and the Diem government. It was comprised of farmers, workers, housewives, students, writers, artists and Buddhist practitioners.

THE UNITED STATES and the Diem government criticized the NLF as a puppet of the Soviet Union and China and dubbed it the Viet Cong (meaning Vietnamese communists). In reality, though, the NLF was not exclusively a communist organization; it enjoyed widespread popular support.

The NLF began a campaign of guerilla warfare, using any weapons its members could get their hands on—guns stolen from the enemy, shotguns made from drainage pipes, simple bows and arrows, and lances and bamboo spears. They were tough fighters who would appear from nowhere and strike before fading back into the forest.

Their attacks battered and exhausted the South Vietnamese government forces.

The NLF also carried out terrorist attacks, and in several cases military advisors sent by the United States to support the South Vietnamese military were killed or injured. The United States responded by increasing the number of advisors, including the Green Berets, a special military force sent to train the South Vietnamese in counter insurgency methods. But the rebels could not be stopped.

In addition, the Diem regime was growing more and more oppressive, leading to mounting antagonism among the South Vietnamese people toward the government and its backer, the United States. In June 1963, an elderly Buddhist monk committed suicide in the center of Saigon (the capital of South Vietnam, now called Ho Chi Minh City) by setting himself on fire in protest against the suppression of Buddhism by the Diem government. This incident caused tremendous shock among the people. But the tyranny continued.

Then, in November, a military coup d'etat with tacit approval from the United States resulted in the overthrow and execution of Diem. From that point, the government of South Vietnam became increasingly unstable and the suffering and apprehension of the people escalated.

In August 1964, the United States announced that a US destroyer had been attacked twice by North Vietnamese torpedo patrol boats in the Gulf of Tonkin in North Vietnam. This would come to be known as the Gulf of Tonkin Incident. Precisely what happened remains unclear to this day—some sources asert that there was never a second attack—but this provided the opportunity for an American counterattack. On February 7, 1965, the United States began its bombing campaign on North Vietnam, which it called Operation Rolling Thunder.

The amount of bombs dropped on North Vietnam in this and successive campaigns eventually totaled more than those dropped in all of World War II.

IN MARCH 1965, the United States began sending Marines to Vietnam, and from that point on, the number of US troops deployed to the Southeast Asian country steadily increased. The United States' role thus shifted from supporter of the South Vietnam military forces to a main player in the conflict. This was the Americanization of the Vietnam War. With the sustained bombing of the North by the Americans and the reciprocal guerilla war of the combined forces of the North Vietnamese and the NLF, the crisis was becoming exceedingly drawn out. By 1966, it had developed into a deep quagmire.

At the end of 1965, there were one hundred eighty thousand US troops in Vietnam. By the end of October 1966, that number had almost doubled, reaching three hundred forty-five thousand. At the peak of the hostilities in 1969, more than five hundred forty thousand US troops had been deployed. Furthermore, in 1966, troops from the Philippines and Thailand had joined up with the forces of other US allies, such as South Korea, Australia and New Zealand, who were already in Vietnam at the request of the United States.

On October 24 and 25, 1966, a summit was held in the Philippine capital of Manila, attended by the leaders of US allies in the Asian and Pacific region to consider the conflict in Vietnam. Though dubbed a peace conference, in actuality, no new steps toward peace were explored; rather, the conference was used as an opportunity to shore up the allies' resolve and unity.

Meanwhile, North Vietnam was receiving support from the Soviet Union and China, turning Vietnam into a bloody battleground where the opposing Cold War camps of East and West collided.

This situation deeply concerned Shin'ichi. Each time the war intensified, his heart ached and his suffering mounted. Young people are the first to die in war, and innocent civilians are war's greatest victims.

At a Tokyo metropolitan area high school division meeting in January 1966, Shin'ichi spoke of a soldier from the National Liberation Front who had been captured and executed by the Saigon government. He said: "Last year, a photograph of the execution of a twenty-one-year-old Vietnamese man appeared in a newsmagazine. He had been fighting for the liberation of his people and the restoration of his homeland, and he was captured by government troops and shot.

"He was still so very young, and surely he had many unfulfilled dreams in life. No doubt he had family waiting for him at home. But he died fighting to free his country and to oust the American forces."

SHIN'ICHI continued speaking, as if addressing each high school division member there individually: "I was very impressed by this young man who died upholding his convictions. But I also couldn't help feeling

tremendous pity for him. At the same time, while etching
the image of him in my mind, I firmly resolved never to
allow our society to become one that causes such suffering to young people like all of you."

Shin'ichi voiced the true feelings of his heart to the
members gathered that day, in the hopes that they would
inherit his spirit and live out their lives working to realize
world peace.

The skies over Vietnam darkened with gun smoke, and
the light of peace could not be detected anywhere. With
each passing day, the number of victims grew. The thought
of the Vietnamese people being subjected to the horrors
of war pained Shin'ichi deeply. At that time, the Soka
Gakkai had a chapter in Saigon.

Shin'ichi knew something had to be done to bring the
war to an end as quickly as possible. He therefore decided
to talk about the Buddhist philosophy of peace and to
make a proposal for resolving the conflict at the youth division general meeting scheduled for November 3 of that
year.

He was fully aware of the strong likelihood that in making such a proposal, he would incur all manner of pressure
from Japanese government officials and politicians who
toed the US line. At the same time, however, he knew that
as a Buddhist and a human being he had to speak out.

The youth division general meeting began before ten
o'clock in the morning on a bright autumn day at the Nippon Budokan Hall in Chiyoda Ward, Tokyo.

When the time came for him to speak, Shin'ichi took
the podium. He started by telling his listeners about a
recent interview he had with John Gunther,[4] a world-

renowned US journalist and author of such books as *Inside Europe, Inside Asia* and *Inside USA*.

Shin'ichi said:"I asked Mr. Gunther if he thought there would be a war between China and the United States. He said that he didn't think so, but that it wasn't entirely impossible. I then asked him how he thought the conflict in Vietnam should be resolved. With a troubled look, he replied that it was an extremely difficult problem to which he didn't have an answer. He also stated that he didn't think anyone else did either."

SHIN'ICHI said to the youth division members gathered that if the world situation continued in the direction it was headed, the result would be disastrous. He also affirmed his belief that the Buddhist concept of the Middle Way was the philosophy for creating world peace.

The Middle Way does not imply moderation in the political sense. It refers to one of the three truths expounded in Buddhist philosophy, the other two being non-substantiality and temporary existence. The term *truth*, in this case, means to clarify or elucidate. The three truths articulate the reality of all phenomena from three separate dimensions.

From the standpoint of life expounded in the Lotus Sutra, the truth of non-substantiality refers to the invisible nature of things, mainly the mental and spiritual functions of existence. The mind and the spirit are non-substantial, meaning they are indefinable in terms of existence or nonexistence. Rather, they lay dormant in our lives until they are manifested through external causes. Human emotions like anger are a good example. Anger flares up in response to certain conditions and then eventually disappears again.

The truth of temporary existence refers primarily to the material and physical aspects of existence, including its appearance, forms and activities. These come into being due to various causes and conditions and exist temporarily. This can be likened to a flower whose petals bloom but then wither and fall.

The truth of the Middle Way refers to the essence of life, its true substance and its totality. Human life, for instance, simultaneously encompasses both the non-substantial aspect of the mind and the temporary aspect of the body, without being solely one or the other. The Middle Way is the ultimate source and essence of life that pervades both of the other aspects.

To use the example of anger once again, even when a person isn't angry, the potential for anger still exists within the mind; it is not that it has disappeared completely. Or in the case of a plant, while its flowers may die, the plant itself continues to exist. The truth of the Middle Way is a clear expression of this mystic principle of life, its totality.

In the pre-Lotus Sutra teachings, however, the three truths were expounded as separate, unrelated principles. It was in the Lotus Sutra that they came to be viewed as an integral whole, with each of the three truths containing the other two. This is a presentation of life's true form, perfect and complete. And it is Nichiren Buddhism—the Lotus Sutra of the Latter Day of the Law—that dynamically articulates this consummate view of life expressed in the unification of the three truths.

The great movement of Soka is working to construct

an age of respect for the dignity of life, basing its actions on Nichiren Buddhism and upholding the principle of the Middle Way—a principle based on the totality of life that is neither exclusively inclined toward the physical and material nor toward the mental and spiritual.

A FTER EXPLAINING the philosophy of the Middle Way in terms of the three truths, Shin'ichi discussed the dominant philosophies of the age in regard to these Buddhist principles.

He said: "Idealism expounds one aspect of the truth of non-substantiality, while materialism represents one aspect of the truth of temporary existence. At the same time, existentialism addresses only a part of the truth of the Middle Way. Moreover, because these three modern concepts are separate and distinct, they ultimately fall into the same category as the pre-Lotus Sutra teachings.

"Philosophies or ideas that do not illuminate the essence of life will not be widely accepted, nor can they lead people to happiness. I wish to declare here and now that the Buddhism of Nichiren Daishonin is the philosophy of the Middle Way that integrates idealism, materialism and existentialism and can lead each to its culmination."

The youth division members present, deeply moved by the depth of the Buddhist teachings Shin'ichi was presenting to them, applauded enthusiastically, their eyes shining with hope.

Shin'ichi went on to discuss government in light of the Middle Way: "A government based on the Middle Way is not a government that adopts a middle-of-the-road stance between two opposing extremes or forces. Nor does it engage in eclecticism, selecting what it regards as the best ideas from both sides.

"Rather, it is a form of government that, grounded in the Buddhist principle of the oneness of the material and spiritual, protects the dignity of human life and seeks to achieve peace and happiness for all. Such a government must never become centered on partisan interests or strategies; it must always give top priority to working for the people and implementing policies for their benefit and welfare. I would like to declare that this must be the eternal aim of the Clean Government Party, which we support. Toward this end, the Clean Government Party will at times need to endorse the policies of conservative political parties and at other times cooperate with reformist parties.

"A politician who lives in accord with the Middle Way will always remain practical while possessing a broad and long-range perspective and working to carry out policies dedicated to a higher good."

Shin'ichi next discussed the specific mission of Japan, saying that, as the world's only nation to undergo a nuclear attack and as a country geographically situated in between the East and the West, Japan must lead Asia in becoming a third force in the world committed to the realization of lasting peace.

It was a call to rouse the Japanese people from their complacent attitude that as long as their own country was enjoying peace and security, nothing else mattered.

SHIN'ICHI then announced a concrete plan for ending the conflict in Vietnam. He said: "Today, as a Buddhist dedicated to the realization of lasting peace, I would like to make the following proposals regarding the crisis in Vietnam. I propose an immediate cessation of hostilities, and that an international peacekeeping conference be held in Tokyo among all concerned nations, including the National Liberation Front in South Vietnam. Once a consensus is reached, I recommend the prompt evacuation of US forces from the area. More, in order to prevent future outbreaks of fighting, I propose that UN troops be stationed in the demilitarized zone established by the Geneva agreements.

"I declare that Japan should submit these proposals to the United Nations as well as rally other nations not involved in the conflict to join in calling for peace in Vietnam. Do you agree?"

Shin'ichi's cry, filled with indignation and a strong determination not to allow the cycle of war and violence to persist, struck deep into the hearts of the youth present. They applauded vigorously in a show of their approval. Many of these youth had been feeling frustrated and disturbed by the war in Vietnam.

Shin'ichi knew that the United States and the other concerned parties were unlikely to readily accept his proposal. Even so, he firmly believed that, in order to bring an end to the morass of the Vietnam War, he had to continue to speak out with his entire being.

In closing, as if imparting his final injunction, Shin'ichi called out to the youth: "I hope that you will raise high the banner of world citizenship and work to build a global alliance that transcends national boundaries."

As they applauded, the meeting participants vowed that

they would take every possible opportunity to communicate Shin'ichi's proposal to others for the sake of world peace.

Demands for peace in Vietnam were increasing. A week prior to Shin'ichi's proposal for ending the conflict, the British philosopher and Nobel laureate Bertrand Russell[5] and others made an official appeal for the establishment of an International Vietnam War Crimes Tribunal. This tribunal, they proclaimed, would present the truth of the Vietnam War by revealing the kind of weapons that were employed and introducing testimony by the victims, as well as expose the war crimes of US leaders. In addition, five months earlier, sixty-four hundred American university professors had taken out a three-page advertisement in the *New York Times* calling for a stop to the war.

It was amid this climate that Shin'ichi, representing a voice from Asia, made this new proposal for peace.

SHIN'ICHI'S appeal for an immediate cease-fire was communicated to Soka Gakkai members around the world via the *Seikyo Shimbun* and other Gakkai publications. It had a particularly strong impact on youth division members in the United States, for whom the Vietnam War was an extremely pressing issue. The views held by these members regarding the conflict varied greatly. While some supported the widespread opinion in American society that its purpose was to defend Vietnam from a Communist takeover, others regarded the war as the US invasion of an Asian nation.

Whatever their sentiments, the members were united in their desire to see the war ended and in their absolute opposition to killing and destruction. They were thus in complete agreement with Shin'ichi's call for a cessation of hostilities. Feeling that his proposal conveyed the correct attitude of a Buddhist, they together reaffirmed their vow to realize peace.

Their determination did not immediately take shape as social activism, however. There were simply too few members in the United States at that time to affect any real social change. In addition, the members were of differing ages, occupations and social positions, and they held a wide range of ideas about what sort of concrete actions should be taken for peace. This made it difficult for the American organization to get a unified movement off the ground. If, for example, the organization were to stage an antiwar demonstration, it could cause problems for members who belonged to the armed forces. It therefore only made sense that each member strove to realize President Yamamoto's proposal in the way he or she felt best.

The war continued to escalate. In 1967, the bombing of North Vietnam intensified, and in August of that year, President Lyndon B. Johnson announced a plan to increase the number of US troops in South Vietnam to a maximum of five hundred twenty-five thousand.

On August 24, at the Tenth Student Division General Meeting held at the Nihon University Auditorium in Ryogoku, Tokyo, Shin'ichi once again made a proposal for peace in Vietnam, this time calling for a halt to the US bombing of the North. This day marked the twentieth anniversary of his taking faith. On August 24, 1947, Tokyo was still pockmarked with the ravages of World War II, and its citizens, faced with severe food shortages, were struggling just to survive. But dire as the times were, at least the war was over and the air raids and blackouts had stopped. The city was at peace and the people had freedom.

SHIN'ICHI knew firsthand the tragedy of war, having lost his eldest brother because of it. He was therefore firmly determined to do everything he could to see the Vietnam War concluded.

When he stood up to speak at the student division general meeting, Shin'ichi told the members how he had been thinking about the Vietnamese people suffering amid the fighting and had been praying in earnest for the conflict to end at the earliest possible date. He then said: "At the youth division general meeting on November 3 of last year, I made a few proposals for a cease-fire in the Vietnam War, to which the youth division expressed their agreement. With the recent escalation of the hostilities, however, I would like to take this opportunity today to make some amendments.

"The increased bombing of the North by the United States threatens to trigger a war between the United States and China. I therefore propose an immediate halt to the bombings. This should be followed by the cessation of all military activity in the demilitarized zone and South Vietnam, and of the further deployment of US troops to the region.

"I also propose once again that an international peace-keeping conference be held in Tokyo between all related parties, including the National Liberation Front in South Vietnam. Upon consensus, US forces should be withdrawn, and then economic assistance should be provided to both North and South Vietnam by the rest of the world.

"In addition, to prevent hostilities from erupting in the future, I propose that UN forces be stationed in the demilitarized zone. And furthermore, the flames of war must absolutely be prevented from spreading to neighboring Laos, Cambodia, Thailand and other nations.

"I would like Japan to submit these suggestions to the United Nations and to rally other nations not involved in the conflict to join in the call for peace. Do you agree?"

For the student division members, who were deeply concerned about the situation in Vietnam, Shin'ichi's words were a ray of hope. Their energetic applause shook the auditorium.

Shin'ichi continued, his voice growing stronger: "This year, UN Secretary-General U Thant made a new proposal for the immediate cessation of hostilities, but lacking any precondition for a halt to the bombing of the North, it was not adopted. Without such a move on the part of the United States, a truce cannot be reached. This is the only way to realize peace.

"Let us continue to advance with hope, rousing international opinion in support of the prompt conclusion of the Vietnam War."

SHIN'ICHI'S proposals struck a resonant chord with the student division members. Filled with pride and confidence, they did their best to convey them to their friends.

Members in the United States were also determined to open the way toward peace. The grim reality of the

Vietnam War weighed especially heavily on them. More than a few of them would be forced to go to Vietnam to fight, either because they would be drafted or because they were career soldiers already. The suffering of these young men and their families was particularly deep.

S. G. Rike was a vice leader of the young men's division in Hawaii and belonged to the navy. He received orders to go to Vietnam just after Shin'ichi's first speech proposing an immediate ceasefire, given at the youth division general meeting in November 1966. He was very distressed about the prospect of serving in Vietnam, realizing that he might be killed, or that he might have to kill others. He wanted to return home safely, both for the sake of his family, whom he loved dearly, and so that he could fulfill his mission for kosen-rufu. Also, as a Buddhist, he knew that taking life was wrong. At the same time, however, he couldn't disobey military orders.

Realizing that fighting for one's country was the job of a soldier, Rike was at a loss as to what he should do. He continued to pray, but was still in this state of mental agony when he finally embarked on a destroyer bound for Vietnam. The waves of the Pacific Ocean were rough and the ship was tossed about, as was Rike's heart.

On the way to Vietnam, the ship Rike was on stopped in Japan. After disembarking at the port of Yokosuka, Kanagawa Prefecture, he immediately went to the Soka Gakkai Headquarters in neighboring Tokyo to see President Yamamoto. Shin'ichi welcomed him with a broad smile, but Rike did not return the gesture. Rather, his imposing figure seemed shrunken and his face was pale. Through an interpreter, he said to Shin'ichi: "I am on my way to Vietnam. I may have to kill others, and I may be killed myself."

After listening to Rike's sincere concerns, Shin'ichi said warmly: "You don't need to worry. You have the Gohonzon, don't you? The Gohonzon answers all our prayers. No matter what the circumstances, don't forget to chant. I will also continue chanting for you until you return safely to Hawaii."

Rike felt new courage rising up from the depths of his being.

Once he arrived in Vietnam, he was assigned as a gunner on a battleship.

RIKE CONTINUED to chant in earnest, praying that he would return home safely and that he wouldn't have to kill another human being. But one day he found himself in battle.

Through his earphones, Rike received the command, "Fire!"

He had no choice but to open fire. He expected to hear a thunderous explosion as he did so, but nothing happened. His gun wasn't functioning.

Rike spent days trying to repair the weapon, but his tour of duty came to an end before he could fire a single shot. He knew this was a benefit of faith.

Several months later, Rike was called up for deployment to Vietnam once again. Wanting to remain in Hawaii, he prayed wholeheartedly not to have to go. Then, just before he was scheduled to embark, he felt a sharp pain in one of his knees. The navy medical doctor decided that he was in no condition to be on board a ship. His tour to Vietnam was thus canceled and he was assigned to onshore duty.

Many members in the United States had similar experiences. Carrying the heavy burden of being military personnel, their greatest protest to war was their personal suffering and anguish about how to avoid killing another human being.

Albert E. Parton was a second lieutenant in the Marines sent to Da Nang in South Vietnam, where he commanded a platoon. Of the sixty soldiers in his charge, most were young men of eighteen or nineteen. Looking at them, he was struck by how young they were and what bright futures they all had awaiting them. He could not allow a single one of them to be killed in the fighting. His responsibility, he felt, lay not in creating dead heroes but living heroes who could return safely to their homes, and he made a vow to see that happen. He chanted fervently each day for the safety and protection of his men.

Other commanders lost numerous troops in battle, and there were many platoons that lost more than half of their soldiers in the space of a single year. By some wondrous circumstance, however, not a single one of Commander Parton's men was killed, and they all returned to America unscathed.

SOME YOUTH division members in the United States opposed the war directly, standing up and raising their voices for peace. Albert Steiner, a student at Boston University, was one of them. He joined the Soka Gakkai in September 1966, two months before Shin'ichi's speech to the youth division members calling for an immediate cessation of hostilities in Vietnam. He did so because he was deeply impressed by the way in which the first and second Soka Gakkai presidents, Tsunesaburo Makiguchi and Josei Toda, had struggled against the Japanese militarist government during World War II.

Steiner and some of his friends organized and led a demonstration demanding an immediate halt to the bombing of North Vietnam and the return of all US forces. He was certain that war, which wantonly slaughtered innocent young people, was utterly and absolutely wrong.

If he had gone to a foreign country, he could have avoided the draft—which was actually what the sons of many wealthy families did. But Albert Steiner did not choose that route. He was deeply troubled by the fact that while other young people his age were dying on the battlefield, he had the privilege of student deferment because he was in college.

One day he went to his local draft board and asked to enlist. His plan was to refuse deployment once he was accepted, and then to serve time in prison for his beliefs. A month later, he received a notice to report for his physical examination for conscription. He passed, but his draft board told him to go back to college. They apparently regarded him as a menace because of the demonstration and other antiwar activities he had been involved in and therefore unfit to be a soldier. Having been prepared to carry on his struggle of conscience in prison, Steiner felt robbed of the opportunity.

With each passing day, a dark cloud descended further over American society. Young people, in particular, felt utterly hopeless. They lived in constant uncertainty and fear, never knowing when they might be sent to war. In their frustration and anger, many turned to alcohol, drugs and rebellion.

Young soldiers returning from Vietnam also suffered terribly. Some had lost arms or legs in the fighting, and all had to deal with painful psychological scars. Others were tormented by ghastly images of comrades with their heads blown open or of the Vietnamese they had killed. Many became living corpses, lost in the depths of despair and apathy.

MANY YOUNG Americans felt powerless in the face of the monolithic machinery of the state as it headed inexorably toward war. Soka Gakkai youth division members in the United States, convinced that Nichiren Buddhism was a teaching that could eliminate war from the world forever, eagerly studied Nichiren Daishonin's writings and President Yamamoto's lectures.

As they pursued their studies, they came to deeply understand that war was a working of what Buddhism calls devilish functions. The Sanskrit term *mara* is translated in Chinese in various Buddhist texts as "murderer," "robber of life," or "destruction." It manifests as earthly desires or other things that vex the minds of people, take life and destroy wisdom.

According to Buddhism, the devil king of the sixth heaven is the epitome of this negative, destructive force. The true nature of this devil king, who is said to dwell in the Heaven of Freely Enjoying Things Conjured by Others, is the desire to enslave others and to manipulate them for self-advantage. While in Buddhism this force is personified as the devil king of the sixth heaven, it is actually something that resides in the human heart. When it gains control over people's hearts, they are led to engage in murderous and destructive behavior and to start wars. What, then, can defeat the devil king of the sixth heaven? Only one thing: the life-state of Buddhahood.

Discussing this point, the American youth concluded that it is people who are ultimately responsible—it is people who make up the government, who start wars and who bring about peace. Unless the devilish nature inherent in human life—a nature characterized by hatred and an urge to destroy and dominate others—is vanquished and replaced by the life-state of Buddhahood, genuine peace cannot be realized.

While it is important that national leaders take part in peace negotiations, the youth realized, the fundamental path to peace can only be found in transforming the inner state of life of each individual. In other words, the only answer is human revolution, a process that establishes an indestructible citadel of peace in each person's heart.

The American youth also understood that while achieving the widespread propagation of the Mystic Law may seem like a long, circuitous route, it is the surest and most essential path to peace. Grasping the Buddhist teaching that all people innately possess Buddhahood and that their lives are infinitely precious, the youth agreed that if this great philosophy were to become established in people's hearts, the desire to take life or start war would be eliminated.

In this way, the US members vowed together that they would dedicate their lives to spreading the Daishonin's teachings toward the actualization of world peace.

THROUGH the *Seikyo Shimbun* and other Gakkai publications, Soka Gakkai members living in South Vietnam learned of Shin'ichi's two proposals for ending the war. Saigon Chapter, which had been established there in September 1962, comprised some eighty families in the Saigon area. Initially, most of the members were Japanese, but gradually Vietnamese people started to practice as well.

When the United States began its bombing of North Vietnam in February 1965, people living in Saigon, which was located some five hundred miles south of the seventeenth parallel, were still relatively unaffected by the hostilities. But as the days passed, the guerilla activities of the NLF against the American and South Vietnamese military forces picked up steam. The two latter groups also became more aggressive, and people began to witness horrific sights, such as the execution of captured guerilla fighters by government firing squads in order to make an example of them.

In addition, fear among the people mounted as they began to worry that North Vietnamese forces might invade Saigon and turn it into a battlefield.

Against this backdrop, spirited Soka Gakkai discussion meetings were being held on a regular basis. Koji Fukase from Japan was serving as chapter leader and his wife, Michie, as women's division leader.

Koji Fukase had been sent to Vietnam in 1962 as an engineer for a Japanese shipbuilding company. He was now in his early fifties. The meetings held at his home in Saigon were attended not only by Japanese and Vietnamese members, but also members from the United States, South Korea and the Philippines who were on military assignment in Vietnam. Because many of them couldn't understand the other members' languages, often three separate discussion meetings would take place in a day—Vietnamese in the morning, English in the afternoon and Japanese in the evenings.

With the imposition of martial law, large gatherings were banned. The members therefore conducted their discussion meetings as lunch or dinner parties. At one point, the police began to regard the members' activities with suspicion and Fukase was taken in for questioning. However, seeing this as an opportunity to let the authorities know about the Soka Gakkai, he cooperated happily. After explaining to the police that he and the others were practicing Nichiren Daishonin's Buddhism in order to realize peace and prosperity in Vietnam, he was allowed to return home without any problems.

It was amid these circumstances that the members in Vietnam learned of the proposal made by President Yamamoto at the 1966 youth division meeting in Japan. Japanese members translated it into Vietnamese for the local members.

WHEN THE MEMBERS in Vietnam heard of Shin'ichi's proposal, they were deeply moved to realize just how much he cared about their country. Together they resolved to work for peace, knowing that the only way to do so was to share the Daishonin's philosophy of peace with others. Thus, in a nation burning with the fires of war, the flame of Buddhist propagation was kindled. By the time Shin'ichi announced his second proposal for ending the war at the student division general meeting in 1967, Soka Gakkai membership in Vietnam had increased to several hundred member-households.

The Tet Offensive, a series of attacks throughout South Vietnam initiated by the NLF and North Vietnamese troops on January 30, 1968, marked a major turning point in the Vietnam War. Tet is the traditional Vietnamese New Year. As a result of these attacks, the tide of the war turned in North Vietnam's favor.

As the Tet festival approached, Ho Chi Minh, the leader of North Vietnam, offered a poem to the Vietnamese people in his annual New Year's message:

> *This spring outshines the previous ones,*
> *News of victory rejoices the whole country*

South and North emulate each other in fighting
the US aggressors,
Forward!
Complete victory will be ours![6]

This poem stirred the hearts of Vietnamese people seeking their country's liberation. Coming from a leader who lived among the people, it emboldened them tremendously.

In the Tet Offensive, NLF rebels lay siege to some forty cities. On January 31, they attacked targets throughout the South Vietnamese capital of Saigon, including the US Embassy, the Presidential Palace, the headquarters of the Army of the Republic of Vietnam Chiefs of Staff, the airport and the Saigon National Radio Station. Less than twenty commandos managed to seize the US Embassy and occupy it for six hours in an attack that took the Americans off guard.

News of the Tet Offensive spread across the globe.

The insurgents also engaged in intensive efforts to persuade South Vietnamese troops to join them, using megaphones to urge them to fight for the happiness of the people and the liberation of their homeland. At first these calls were answered with a shower of bullets, but as more and more people began to question why fellow Vietnamese should be killing each other, the number of South Vietnamese soldiers defecting to the other side increased.

SAIGON was no longer safe, and there were frequent gun battles in the streets. But the Soka Gakkai members there continued to practice their faith in earnest.

Many of them even experienced close brushes with death.

One such member was an American serviceman, who was captured by an NLF soldier one day. Discovering the Buddhist prayer beads the American had in his pocket, the rebel asked him what they were. "I use them when I pray," the member replied. "If I pray, my life is protected."

"Give them to me!" his captor demanded. "If you do, I'll let you go."

The American soldier handed him the prayer beads and, as promised, he was set free. He then ran at full speed to Fukase's home, where a discussion meeting was under way. Panting to catch his breath, he emotionally told the members gathered there what had just happened. The members wept, too, as they listened attentively to his story, and their conviction in the power of faith deepened.

On another occasion, a member happened to be carrying a set of prayer beads wrapped in a purple *fukusa* cloth when fighting erupted in the street. Clasping the cloth-wrapped beads in her hand, she chanted fervently as she fled. Word of her narrow escape got out and a rumor spread that anyone who followed someone holding a purple cloth when fighting broke out would be saved. From then on, whenever there was an attack, there would be a string of people trailing behind members running to safety.

Among the Soka Gakkai members in Saigon, there were not only American and South Vietnamese soldiers but also some who secretly belonged to the NLF. While they may have been pitted against each other on the battlefield, at discussion meetings, these fellow members came together to recite the sutra and chant Nam-myoho-renge-kyo for peace to be realized in Vietnam as soon as possible. At these activities, there were no enemies or allies. There were only children of the Buddha united by an eternal vow; members of the Soka family linked by a fraternal bond.

The members looked at their gathering as a model for peace, and they were determined to expand it widely. Each time they chanted their prayer was infused with their firm resolve.

Shin'ichi was deeply concerned about the members in Vietnam. Whenever he heard that members of Saigon Chapter were attending the annual summer training course or other meetings in Japan, he would meet with them several times during their stay and encourage them with his entire being.

On one such occasion, he said to them: "The situation in Vietnam right now is extremely difficult, but our faith exists so that those who experience the greatest suffering will enjoy the greatest happiness. Please continue to plant the seeds of peace and happiness in the hearts of the Vietnamese people. I am also sending you prayers in earnest."

Shin'ichi's heart was with the Vietnam members.

THEIR CONFIDENCE severely shaken by the Tet Offensive, frustrated US forces began indiscriminate attacks on towns and villages where they believed rebel forces to be entrenched. In March 1968, the My Lai Massacre took place in the coastal village of My Lai in Son My district, South Vietnam. American soldiers killed more than one hundred (some accounts put the number at more than five hundred) unresisting women, children and elderly. The massacre came to light a year and eight months later, when it was first reported in the newspapers.

US forces also began spraying the jungles, where NLF guerillas and North Vietnamese soldiers often hid, with powerful and poisonous defoliants, such as Agent Orange. Not only did these chemicals later produce numerous birth defects among the population of Vietnam, they also had devastating effects on the natural ecosystems.

Images of the Vietnam War were broadcast to the world through television and other mass media. As the horrors of the war became more widely known, criticism of the American government for allowing such cruelty and destruction to continue rose from people within and outside the United States. In Japan, as well, the Peace for Vietnam Committee and other citizen's movements opposing the war became active.

The huge military expenditures for the war also became an issue in the United States, and the Johnson administration eventually had no choice but to seek talks with the Hanoi government. At the end of March 1968, two months after the Tet Offensive was launched, President Johnson proposed a partial halt to the bombing of the North and the opening of peace negotiations. In May, representatives of the United States and North Vietnam met in Paris and preliminary talks began.

The negotiations were rough going, but toward the end of 1968 Johnson announced a complete cessation of the bombing of the North. In January 1969, the first plenary session of peace talks opened in Paris, with the participation of the United States, the governments of North and South Vietnam and the NLF. In the same month, Richard Nixon replaced Johnson as president of the United States and announced a partial withdrawal of US troops from

Vietnam. This was part of a policy known as "Vietnam-ization," whereby the capacity of the South Vietnamese forces to defend themselves would be strengthened and the burden of the war would be transferred to the Vietnamese people.

On September 2, 1969, as the withdrawals were getting under way, Ho Chi Minh, who had come to be affectionately and respectfully known by the people as "Uncle Ho," died of a heart attack. He was seventy-nine. His last words to his people were: "Our Homeland will certainly be reunified. Our fellow countrymen in the South and in the North will certainly be reunited under the same roof."[7]

IN MAY 1970, the United States and South Vietnamese forces entered neighboring Cambodia in an attempt to eliminate NLF and North Vietnamese forces taking refuge there. Then, on February 8, 1971, the South Vietnamese president ordered the invasion of another neighbor, Laos, in order to cut off NLF and North Vietnamese supply lines, which ran throughout the country on what was known as the Ho Chi Minh Trail. This invasion was carried out with support from US forces.

As Shin'ichi had feared, the war was spreading to the rest of Indochina. The thought of the suffering being inflicted on the people there filled him with outrage.

In March 1972, North Vietnam and the NLF launched the Eastertide Offensive in an all-out effort to take back South Vietnam. In response, the United States renewed its bombing of the North, with heavy attacks on Haiphong and Hanoi. The aerial mining of North Vietnamese harbors was also initiated.

Peace negotiations started again in July, and the United States scaled down its bombing of the North. A stalemate in the talks in December, however, led to the most intense bombardment of the war yet with the carpet bombing of the North by the United States. The horrific effects of this new campaign were carried in newspapers around the world.

There is not a moment to be lost, Shin'ichi thought. He was determined to do whatever he could to see the war end as quickly as possible. After pondering long and hard about how to bring peace to Vietnam, he finally decided to write a letter to US President Nixon urging him to stop the war.

With a prayer in his heart, Shin'ichi picked up his pen. Stating his intent to speak his thoughts frankly, he began by calling for an immediate cessation to the bombing of North Vietnam. He then asserted that any delay by the president in coming to a decision could have effects on the US leader and his country that no amount of time could erase. He also said that whether history would praise Nixon as a president of peace or condemn him as a person who betrayed the hopes of humankind hinged on that point.

Stressing that the desire of the Vietnamese people for independence was not something that could be suppressed by military force, Shin'ichi further urged President Nixon to announce to the world the cessation of all bombing and that the United States was prepared to resume talks for peace.

He also asserted that in effect the United States was not fighting a war against Communism but against the Vietnamese people, and called for the withdrawal of the United

States from Vietnam based on the principle of ethnic self-determination.

S HIN'ICHI went on to offer suggestions on the direction American policy toward Vietnam and the rest of Indochina should take in the future. One proposal he made was that the United States assume leadership in forming an international coalition of scientists, educators and doctors committed to the spirit of friendship and goodwill to assist in the reconstruction of Vietnam. He further suggested that, for the sake of Vietnam's future, other international groups be established to deal with the specific areas of economics, education, and health and welfare.

He then outlined the requisite characteristics for such organizations, listing them as: (1) possessing a fundamental commitment to humanism and friendship; (2) aiming for the realization of lasting peace by eliminating threats to human dignity and all violence and oppression; (3) functioning as part of the structure of the United Nations, rather than representing the interests of any one country; (4) having a solely humanitarian, nonmilitary objective, dedicated to improving the lives of the Vietnamese people, promoting education and developing health, welfare and sanitation facilities; and (5) respecting Vietnam's right of self-determination and offering only indirect support.

In order to prevent similar conflicts from arising in the future, Shin'ichi then proposed the formation of an international committee for peace in Asia. The members of this body would consist of representatives from the countries of Southeast Asia as well as India, Japan, North and South Korea, the United States, China and the Soviet Union and be responsible for dealing with any conflict that should erupt in Asia. In addition, nations or groups directly involved in the conflict would also be included in discussions, with all parties working together to find a peaceful solution. He also proposed that the headquarters of such a committee be established in Okinawa.

During World War II, the Okinawan islands had been the site of horrible atrocities, and after the war, large portions of the prefecture had been turned into US military bases. Okinawa also had deep historical connections to the United States, China and the countries of Southeast Asia. Shin'ichi believed that it was Okinawa's mission to be the starting point for lasting peace in Asia.

He concluded his letter to President Nixon stating that the entire world was eagerly awaiting his decision and subsequent action and that thinking people everywhere had faith in his humanity.

SHIN'ICHI'S LETTER to President Nixon came to thirty-eight pages when translated into English. Every page flowed with his deep concern for both the Vietnamese and American people and his fervent wish for peace. It was at once a proposal and a pledge for peace, as well as an admonition.

Dated January 1, 1973, the letter was written with the prayer that a brilliant sun of hope would rise in the coming year. Shin'ichi had it hand-delivered to US National Security Advisor Henry Kissinger, who in turn passed it on to the president. From 1969, Kissinger had been involved in secret negotiations with Le Duc Tho, the head of the North Vietnamese delegation to the Paris Peace Talks.

In January 1975, two years after Shin'ichi sent his letter to Nixon, he and Kissinger met for the first time. A discussion ensued and they later published a dialogue together.

It is unclear how Nixon reacted to Shin'ichi's letter or how it may have influenced him. At any rate, on January 23, 1973, Kissinger and Le Duc Tho reached a cease-fire agreement in Paris, and on January 27, the Paris Peace Accords were officially signed by the foreign ministers of the Democratic Republic of Vietnam (North), the Republic of Vietnam (South) and the Provisional Revolutionary Government of South Vietnam (established in June 1969 as the Communist rival to the South Vietnamese government), and the US secretary of state. The agreement was thus accepted, and the Vietnam War officially ended on January 28, 1973.

Among the stipulations set forth in the pact were the full withdrawal of all US forces from Vietnam and the release of all prisoners of war within a sixty-day period of its signing. Although this marked an end to the fighting between the United States and the people of Vietnam, peace was still long in coming. The Saigon government insisted that it was the only legal government in the South and began fighting against the opposing provisional revolutionary government.

With the Americans gone, however, the South Vietnamese forces soon lost their will to fight. Consequently, Communist troops quickly gained control of several outlying areas before invading Saigon. South Vietnam surrendered unconditionally on April 30, 1975.

PEACE IN VIETNAM was finally realized nearly three decades after the start of the First Indochina War with France, and a decade after the start of the US bombing of the North. In July of the following year, 1976, Vietnam achieved its long-awaited goal of unification and the Socialist Republic of Vietnam was born.

The turmoil of the war, however, had forced most Japanese Soka Gakkai members living in Saigon to return home and scattered the local Vietnamese members across the country. But Saigon Chapter Leader Fukase and his wife, Michie, the women's division leader, while being aware of the impending danger, resolved to stay in Vietnam as long as possible. They wanted to be there to encourage any other members who might come to them.

When fighting broke out on the streets of the capital, the couple took refuge in a basement room with their three children. Many homes in the area had been burned down, and there were bullet holes in the posts of their own front gate. They once even found a bloody corpse with the arms ripped off in the street in front of their house. But they remained in Saigon.

Eventually, the Japanese Embassy issued an advisory recommending that all Japanese nationals leave the country and in January 1973, the Fukase family reluctantly decided to say farewell to their adopted homeland.

Shin'ichi did whatever he could to support the reconstruction of Vietnam after peace was achieved. When, for example, there was a sudden increase in the outflow of refugees from the country, he endorsed fund-raising efforts of the Soka Gakkai youth division members in aid of the refugees.

In 1990, the Soka Gakkai-sponsored *War and Peace: The Course of the Vietnam War* exhibition toured Japan as an appeal for peace, and in July and August 1994, the SGI-sponsored *World Boys and Girls Art Exhibition* was held in Hanoi and Ho Chi Minh City. The Hanoi showing was attended by then vice president Madame Nguyen Thi Binh, who had been one of the representatives of the Provisional Revolutionary Government of South Vietnam at the Paris Peace Talks and an activist of the resistance movement.

The United States Department of Defense reported that during the war, which cost the United States $139 billion, some sixty thousand Americans were killed either in action or through accidents. Vietnamese casualties were put at one million North Vietnamese and NLF soldiers, two hundred forty thousand South Vietnamese soldiers and half a million civilians.

And what purpose did the war serve?

No matter what high-sounding justifications are offered and no matter how cloaked in righteousness it is, war is the most barbaric and foolish of all acts, perpetrated by the devilish forces that reside within the human heart.

The Soka Gakkai is opposed to all war, and we will continue our struggle until it is eliminated from this world, completely and forever.

NOTES

1 Simone Weil, *The Need for Roots: Prelude to a Declaration of Duties Towards Mankind*, translated by A.F. Willis (London and New York: Routledge, 1952), p. 194.

2 In *The Writings of Nichiren Daishonin*, the title of this work was retranslated as "The Object of Devotion for Observing the Mind."

3 Ho Chi Minh, "Appeal to Compatriots and Fighters Throughout the Country." From the official Web site of the Communist Party of Vietnam. http://www.cpv.org.vn/hochiminh_en/publications/selectedwritings/307-310.htm (February 5, 2003).

4 John Gunther (1901–70).

5 Bertrand Russell (1872–1970).

6 Ho Chi Minh, "New Years Greetings," 1968. From the official Web site of the Communist Party of Vietnam. http://www.cpv.org/vn/hochiminh_en/publications/selectedwritings /337-338.htm (April 17, 2003).

7 "President Ho Chi Minh's Statement," dated May 10, 1969. From the official Web site of the Communist Party of Vietnam. http://www.cpv.org.vn/hochiminh_en/testament/president.htm (April 17, 2003).

Dynamic Advancement

MOMENTUM gives rise to greater momentum. Just as a strong blaze is fueled by fierce winds, dynamic advancement is powered by adversity and can break through the walls of any hardship. Who can possibly stop the surging tide of an awakened people's determination to change society? Who can obstruct their joyous movement in that direction? No authority can reverse the current of the times. This is the lesson of history.

The Soka Gakkai was forging ahead into the new year

with even greater momentum, moving from the Year of Dawn, 1966, to the Year of Dynamic Advancement, 1967.

At the end of November 1966, the organization surpassed its long-cherished goal of six million member-households, reaching a total of 6.1 million. Shin'ichi had announced the goal of six million at the May 3, 1964, Headquarters general meeting as the target for the next seven years. At that point, the membership stood at about 4.3 million member-households, which meant that in the intervening two-and-a-half years, it had grown steadily by 1.8 million.

The year 1967 would mark the seventh anniversary of Shin'ichi's presidency. Everyone burnt with enthusiasm, feeling that through their earnest efforts, the unprecedented undertaking of worldwide kosen-rufu was becoming a reality, and society and the times were definitely changing. For these fellow members, each day was filled with excitement and brimming with hope. Keenly aware of their individual roles as leading protagonists in the endeavor to spread Nichiren Daishonin's teachings, their passion to achieve tremendous victory in the coming year blazed even brighter.

Shin'ichi's determination at the start of this Year of Dynamic Advancement was solid and profound. He was resolved to make it a year of incredible growth in the kosen-rufu movement.

Time is shared equally by all people, but there is never enough of it for the person determined to accomplish a great objective. To Shin'ichi, time seemed to be rapidly flashing by, and so he regarded each moment as a win-or-lose struggle. He continuously exerted himself to such an extent that he could declare himself ready to die at any moment without a single regret. Not begrudging one's life is the spirit of giving one's utmost to each instant, each day, with the awareness that now is the last moment of one's life.

How could Shin'ichi make great strides in kosen-rufu? The answer was clear—it was by praising, encouraging and inspiring his fellow members working on the front lines of the organization, showing them the same respect he would a Buddha.

TO MARK the start of this next phase of development, Shin'ichi planned to spend January traveling around Japan meeting with members. On January 9, he visited Hyogo and Osaka in the Kansai region. He then moved on to Sapporo in Hokkaido, Fukuoka Prefecture in the Kyushu region, Aichi Prefecture in the Chubu region, Chiba Prefecture, Okayama Prefecture in the Chugoku region, Shizuoka Prefecture and Kanagawa Prefecture, crisscrossing the entire country in just two weeks. It was an intense struggle without a second's rest.

When members throughout Japan read of Shin'ichi's activities in the Soka Gakkai publications, they felt that the time of dynamic advancement had indeed arrived. They thought: *Sensei is exerting himself wholeheartedly. He is striving with all his might. Let us also take action and speak with others to the best of our ability—for the sake of the Law, our friends and society.*

The effect of Shin'ichi's activities rippled far and wide.

It is a leader's actions, not words, that people will support and follow. Leaders who only pay lip service to the people will have their true colors exposed and be abandoned and forsaken in the end.

And so it was that the kosen-rufu movement began to pick up speed in 1967.

On January 29, the Thirty-first House of Representatives (Lower House) elections were held. It was the tenth such election since the end of World War II, and the first general election to be held during the Eisaku Sato Cabinet, which had been formed in 1964. The previous election had taken place three years and two months earlier, during the second Hayato Ikeda Cabinet. This was also the first Lower House election in which the Clean Government Party participated.

Elections were being held due to the dissolution of the Lower House, which had resulted from a series of scandals involving abuse of power and corruption among cabinet ministers and representatives. Dubbed the "Black Mist Scandal," it had aroused public distrust of politics. The major focus of the upcoming election was therefore whether the political arena could be cleaned up, the public's confidence restored and a true representative government established.

For this reason, both Soka Gakkai members and society at large placed high expectations in the Clean Government Party, which had made positive strides in weeding out political corruption. Gakkai members were convinced that without the Clean Government Party, there wasn't much hope for Japan's future. They also felt a renewed determination to support the Clean Government Party in achieving total victory in its first run in Lower House elections and to bring a new dawn to Japanese politics.

THE DECISION to run candidates for the Lower House was officially made by the Clean Government Political Federation (forerunner of the Clean Government Party) in May 1964. When the Clean Government Party was formed in November of that same year, it thus announced that it would field candidates in the next Lower House elections. But the political and religious establishments of the day perceived this as a threat and began putting various kinds of pressure on the Soka Gakkai. Shin'ichi was even approached by a major political figure who was by turns belligerent to the point of intimidation and conciliatory. The Soka Gakkai Headquarters was also swamped with hostile and threatening phone calls and letters.

In addition, just around the time the Clean Government Party was founded, efforts of the ruling Liberal Democratic Party to change the electoral system for the Lower House were gaining momentum. In those days, the Lower House operated on a medium-sized constituency system, whereby three to five representatives were sent from each district to the Japanese parliament. The LDP was seeking to change this to a single-seat constituency system with smaller electoral districts. Allowing for only one candidate to be elected per district, this new system would increase the likelihood that the winner would be from a large, powerful party and was therefore highly advantageous to such parties. All the votes cast for the candidates who came in second and below would essentially be wasted votes, since they elected no one; this made the proposed system ineffective in truly representing the will of the voters.

The Election System Council also considered implementing a proportional representation system in conjunction with the single-seat constituency system, but in actual practice, this wouldn't have been much different than the single-seat plan. In any event, the proposed reorganization of electoral districts was very likely to lead to single-party rule and sound the death knell for representative parliamentary democracy in Japan.

The members of the Soka Gakkai youth division responded swiftly to these developments in the political arena. Seeing this as an attempt by the ruling party to maintain its power and block the entry of the Clean Government Party into the Lower House, they voiced a desire to hold demonstrations to protest this move.

But Shin'ichi was circumspect. He didn't want his fellow members, who were already exerting themselves wholeheartedly in Gakkai activities, often while struggling with such personal problems as illness and financial difficulties, to take on the added burden of political protest. Furthermore, if at all possible, he also didn't want the organization to become involved in political activities beyond offering election campaign support.

The youth division members determined, however, to carry out their protest. And the men's, women's and young women's division members also voiced their wish to join them. All burned with righteous indignation at the injustice they felt was being perpetrated by the powers that be.

SHIN'ICHI considered the matter carefully. He was deeply concerned about the state of the Japanese political realm, into which the East-West rivalries of the

Cold War had been brought just as they were. This made genuine debate or discussion between the opposing conservative and reformist camps within the government impossible. He believed that in order to bridge this ideological gap and break through the impasse, a new, third pillar needed to be established in addition to the two major forces of the Liberal Democratic Party and Socialist Democratic Party of Japan. And he was convinced that the Clean Government Party, which upheld the Buddhist principle of the Middle Way, was the very party to fulfill that role.

If, however, the single-seat constituency system was adopted and the Clean Government Party was prevented from gaining entrance to the Lower House, even this would be impossible. This was a problem that the Soka Gakkai, which had formed the party to realize the happiness of the people and the prosperity of society, could not overlook.

Furthermore, given the statements and actions of LDP representatives thus far, there was justifiable cause for concern that the implementation of the proposed new system could result in the LDP's entrenchment as Japan's unchallenged ruler, increasing the probability of the country advancing once more down the path of militarism. *If we remain silent and do nothing now*, Shin'ichi thought, *the situation is certain to get out of hand.*

At the youth division general meeting held on November 23, 1965, at the Nihon University Auditorium in Ryogoku, Tokyo, Shin'ichi touched on the matter of the proposed change in the electoral system and, after pointing out the dangers it presented, stated emphatically: "If the Soka Gakkai does not take action now, what will happen to Japan? If we go to war again, what will become of the Japanese people? In light of these questions, I propose that, in the event there is an attempt to railroad this new system through the Diet next year, we hold mass demonstrations of half a million in Tokyo and three million around Japan. What do you think?"

Shouts of approval and a thunderous wave of applause echoed throughout the auditorium.

Keeping in mind Japan's history of demonstrations turning violent, Shin'ichi added when the noise subsided: "Out of consideration for the safety of our women's and young women's division members, I would like to ask that they refrain from participating in these proposed rallies."

With the impassioned fervor of a lion's roar, Shin'ichi's voice then rang out: "I will take the lead in such a demonstration when the time comes! We must not allow the people to be trampled on any longer!"

SHIN'ICHI'S announcement struck a deep chord in the hearts of the youth and roused their fighting spirit. The Soka Gakkai, then comprising a total of eight million people of every social level, age and profession, could be described as a great movement of the Japanese people. It was these very representatives of Japanese society who had been galvanized to rise up in opposition to the government's plan to revise the Japanese election system.

This was neither a ploy nor false bravado; a demonstration of three million people was bound to shake the nation. The righteous anger of the members and their iron will to stop this proposal awakened public opinion. As a result, the leaders of the LDP began to realize that if they went through with their plan, they would lose the support of the people and their party's foundations would be rattled to the core.

At the same time, the Clean Government Party and the other opposition parties actively challenged the LDP proposal and joined forces to oppose it. In January 1966, it was reported that the LDP leadership had decided to put off the new electoral plan for the foreseeable future. Their reasons were cited as wanting to avoid the head-on collision that was sure to arise with the other parties if they forced this change through, as well as staunch resistance from elements within their own party.

Just before the end of the year, on December 27, 1966, the Lower House was dissolved and elections were scheduled for the following month under the already existing medium-sized constituency system. In the end, the LDP's scheme to institute a self-advantageous electoral system was frustrated and so a protest demonstration by the Soka Gakkai didn't take place.

The Clean Government Party's participation in the Lower House elections was fiercely contested by other religious groups in Japan. In August 1965, an association of established Buddhist schools held a conference to address the urgent issue of taking decisive measures against the Soka Gakkai.

According to an article that appeared in the religious newspaper *Chugai Nippo* on September 1, 1965, the conference concluded: "The Soka Gakkai's establishment of the Clean Government Party and entry into the political arena will have a major impact on the future of Buddhism.

Buddhist practitioners need to therefore resolutely unite, make a major shift from the defensive to the offensive and initiate a holy war in order to refute the erroneous and reveal the true."

Among the concrete measures proposed at the conference was a plan to seize the best opportunity and petition the Diet and government to have the Soka Gakkai outlawed as a pernicious religion. This was no more than a plot to enlist the authorities in an effort to clamp down on the Soka Gakkai.

A GROUP of the so-called new religions held a directors meeting in early September to draw up a strategy to oppose the Soka Gakkai and the Clean Government Party. They decided to mobilize the approximately seven million members of the group's more than ninety affiliated religious organizations and launch a campaign of counter propagation, whereby they would seek to disassociate members from the Soka Gakkai. They also announced (according to the September 8, 1965 edition of *Chugai Nippo*) that they were "prepared to take a hard stand against any newspaper or other mass media that appeared to curry favor with the Soka Gakkai and the Clean Government Party, and to initiate a boycott movement countering such media if need be."

It was against this backdrop of fierce mudslinging that the Clean Government Party participated in its first Lower House election campaign. The Clean Government Party fielded thirty-two candidates, but because the LDP and other established parties reduced the number of candidates they were fielding in each district, the election became a tight race between 917 candidates vying for a limited number of seats.

As the campaign got under way, Shin'ichi took great pains to make certain that Soka Gakkai members, who were working hard to support the party, had a solid understanding of the direction the party should be heading in and could carry out their election activities with confidence.

At the New Year's leaders meeting held on January 6, 1967, at the Nippon Budokan in Chiyoda Ward, Tokyo, he clarified the future course of the Clean Government Party, saying: "As the founder of the Clean Government Party, I have a responsibility to lay out a vision for the party as well as to watch over it. Because the Clean Government Party came into being through the support of the Soka Gakkai, at present both its members and supporters are mainly Gakkai members. I therefore think it's of utmost importance that I speak to my fellow Gakkai members about this goal. I would like to take this opportunity today to do so.

"I would like us to advance with the motto, 'Building a Peaceful and Prosperous Society through Government Based on the Middle Way.' The first step we must take in that direction is to ensure that our government is democratic and corruption-free. Concretely, this means protecting Japan's peace constitution, establishing a true parliamentary democracy and safeguarding the freedoms of speech, association and religious belief.

"As far as domestic affairs are concerned, I'd like our slogan to be, Creating a Higher Standard of Living by Working for the People's Welfare. In that sense, let us strive to foster an economy that protects the interests of ordinary citizens by encouraging mutual assistance, an extensive social security system and a richly humanistic culture."

With regard to foreign policy, Shin'ichi called on the party to endeavor for the abolition of all nuclear weapons, the reform of the United Nations and complete international disarmament toward the realization of a peaceful world without war.

SHIN'ICHI spoke further of the concept of government based on the Buddhist principle of the Middle Way: "Simply put, what we are aiming for is a compassionate government that values humanity in accord with the philosophy of life of the Middle Way. To value humanity means valuing the distinct individuality of each person based on profound respect for the dignity of human life, and enabling each individual to enjoy a life of the greatest possible happiness. It means regarding all social organizations and cultural activities as existing for this purpose, and governing in a way that respects life. The ideal society we seek is one that is built on such principles."

Shin'ichi went on to state that both capitalism and communism result in government that neglects the human being, losing sight of their original purpose of serving the people. This, he pointed out, was the fundamental cause of societal deadlock.

"In capitalist societies," he elaborated, "the pursuit of profit is the primary goal, which in many cases leads to the sacrifice of individual happiness. In communist societies, the uniform economic system and totalitarian state harshly suppress individual liberty. As a result, it has become necessary for capitalist societies to implement reforms in order to reduce the sacrifice made by the people, and communist societies have been forced to enact major reforms to recognize individual freedoms.

"Clearly, the trend of the times is to seek a Middle Way government that bases itself on genuine humanism. I am convinced that we have entered the age when people throughout the world are yearning for the creation of a new society of peace and prosperity based on the philosophy of the Middle Way."

Vigorous applause filled the auditorium. The members felt as if a dark veil had instantaneously been lifted from their eyes. Shin'ichi had illustrated that the society created through the Middle Way would be a new society founded on the principles of trust and harmony. He also argued that conflict between nations as well as various domestic conflicts all arose from a lack of mutual trust, and that the only way to overcome such discord was to foster a society built on trust and harmony.

After outlining specific guidelines for the establishment of an economy that protects the interests of ordinary citizens, which he had mentioned earlier, Shin'ichi concluded his speech. Overall, he had defined not only the path the Clean Government Party should take but also that of Japanese politics.

WHEN WE HAVE a clear image of our future and goals we are working toward, we feel hopeful. Hope gives rise to courage and becomes the driving force for advancement.

After hearing Shin'ichi's vision for the Clean Government Party, the activities of Soka Gakkai members to support the party became infused with even greater passion.

Holding their heads high, they were able to confidently articulate to others their view of the way government should be.

January 29, Election Day, arrived. The polls closed at six o'clock in the evening and the counting of votes began soon thereafter. As the counting proceeded, the Clean Government Party gained seats steadily, with twenty-five of its thirty-two candidates elected. It was a great step forward and a tremendous victory.

The Liberal Democratic Party lost seats, dropping from its previous 283 to 277. The Japan Socialist Party won 140 seats and the Democratic Socialist Party won 30. This meant that the Clean Government Party had, on its first time out, leapt to the position of the fourth-ranking party in the Lower House.

On the evening of January 30, when the election results were confirmed, several leaders of the Clean Government Party came to see Shin'ichi at the Soka Gakkai Headquarters.

With a smile, Shin'ichi expressed his appreciation for their hard work. "Congratulations!" he said. "You really gave it your all. I know you suffered some losses, but you can make that a springboard for your next campaign. It's impossible to get all your candidates elected on the first run. For a first time, you achieved an incredible victory."

The Clean Government Party Chairman Hisao Seki responded: "Thank you very much. The dust has finally settled. Thank you so much for your support."

"Mr. Seki," Shin'ichi said, "the battle has just begun. In the old days, power was seized through war and bloodshed. Though times have changed, the established parties are engaged in a fierce, dog-eat-dog struggle to gain control of the government. The more your party grows in the future, the more various forces will try every possible means to bring it down. That is the harsh reality.

"I hope you will all be courageous and keep your party clean and uncorrupted. This is also the hope of the people. No doubt the Clean Government Party members will be approached with conciliatory offers in the future. If anyone has even the slightest personal ambition to line their own pockets, others will detect it and try to exploit it to the hilt.

"Those who seek to use the Soka Gakkai or the Clean Government Party for personal gain will eventually fall by the wayside. If any Clean Government Party representative should grow corrupt and betray the public trust and that of the Gakkai members who have supported them so sincerely, they should immediately be expelled from the party."

SHIN'ICHI fixed his gaze on each of the Clean Government representatives: "In addition, you must never forget the spirit of struggling against the devilish nature of power in order to safeguard people's happiness. In the future, there may be times when your party will have to join forces with reformist parties and times when you have to work with conservative parties. There may also be times when, as part of the opposition, you will need to correct the course of the ruling party, and times when you will merge with it to promote reforms. And there may be situations where you will have to compromise in order to see certain policies enacted.

"You will face all kinds of choices, but you must never forget that your fundamental goal is the happiness of the people. Furthermore, even if some day you should become part of the ruling administration, you must never cease in your efforts to battle the corrupt nature of authority. Otherwise, there is no reason for the Clean Government Party's existence."

When Shin'ichi returned home that evening, he prayed deeply for the growth of the twenty-five representatives and the great development of the Clean Government Party as a whole. He felt that he had finally fulfilled his responsibility as the party's founder. Now that the party had gained a foothold in the Lower House, it could continue with its activities autonomously. The time had come at last for the Clean Government Party to venture out on its own.

Shin'ichi turned his mind to the twenty-first century. "The twentieth century has been a time of ceaseless war and conflict," he thought. "If things continue as they are, what will the twenty-first century be like? All we will have to look forward to is an unending nuclear arms race and the threat of a third world war, not to mention the prospect of environmental destruction and pollution, food shortages, racial and ethnic discrimination, violence, human rights abuses, poverty, hunger and the desolation of the human spirit. But we mustn't allow the twenty-first century to be an age of devastation and despair. We must make it a century of hope, of peace, of life—a century in which the dignity of human life is revered and protected."

It was for that purpose as well that Shin'ichi had articulated his vision for the Clean Government Party. He believed that the fate of the next century rested on whether the Clean Government Party's goal of government based on the Middle Way—in other words, a humanistic government—became the main current in Japan as well as the prevailing philosophy of government around the world. That was why he had devoted himself with such passion to the development of first the Clean Government Political Federation and then the Clean Government Party.

Shin'ichi chanted in earnest. As he did so, he felt as if he could hear the resonant sound of the Clean Government Party's dynamic advance and the joyous cheers of the people reverberating into the skies of the twenty-first century.

FROM JANUARY through early February 1967, no matter where he was, Shin'ichi could be seen writing whenever he had a spare moment. It was true that he always had a stack of manuscripts with him, whether it be installments for his serialized novel *The Human Revolution,* the editorial for *The Daibyakurenge* study journal or some other piece he was working on. It wasn't uncommon for him to have these on hand even during his travels. But this was not one of his usual writing projects, nor was it anything that a publishing company or newspaper unrelated to the Soka Gakkai had requested. Shin'ichi was writing reports that would enable him to graduate from junior college.

After graduating from the night school of Toyo Commercial High School in the spring of 1948, he entered the political science and economics department of Taisei Gakuin's night school. During the day he worked at the

Jonan Industrial Association, an organization that assisted medium and small businesses, and in the evening he took classes at Taisei Gakuin.

Originally called Toa Gakuin, the school had been founded by the political scientist Yumichi Takata.[1] The name was later changed to Taisei Gakuin, and when Shin'-ichi studied there the campus was located near Nakai Station (in Tokyo's Shinjuku Ward) on the Seibu train line. The school rented buildings that had survived the bombings of World War II. The rooms were dark and dim, the floors creaked, and wind and rain blew in through the broken windows.

But whenever Professor Takata appeared and addressed the students in his warm and friendly manner, the classroom filled with light. Suffering from a lung infection, Professor Takata was thin and pale, but when he stood before the class his face shone with life and his voice flowed with enthusiasm.

Shin'ichi studied political science with Professor Takata, and he loved the lectures. There were times during class when the professor would start coughing painfully, but when the fit had passed he would resume his lecture as if nothing had happened. Shin'ichi himself had tuberculosis, which made the image of Professor Takata teaching with such passion as he struggled against his illness even more inspiring to him. Shin'ichi was strongly drawn to his teacher's character.

Professor Takata regarded political science as a practical means to manage society and alleviate the suffering of the people. He also strongly advocated establishing global peace based on humanitarianism and the importance of developing one's humanity.

Even after class, he would meet with the students and engage them in casual conversation. When Shin'ichi offered his opinions on philosophy and literature, Professor Takata would nod approvingly as he listened. It was in those moments that Shin'ichi felt his teacher's unlimited warmth and compassion.

IN JANUARY 1949, the year after Shin'ichi had enrolled in Taisei Gakuin, he began to work at Josei Toda's publishing company, where he was assigned the responsibility of editing a boys' magazine. In the autumn of that year, however, Toda's business hit hard times and the company collapsed. Shin'ichi became extremely busy liquidating the company, and he could no longer attend his night courses. He eventually took a leave of absence from school, hoping to return after things settled down at work. But that was as good as impossible as Shin'ichi bore the entire responsibility for handling all of Toda's business affairs.

One day in January 1950, Toda said to Shin'ichi: "The Japanese economy is still in a period of turmoil, and I have to concentrate fully on the business, which is bound to become busier and busier from now on. Would you consider giving up school and helping me full time?"

Without hesitation, Shin'ichi replied: "I'll be happy to do whatever you ask."

A glimmer of kindness shone in Toda's stern eyes. "I'm very grateful. In exchange, I'll take responsibility for your education as your private tutor."

True to his promise, Toda invited Shin'ichi to his home every Sunday and lectured him on a wide range of college-level topics. He devoted both mornings and afternoons to these lectures.

Shin'ichi thus found himself in the fortunate position of having one-to-one lessons at "Toda University." Eventually, however, Sundays alone were not enough, so Toda began giving lectures at the office in the morning before work. Several other employees were later permitted to join in these sessions as well.

One day Toda said: "I want to provide you with a better education than what you could receive at a top university. I would like to teach you all kinds of living fields of study."

And in fact Toda poured his entire life into his lectures, which covered such subjects as economics, law, political science, chemistry, astronomy and life science. There were also classes in Japanese history, world history and classical Chinese literature. A great mathematician and unparalleled educator, Toda's impassioned lectures continued up to the year before his death.

From about the time Shin'ichi entered Taisei Gakuin, a movement began to expand the institution into an accredited university. In March 1951, accreditation was finally granted and the institution held its first entrance ceremony under the new name of Fuji Junior College.

IN 1950, the year before Fuji Junior College received accreditation, Shin'ichi made a modest donation in response to a call to alumni by the school's students. He had already left Taisei Gakuin, and Toda's company was in such dire straits that his salary had been in arrears for some time. But founding a college had been Professor Takata's dream and Shin'ichi wanted to support his former teacher who was working so hard to realize that dream while battling illness. He also had a strong desire to help his alma mater. In fact, Shin'ichi felt bad that he couldn't do more, but it was impossible under the circumstances.

Professor Takata died in May 1951, at the age of forty-two, just a month after the first entrance ceremony to the new Fuji Junior College took place. A month before his death he had written in his notebook: "Education is to give one's life to one's students." This was the spirit of a great educator who had devoted his life to his vocation.

In 1966, Shin'ichi was approached by Fuji Junior College with a strong suggestion that he write several papers so that he would qualify for graduation. Shin'ichi was incredibly busy at the time. Initial planning for the establishment of Soka University had begun in earnest, and the preparations for the opening of Soka Junior and Senior

High Schools in 1968 were proceeding at a rapid pace.

Top Soka Gakkai leaders who had heard about the proposal didn't think Shin'ichi would accept, but he did, saying: "Since they have been kind enough to make the suggestion, I'd like to give it a shot." The leaders were dumbfounded. They responded vaguely, but it was clear that they wanted to say, "What's the use of getting a junior college certificate at this point?"

Shin'ichi had no special wish for graduation credentials, but he looked on this opportunity as a way of showing gratitude to Professor Takata's passion for education, and he also wanted to repay the kindness of Fuji Junior College.

He had been asked to submit ten papers on such topics as "Japanese Industrial Trends from the End of World War II to the End of the Korean War" and "The Establishment and Special Features of Japanese Industrial Capital."

SHIN'ICHI spent whatever time he could—even while en route during his travels—reading the necessary materials for writing his graduation papers. He also sat down and worked on them whenever he had a spare moment. Actually, he was grateful for this opportunity to review the basics of his studies.

When he met with leaders of the Soka Gakkai young men's, young women's and student divisions, he would encourage them, saying: "I'm currently writing papers to submit to my college. Learning is enjoyable, and something that every person has a right to. That's why no matter how busy you are, no matter how full your schedules are, you must never stop studying.

"Even when we were thoroughly immersed in all the activities taking place during the month when the Grand Lecture Hall at the head temple was completed, Mr. Toda would frequently question me about what book I had read that day.

"When we stop learning, we stop advancing and growing. It is shameful to neglect learning. I hope you will keep studying throughout your lives."

Shin'ichi submitted his papers to the school on February 9. They totaled nearly one hundred pages. And with that he completed his requirements and graduated from the economics department of Fuji Junior College.

On February 10, Shin'ichi participated in the groundbreaking ceremony for the Nagoya Culture Center, and the following day he attended a Kansai Headquarters leaders meeting in Amagasaki City, Hyogo Prefecture. During these events, he strove to encourage the leaders working on the front lines of the organization.

On March 3, Shin'ichi attended a district leaders meeting in Gifu Prefecture, and the following day he went to the opening ceremony for the Chugoku Culture Center in Okayama City. This was the Soka Gakkai's very first culture center. There was another under construction adjacent to the Soka Gakkai Headquarters building in Tokyo, but it wouldn't be completed for another six months.

The culture centers had the same function and objective as any other Soka Gakkai community center, but Shin'ichi added the word *culture* because he believed that kosen-rufu was a movement for the creation of a truly humanistic culture.

What is the purpose of religion? It is to enable people to become happy. It is to give meaning to life. Toward that end, it is essential to build a society that respects humanity and allows a truly humanistic culture to blossom. In other words, only when religion contributes positively to society can it be said to be fulfilling its mission.

S HIN'ICHI was very happy that the Chugoku Culture Center was the first to open in Japan. This was because he had high hopes that the Chugoku region would become a model for kosen-rufu—that it would see the creation of a society where a truly humanistic culture flourished. He regarded this region as extremely important for the fresh development of kosen-rufu in Japan.

As the pivotal center of the western part of the country, the great advancement of Chugoku would have a powerful influence on the neighboring Kansai, Shikoku and Kyushu regions. Indeed, Shin'ichi viewed Chugoku as the linchpin to the progress of kosen-rufu in western Japan.

It was important that Chugoku—which embraced the city of Hiroshima, the site of the world's first atomic bombing—become a transmission point for the supreme life philosophy for realizing lasting world peace. Furthermore, the region had produced a large number of political and other leaders since the late nineteenth century. Many prime ministers were from the area—Hirobumi Ito, Aritomo Yamagata, Tsuyoshi Inukai, Nobusuke Kishi, Hayato Ikeda and Eisaku Sato, the latter of whom was in office at the time. Reformist leaders such as Sanzo Nosaka of the Japan Communist Party also hailed from Chugoku.

Shin'ichi was certain that in the future great leaders who upheld the principle of the Middle Way would emerge from Chugoku one after another and be active in every field of endeavor. As the seventh anniversary of his presidency approached, Shin'ichi thus focused his activities on establishing a base for Chugoku's tremendous development. That was why he made some space in his packed schedule for a guidance tour of the region, starting with attending the opening ceremony for the Chugoku Culture Center.

On March 5, he participated in a commemorative photo session with three thousand group leaders and group women's division leaders of the Sanin Headquarters in Matsue City, Shimane Prefecture. Among the participants were some fifty members from the Oki Islands, which were known as the place of exile of such historical figures as Retired Emperor Go-Toba[2] and Emperor Go-Daigo.[3] The islands' first Soka Gakkai chapter had been established just one month earlier, and the members, filled with excitement at their new start, had gathered together in the light rain for the commemorative photos. The session would be conducted in nine sittings.

In between pictures, Shin'ichi spoke with the members, offering guidance and encouragement with his entire being. In the last sitting, he took a photograph with leaders on the chapter level and above. As he stood in front of the bleachers set up for the purpose, he said: "Thank you for your hard work! Did any of you travel more than five hours to get here?"

Several people raised their hands. Shin'ichi addressed a woman standing toward the top of the bleachers, asking, "Where did you come from?"

"From the Oki Islands!" she replied. It was Yorie Tsutsui, who had been appointed the Oki Chapter women's division leader.

"Thank you for coming from so far!" Shin'ichi said.

YORIE had tears in her eyes as she spoke. "Our organization in Oki has just been made a chapter," she said. "We will all unite and do our best!"

Yorie, who worked diligently for kosen-rufu in the Oki Islands, had joined the Soka Gakkai in 1958. Her husband, Shigeyoshi, joined four months later after seeing his sickly wife turn her health around through faith. They also overcame the failure of their family business by chanting Nam-myoho-renge-kyo and, with their faith deepened as a result, enthusiastically set out to spread Nichiren's teachings.

Yorie rode on the back of Shigeyoshi's motorbike, and together they traveled all over the island talking to people about Buddhism. On one occasion, the bike broke down on a mountain pass and they had to push it all the way home. It was morning by the time they arrived. Their efforts to share the Daishonin's teachings with others bore fruit and gradually the number of members in the islands grew. Experiencing tremendous joy from their practice, these new members in turn went out and spread the flame of propagation even further.

At the time, many people in Oki were conservative and held firmly to the islands' entrenched beliefs and customs. The mere mention of the Soka Gakkai brought a negative reaction and refusal to hear more. It was not unusual for members trying to introduce Buddhism to others to have salt or even a bucket of water thrown at them.[4] But in spite of this, their spirits remained high. "Thanks to these hardships, we've been able to extinguish some of our bad karma!" "It's really too bad that they refuse to listen to what we have to share about this wonderful Buddhism!" Talking cheerfully among themselves and singing Gakkai songs together, they went about their activities for kosen-rufu day after day.

The lives of the members in Oki were by no means easy. The islands' industries included fishing, farming and forestry, but with the influx of outside competitors, the local fishing industry, which was their major source of income, was struggling severely. In order to improve their catches, the locals needed to update their boats and fishing equipment, but few had the financial resources to do so.

Without money, prestige or social position, many of the Soka Gakkai members there were showered with unceasing scorn and abuse. However, aware that they shouldered the responsibility for paving the way to a bright future for Oki, they continued to pray for the happiness of their fellow citizens, refusing to be discouraged no matter what opposition or maltreatment they encountered. That is the Soka Gakkai spirit.

To the Oki members, it seemed that the stars illuminating the night sky as they made their way home from Gakkai activities were congratulating them on their future victory and good fortune.

ATTENDING MEETINGS on mainland Japan was a major effort for the members on the Oki Islands. In 1961, the only ferry connecting the islands and Honshu was one that departed from the port of Saigo on Dogo, the largest of the Oki island chain, at nine o'clock in the evening. From there, it stopped at each of the islands' ports, arriving at the port of Sakai in Tottori Prefecture on Honshu at half past four in the morning. The return trip was also arduous, leaving Sakai at half past eleven in the evening and reaching Saigo at seven o'clock the following morning. Not only was the journey time-consuming, but it was also difficult for the members to come up with the fare.

In order to cut costs, some members traveled to the mainland on cargo ships or fishing boats, but unlike passenger ships, such vessels were tossed about so much at sea that many members experienced extreme seasickness. Nevertheless, Oki members were always found at meetings in the region, an unrivaled seeking spirit burning in their hearts.

Shin'ichi had continued to do whatever he could to support the Oki members. In March 1962, when he learned that some of them were traveling all the way to Tottori's Yonago City and staying overnight to sit for entrance examinations for the Soka Gakkai Study Department, he made arrangements for the test to be held on the islands thereafter.

And in January 1965, at a district leaders meeting held at the Yonago Community Center, Shin'ichi encouraged a leader from Oki with all his might. He said: "Oki is a place with a profound relationship to Nichiren Buddhism. It is mentioned several times in the Daishonin's writings. I hope you will make your islands the happiest place in Japan and the entire world. One determined individual can change everything. I will be watching the development of our organization in Oki." To commemorate the occasion, Shin'ichi then presented the leader with a cloth for wrapping prayer beads printed with the Chinese characters for *sincerity* in his own handwriting.

Now a chapter had been established in the Oki Islands, with Shigeyoshi and Yorie as chapter leaders. Seeing the faces of Yorie and the other members who had been working so hard in the Sanin area, Shin'ichi was glad that he had made the time to come to Matsue in Shimane Prefecture to participate in the photo sessions, despite his busy schedule.

In the seven years since he had become president, Shin'-ichi visited every region of Japan as well as many other countries. Now he was determined to devote every ounce of his being during the next seven years to searching out and visiting those areas that were most challenging and where people were suffering the most.

Shakyamuni had spent his life traveling from place to place in order to help the suffering. He was truly a person of action. Shin'ichi was also firmly determined that his life would be a journey to widely propagate the Mystic Law.

ON MARCH 6, Shin'ichi went to Hagi City in Yamaguchi Prefecture where he participated in a commemorative photo session with men's and women's division group leaders of Hagi Joint Chapter. On March 7, he attended the Chugoku No. 3 Headquarters Leaders Meeting held at the Hiroshima Prefectural Gymnasium.

Shin'ichi's guidance tour of the Chugoku region was being carried out at lightning speed. He spent the rest of March and April visiting Kyushu, Kansai and Chubu, taking not a moment's rest in his journey for kosen-rufu.

In April of this year, 1967, the sixth nationwide local elections were held. Election day was April 15, and for the first time the Clean Government Party fielded its own candidate in the Tokyo gubernatorial race. The candidate's name was Koichi Yabe, and he was the fifty-seven-year-old president of a maritime shipping company. He was known as a businessman with an international perspective.

Yabe had broad experience working overseas, including as the branch manager of the New York office of another shipping company, and he was well acquainted with urban issues. At the time, the population of Tokyo had surpassed ten million and it was showing no signs of leveling off. As a result, the city faced many pressing problems, among them housing shortages, traffic congestion, rush-hour crowding on commuter trains, an inadequate sewage system and increasing pollution. The situation was reaching such a point of crisis that temporary stopgap measures simply would not suffice.

Residents of Tokyo therefore looked for a governor who aimed toward the future with completely new ideas; someone who would outline a vision for Tokyo based on a global perspective and would strive to actualize it. Yabe fit the bill perfectly.

The Clean Government Party had decided to field its own candidate in the Tokyo gubernatorial election because it saw this as an opportunity to publicize its social welfare policies as well as its goal of realizing a government based on the principle of the Middle Way. This was also the strong wish and request of Soka Gakkai members and the party's other supporters.

The Clean Government Party achieved tremendous victory in these nationwide elections. In local prefectural assemblies, it won eighty-four seats—a giant increase over the thirty-nine it formerly held—and in the five major cities of Yokohama, Nagoya, Kyoto, Osaka and Kobe, sixty-one of the sixty-seven Clean Government Party candidates running were elected.

In the gubernatorial race, Ryokichi Minobe, who was supported by the Socialist and Communist parties, surpassed Masatoshi Matsushita, the candidate backed by the Liberal Democratic and Social Democratic parties, by about one hundred thirty-six thousand votes. The Clean Government's Koichi Yabe, while having put up a good fight, came in third. Even so, the Clean Government Party's

emphasis on policies that reflect a Middle Way philosophy greatly expanded public understanding of the party
as seeking to protect the dignity of life and to create a
people-centered government.

THE LAST PLACE that Shin'ichi visited prior to the
seventh anniversary of his presidency of the Soka
Gakkai was Niigata. On April 22, he went there for the
first time in three-and-a-half years to attend a groundbreaking ceremony for the new Niigata Headquarters
building and participate in a photography session with
men's and women's division group leaders.

Shin'ichi had proposed the establishment of a new community center that would function as the Niigata Headquarters immediately after the area was hit by a major
earthquake in June 1964. The original Niigata Community Center had been acquired in 1959 and was located in
Kawabata-cho, Niigata City. But a tidal wave following the
earthquake had caused the nearby Shinano River to over-
flow its banks, and the flooding had damaged the building. In addition, a room that had been added on to the
existing structure to serve as an office had begun to tilt.

When this was reported to Shin'ichi, he suggested they
find a strong, magnificent, new center on firmer ground.
He believed that the main community center of each prefecture should be a large, solid building, so that it could
serve as a relief headquarters and emergency evacuation
center for local residents in case of a natural disaster.

At first, then Niigata Joint Chapter Leader Takao Osabe
and Vice Leader Kinji Eda looked for an existing building that could be purchased and remodeled for the pur-

pose. But they had a hard time finding one on firm ground that was close to the station and suited for large gatherings. In August 1964, Niigata Joint Chapter became Niigata Headquarters, and Eda was made headquarters leader. Soon after that, when Eda paid a visit to the Soka Gakkai Headquarters on a trip to Tokyo to attend a Headquarters leaders meeting, Shin'ichi asked him if he had found a suitable structure for the center.

"No, not yet," Eda replied.

With a pensive expression, Shin'ichi said: "I see. That's too bad."

Eda felt Shin'ichi's sincere concern.

When Eda met Shin'ichi again in Tokyo the following year, the latter repeated his inquiry about the center.

When Eda responded that they were still unsuccessful, Shin'ichi said: "If you can't find an existing building that will suffice, let's look for some land and construct our own. Niigata had a terrible experience with the earthquake, so I'd like to build a grand new citadel of happiness for our members there. Let's make it the first community center made of reinforced concrete on the Sea of Japan coast."

Eda was joyed.

WHEN EDA returned to Niigata after meeting with Shin'ichi in Tokyo, he and other local leaders stepped up their search for land on which to build a new community center. After scouring the area, they found a site located about a ten-minute walk from Niigata Station. A high school campus nearby had suffered minimal damage during the previous earthquake, attesting to the firmness of the ground.

The groundbreaking ceremony took place on April 22 amid great joy. In the preceding days, the weather in Niigata had been cloudy and rainy, but a little after noon, just before the ceremony was due to begin, the clouds parted and gave way to patches of blue sky.

When Shin'ichi arrived at the site that day, he took a look around and said to the members who had assembled to greet him: "You really found a great site. It's perfect. I'm so happy for you." The members were deeply moved by Shin'ichi's evident delight.

During the ceremony, Shin'ichi prayed earnestly that the Niigata members would become happy and would be protected from natural disasters. As soon as the event was completed, he headed for the venue where the photography session with the men's and women's division group leaders was to be held.

A total of forty-seven hundred members were to be photographed in fifteen sittings. At the beginning of each, Shin'ichi took the microphone and spoke to the members, encouraging them with all his might: "No matter how difficult your circumstances may be, Buddhism enables you to turn poison into medicine." "Hardship provides you with an opportunity to transform your karma." "Have courageous faith!" "Please challenge yourselves to study the Daishonin's writings and chant every day!"

When the photo session was finished, more than twenty members, most of who were from Sado Island, performed local folk songs and dances in the gymnasium where the shoot took place. Wearing light cotton kimonos and braided straw hats, they danced joyfully.

Next, Niigata high school division members performed

a song that they had written and composed, titled "Together with Our Mentor."

Afterwards, Shin'ichi said to them: "Thank you. I will continue to clear the way so that all of you, the members of the high school division, will be able to soar freely into the great skies of your mission in the future. The twenty-first century is your time. What you do then is very important, as is what you do now in preparation for that time. I'm counting on you."

As an expression of his appreciation, Shin'ichi took a commemorative photo with the folk dancers as well. He had visited Sado Island nine years earlier and recognized some the members present as people he had spoken to at that time. Fond memories of that trip came rushing back to him.

SHIN'ICHI addressed the members: "If I remember correctly, there are no trains on Sado, are there?"

"That's right," one of them answered. "Buses are our only means of public transport."

"And you don't have a community center, either, do you?" Shin'ichi inquired further.

"No," the members replied.

"Sado is the place where Nichiren endured persecution and composed his most important writings," Shin'-ichi said. "It therefore has great significance from the perspective of kosen-rufu. Let's build a community center there soon."

Just then the photographer announced that he was ready to take the group's picture.

"It's time for our photo now." Shin'ichi continued, "But

if you are experiencing any problems on Sado, no matter what they might be, please jot them down on a piece of paper and let me know what they are. I'd like to also present you with some sweets for you to enjoy together on the boat ride home."

After the photograph was taken, Shin'ichi said: "Let's all sing 'Sado Okesa' together. That song always reminds me of you."

The members on *shamisen* (a traditional Japanese stringed instrument) and *taiko* drums began to play and everyone joined in singing: "To Sado, to Sado, the grasses and plants bending in the breeze...."

The members sang vigorously, their harmonious voices echoing throughout the gymnasium. Shin'ichi vividly recalled his last visit to Sado.

It was July 20, 1958. On April 2 of that year, second Soka

Gakkai president Josei Toda had passed away, and the members remained sad and dejected. Many people in society thought that with President Toda's death, the Soka Gakkai would collapse.

In June, Shin'ichi was appointed to the newly established post of general administrator and effectively assumed full responsibility for leading the entire organization. In this capacity, he wanted to go out and meet the members as quickly as possible and offer them encouragement and hope.

On July 19, Shin'ichi arrived in Niigata City with then Director Hisao Seki, youth division leader Hiroshi Yamagiwa and other leaders. They had gone to attend Niigata Chapter's first athletic meet, which was scheduled for the next day. It was there that he learned a meeting was also scheduled on Sado the following evening.

SHIN'ICHI said to Seki and the other leaders: "If there's a meeting taking place on Sado, let's go there after the athletic meet and encourage the members there. They are engaged in a lonely struggle on an island with many temples of other Buddhist schools, and they deserve our highest praise." The decision to visit Sado was thus made.

On July 20, it had been raining since morning. The Niigata leaders agreed to observe the weather a bit before deciding what to do about the athletic meet. While they waited, Shin'ichi held a guidance session for members who had come from all over Niigata Prefecture. It was an enjoyable gathering, filled with the members' seeking spirit and warm laughter.

Eventually, there was a lull in the rain and preparations went ahead to hold the athletic meet in the afternoon. Because of time constraints, it was decided that Yamagiwa and the other youth division leaders would attend the sporting event, while Shin'ichi and Seki would go to Sado on the noon ferry. There was one more ferry from Niigata to Ryotsu on Sado in the evening, but the seas were rough and there was a possibility it would be canceled. Shin'ichi and Seki therefore hurried to catch the earlier boat.

The rain kept falling intermittently, and in the end the athletic meet had to be called off an hour after it started because it turned into a downpour.

The five hundred-ton ferry *Okesa maru* that Shin'ichi and Seki were traveling on was tossed about like a leaf on the stormy seas. The rain beat heavily against the portholes and the waves struck violently at the hull. The boat seemed to be at the mercy of the powerful currents, and many of the passengers were queasy from its constant lurching.

"It's really rough," croaked Seki. His face was pale, most likely from seasickness.

"Please hang in there, Mr. Seki," Shin'ichi said. "Remember, our Sado members are waiting for us."

Seki nodded and wiped the perspiration from his forehead.

The normally three-hour trip had taken nearly four when the boat finally arrived at the wharf at Ryotsu. It was raining on Sado, too. The guidance meeting was held from seven o'clock in the evening at a public hall that had been rented for the occasion. Though there was no Soka Gakkai district on Sado yet, nearly two hundred members attended. Their excitement filled the auditorium.

Addressing the members, Shin'ichi said: "I have wanted to visit Sado and see you all for a long time, and at last my wish has come true!"

BECAUSE SADO was famous for its gold mines, Shin'ichi decided to talk about leading a "golden life." Quoting from Nichiren Daishonin's writings, he said: "In the *Record of the Orally Transmitted Teachings*, the Daishonin compares birth, old age, sickness and death to gold, silver, copper and iron. Gold symbolizes birth. Silver symbolizes our bones or death. Copper represents old age, and iron, sickness. These four human conditions are the true reality of life, and each has profound meaning and value. Among these four, the Daishonin calls birth, or life itself, gold (see OTT, 75–76).

"But human beings tend to allow themselves to be defeated by suffering and as a result lose their joy and shining smiles, their lives becoming dark and spiritless, filled with sorrow and regret. Buddhism, however, teaches the path to overcoming those sufferings and bringing one's life to shine with brilliant splendor.

"So how do we do this? The first step is to establish a fundamental purpose in life. The Daishonin teaches that this is accomplished not by wishing solely for our own happiness and seeking such things as wealth, status, honor, fame, authority or power, but by dedicating our lives to kosen-rufu.

"Where do we see the brilliance of humanity in people? Isn't it found in those who have broken through the shell of their ego and who dedicate themselves to helping their suffering friends, to their fellow human beings and to society at large, even though at times they must make sacrifices to do so? This is what it means to dedicate one's life to kosen-rufu.

"Furthermore, nothing is wasted on the path of kosen-rufu. Every hardship we encounter becomes a source of great good fortune and benefit."

The members listened attentively as Shin'ichi spoke.

"Life's true brilliance is born from awakening to our personal mission and initiating courageous action to advance kosen-rufu. Faith is not a duty. It is a right. But if we become passive and just do as others tell us, our faith will come to feel like a duty and we will experience no real joy.

"On the other hand, if we stand up on our own and take bold action, we will savor the greatest joy that life has to offer. It is also important to strive to improve ourselves day after day. This means persevering in faith. To persevere doesn't mean simply doing today what we did yesterday. It is to challenge ourselves anew and to make a fresh resolve each day. Faith is a constant struggle against devilish functions, and a Buddha is one who never ceases in that struggle.

"I want you all to know that it is by engaging in such struggle that we bring our lives to shine; it is here that a golden life is realized."

SHIN'ICHI next discussed the mission of the members living on Sado. "To change the subject a bit," he said, "the places on Sado linked to the Daishonin, such as the former sites of the Sammaido at Tsukahara (a dilapidated shrine in the middle of a graveyard) and his dwelling at Ichinosawa (the lay priest Ichinosawa Nyudo's home), are all occupied now by temples of Nichiren Shu, which betrayed the Daishonin's spirit. The correct teachings of Nichiren Buddhism do not exist in those temples. They are no more than empty religious ruins.

"Sado Island is a place where the Daishonin deeply engraved his spirit. The mission of the Soka Gakkai is to revive the great teaching and spirit of Nichiren Daishonin here on Sado and to make this the happiest island in the world. I wish to state that the kosen-rufu of Japan as a whole depends on the kosen-rufu of Sado. In order for Sado to fulfill its mission, it's important that all of you first and foremost drive out even the slightest sense of defeat from your hearts, the feeling that 'It's too hard' or 'It's impossible.' When the Daishonin was exiled to Sado, didn't he say: 'But still I am not discouraged' (WND, 748)?

"And the secret to strength is unity. If you are working at cross-purposes and not united in spirit, nothing can be constructed. In addition, just as the Daishonin led propagation efforts from Sado, I hope you will look beyond this island as well with the conviction that you are shouldering responsibility for the entirety of our movement in Japan. I would like you to travel throughout the country in your efforts to spread the Mystic Law. The momentum you thereby create will in turn become a fresh and dynamic driving force for kosen-rufu in your own community.

"Sado was once a hub of maritime trade in the Sea of Japan and an important point of economic and cultural exchange. Now that President Toda has died, it is especially important for us as his disciples to stand up. I hope that you, the members of Sado, will join me in initiating a new struggle!"

The members applauded vigorously, fresh resolve and a strong fighting spirit burning in their hearts.

When the meeting ended, Shin'ichi and Seki, along with the other leaders from Tokyo who had joined them on Sado, went to the inn where they would be staying for the night. No sooner had they arrived than a dozen or so members came to see them. Seki and the other leaders held a discussion with the men's and women's division members while Shin'ichi met with the young men's and young women's division members.

Wanting to somehow encourage the youth, Shin'ichi suggested that they play Ping-Pong. "We are all President Toda's disciples," he said. "No matter what happens, let us continue to advance together throughout our lives, holding high the banner of kosen-rufu! Now that we've confirmed our resolve, let's have a good time and enjoy a game of Ping-Pong."

AS SHIN'ICHI and the young men's division members began to play Ping-Pong, the young women's division members talked among themselves. The young women decided that since Shin'ichi had traveled all the way to Sado, they wanted to give him a performance of the "Sado Okesa" folk dance. But none of them had brought the light cotton kimono that dancers wear, nor were they confident in their dancing ability. They consulted the staff of the inn and were able to borrow the kimonos. In addition, they persuaded some of the staff members who knew the traditional dance to join them in the performance.

When the Ping-Pong games were done, the young

women's division members addressed Shin'ichi: "Mr. Yamamoto, we'd like to present you with a performance of 'Sado Okesa.'"

"That would be wonderful," Shin'ichi replied.

The strains of the music floated out from a record player that the inn staff had prepared for them. Although their movements were slightly awkward and unrefined, the young women put their whole hearts into their performance. Shin'ichi was touched by their sincerity.

While they were dancing, the leaders from Tokyo who had been talking with members of the men's and women's divisions in another room came down to the floor where Shin'ichi was. When the young women finished, Shin'-ichi said to them: "It was a beautiful dance. You really gave it your all. That made my trip to Sado worth it."

One of the leaders who had entered the room in the middle of the performance said to Shin'ichi: "Was that a show put on by the inn? The dancers must be members of the staff. They weren't very good, were they?"

His words had an arrogant ring that disrespected the sincere spirit of the young women's division members. With a flash of anger, Shin'ichi immediately replied: "What are you saying? Some of the performers were staff members, but those three are my younger sisters."

"You have sisters on Sado?" the leader asked in bewilderment.

The young women's division members heard this exchange and were deeply moved. Hearing Shin'ichi refer to them as his sisters made them aware of his kindness and high expectations of them.

Shin'ichi wanted to present the youth division members

with a memento of his visit and thought that he would purchase something at the inn's gift shop, but by then the shop was closed. He therefore walked over to the piano in the room and, with a smile addressed the members, saying: "I wanted to give you all something, but the gift shop is closed, so I will play a song for you on the piano as my offering." His fingers began to move across the keys and the melody of "The Great Hero Kusunoki"[5] emerged.

"Let's sing together," he said.

THE YOUTH DIVISION members began to sing along to Shin'ichi's playing: "Dusk falls on the lush greenery of the village of Sakurai...."

When he was alive, President Toda would frequently ask the members of the young men's division to sing this song. It told the story of the parting of the warrior chieftain Kusunoki Masashige[6] and his eldest son Masatsura as the former prepared to leave for the Battle of Minatogawa[7] to defend the imperial court in Kyoto from the invading forces of Ashikaga Takauji[8] in 1336. As his army headed into the battle, where defeat was imminent, Masashige summoned his son to a place called Sakurai and urged him to return home. But Masatsura was prepared to die with his father and refused to obey his father's wishes. In the end, Masashige persuaded his son to go by saying that if they both were to die in the battle, Takauji would be left to rule the nation. He told Masatsura to live and grow into a fine man as quickly as possible so that he could serve his country.

President Toda regarded this song as exemplifying the spirit of mentor and disciple sharing the mission of kosen-rufu. That is why he often had youth division members sing it and would strictly critique their performance. In particular, he would ask each person again and again to sing the part that expressed Masatsura's determination to join his father in fighting against Takauji: "Father, no matter what you say, how could I desert you...." Toda would interrupt them as they sang and make comments, such as, "Your spirit is nothing like Masatsura's! How can you fight for kosen-rufu with such an expression in your eyes! Look at me when you sing!" He was staunchly determined to train and foster youth of lion-like courage who would inherit the resolve to dedicate their lives to kosen-rufu.

Quoting the line, "Quickly rise up and serve your lord, for the sake of your country," Toda would encourage them to likewise quickly develop into capable leaders and devote their lives to working for kosen-rufu and society.

The Sado youth division members had heard from their leaders many times about the significance President Toda accorded to "The Great Hero Kusunoki." When they therefore sang it to Shin'ichi's piano accompaniment, an image of their late mentor came to their minds and their hearts grew warm with emotion.

When the song was finished, Shin'ichi said in a rousing voice: "'Quickly rise up'this was President Toda's wish and hope for us. I hope all of you here on Sado will stand up and develop yourselves with the same spirit. I have already risen to the challenge. I hope you will, too, as quickly as possible."

O N THE MORNING of July 21, some fifty or sixty Sado members gathered at the Ryotsu port to see

Shin'ichi and his party off. Unlike the day before, the rain had stopped and the seas were calm. The summer sun streamed down through the clouds in the sky.

"Thank you for coming so early in the morning!" Shin'-ichi said as he stepped out of the car and bowed to the members. The *Kogane maru,* the ferry on which the group would be returning to Niigata, was already at the pier waiting for its scheduled departure.

At Shin'ichi's suggestion, everyone gathered for a group photo in front of the ferry. When they finished, it was time for Shin'ichi to go. "Thank you! Please take care!" he called, shaking hands with the members as he boarded. A gong sounded and the boat pulled away. The members standing on the pier vigorously waved good-bye, some even jumping up so they could keep the vessel in sight for as long as possible. From the ferry, Shin'ichi also waved back.

Addressing the Niigata leaders standing with him on the deck, Shin'ichi said: "I'd like to suggest that the Sado young men's division members aim toward having one hundred members gathered on that pier. If you can achieve that, you'll be able to build a solid foundation for kosen-rufu on Sado and the future will be secured."

The ferry moved through the water, white foam trailing behind in its wake. The form of Sado, resembling outstretched arms, lay across the deep blue sea. Gazing at the line of the islands' mountain ridge in the distance, Shin'ichi thought about Nichiren Daishonin's valiant struggle there.

It was on October 28, 1271, that Nichiren Daishonin arrived at Matsugasaki in Sado. This was according to the old lunar calendar, which meant that winter had already begun. During this season, the Sea of Japan is often very rough and the winds blow fiercely. Nichiren stayed for several days at the harbor town of Teradomari in Echigo Province (present-day Niigata Prefecture) waiting for the seas to calm so that a boat could take him to Sado. There were seven or eight people in the boat—Nichiren, his disciple Nikko, officials of the military government and the boatman.

No doubt the boat rocked violently as it crossed the turbulent seas. It was November 1 when Nichiren finally arrived at Tsukahara on Sado, his place of exile.

TSUKAHARA was located approximately in the center of Sado Island. It was a barren field behind the mansion of Homma Rokuro Saemon, the local steward of this area, whose main fief was in Echi, Sagami Province (present-day Kanagawa Prefecture). At this site, where corpses were often abandoned, the locals had built a small, dilapidated one-room shrine for the purpose of offering prayers for the dead. The shrine was called the Sammaido and it became Nichiren's residence after he arrived on Sado.

Nichiren, who was fifty years old at the time, passed the bitterly cold Sado winter in the Sammaido together with Nikko. In his writing, "The Actions of the Votary of the Lotus Sutra," he describes the Sammaido as follows: "The boards of the roof did not meet, and the walls were full of holes. The snow fell and piled up, never melting away. I spent my days there, sitting in a straw coat or lying on a fur skin. At night it hailed and snowed, and there were continual flashes of lightning. Even in the daytime the sun hardly shone. It was a wretched place to live." (WND, 769).

It is a well-known fact that Nichiren's life was a succession of persecutions. Of all his trials, the persecution that comprised his near-execution at Tatsunokuchi and subsequent exile to Sado was the most severe. The persecutions that befell Nichiren all stemmed from his admonition to Hojo Tokiyori, the de facto ruler of his day, through the treatise "On Establishing the Correct Teaching for the Peace of the Land," which he submitted on July 16, 1260.

Nichiren wrote this treatise in an effort to save the people of Japan from the uninterrupted onslaught of calamities such as destructive gales, floods, famine, epidemic and earthquakes that were afflicting the land. Using passages from the sutras, he elucidated the causes of these disasters. He declared, in other words, that the fundamental source of all this suffering was the fact that the correct teaching was being rejected while erroneous teachings were revered. He also exhorted Tokiyori to discard the teaching of the Pure Land school of Buddhism, which was flourishing under strong government patronage and protection, and to embrace faith in the Mystic Law.

This, Nichiren urged, was the path to realizing the peace and security of the land and the happiness of the people. He also warned that if Tokiyori continued to support false teachings, one of the three calamities[9] that had not yet arisen—warfare—would be sure to occur. This calamity corresponded to two of the seven disasters[10] elucidated in the sutras; in other words, internal strife and foreign invasion.

Through this remonstrance, the other Japanese Buddhist schools, in particular the Pure Land school priests, who had flourished under government patronage, realized that Nichiren posed a dangerous threat to them.

JUST A MONTH LATER, on the evening of August 27, a party of Pure Land followers launched a surprise attack on Nichiren's dwelling at Matsubagayatsu in Kamakura. It is believed that Hojo Shigetoki, an important figure in the military government, had condoned this action.

In May of the following year, 1261, the sixth regent, Hojo Nagatoki, unjustly banished Nichiren to exile in Ito on the Izu Peninsula. This period of exile lasted twenty-one months. After he was pardoned, Nichiren returned to Kamakura, but hearing that his mother, Myoren, was gravely ill, he went to his hometown in Awa Province (in present-day Chiba Prefecture).

While in Awa, Nichiren was attacked by Tojo Kage-nobu[11] along with numerous armed warriors and others at a place called Komatsubara. Kagenobu, whose hatred for Nichiren dated far back, was the local steward of Tojo Village and had links to Hojo Shigetoki. The followers who were accompanying Nichiren defended him valiantly, but the attacking warriors, wielding swords and arrows, killed one called Kyonin-bo and seriously wounded two others. Nichiren suffered a sword cut to his forehead and his left hand was broken.

The persecutions continued. In intercalary January 1268, a letter from Kublai Khan of the Mongol Empire was delivered to the Kamakura government by a Korean emissary. Though ostensively a request for exchange between the two countries, it was really a threat of invasion if Japan failed to submit to Mongol dominion.

Nichiren's prediction of foreign invasion had become a possibility, and both the military government and the Imperial Court were completely taken aback. The letter was passed from the government to the court, but the latter declared its menacing tone offensive and returned the emissary without a reply.

Fear and anxiety of an attack by the Mongols spread throughout the country. The military government ordered temples and shrines to offer prayers for the defeat of the invaders. Meanwhile, the retainers of the shogunate in the western provinces began making preparations for defense. It was at this juncture that the aged Hojo Masa-mura, the seventh regent of the Kamakura regime, ceded power to the eighteen-year-old Hojo Tokimune.

When Nichiren learned that a letter had arrived from

the Mongols, on April 5 he sent "The Rationale for Writing 'On Establishing the Correct Teaching for the Peace of the Land'" to a Zen priest named Hogan-bo, who was highly influential in the military government. In this writing, Nichiren stated that his predictions in his previous treatise had come true and declared that he alone knew how to save Japan from its predicament. He also urged the government to reflect on its errors.

But Hoganbo did not reply.

NICHIREN WROTE and sent letters of remonstrance one after another to eleven members of the military government, including the regent Hojo Tokimune and Hei no Saemonnojo Yoritsuna, as well as to highranking priests of other Buddhist schools, such as Doryu of Kenchoji temple and Ryokan of Gokurakuji temple. Nichiren urged Tokimune to cease his sponsorship of prayers by erroneous Buddhist schools and to host a debate between Nichiren and representatives of those schools so that he could judge the validity of the various teachings.

Nichiren also wrote to his followers at the time, stating: "It is a certainty that we will be exiled and sentenced to death. Please do not be the least surprised by this. . . . Do not think of your wife, children or relatives. Do not fear the authorities. Rather, make this an opportunity to break the shackles of the sufferings of birth and death and attain the fruit of Buddhahood" (GZ, 177).

Nichiren was perfectly aware of the possible repercussions that his strict admonition of the nation's rulers as well as the high-ranking priests of the established Buddhist schools who were in collusion with them. But his concern for his country and desire to alleviate the suffering and misfortune of the people motivated him to take this action, in spite of the danger he knew it could bring upon him and his followers.

The recipients of Nichiren's letter of remonstration displayed various reactions, but none of them took it seriously or heeded its warning. Instead, it gave them cause to express their hatred and animosity toward Nichiren and sparked discussion of ways to dispose of him, including beheading or banishment. Utterly unreasonable suggestions for dealing with his followers were also proposed, such as confiscation of their estates, execution, imprisonment or exile.

Those who received the letters were all highly respected public figures. Ryokan and the other Buddhist leaders in particular were widely revered, and they readily exploited their positions. But when subjected to Nichiren's scathing indictment, their true natures as "animals dressed in priestly robes" (*see* WND, 760) were revealed and they began to fight furiously in their efforts to destroy Nichiren.

They were desperate. They knew better than anyone that they didn't stand a chance of winning in a public debate with Nichiren. If their defeat were exposed to all, they would lose their authority and reputations and imperil their stature. This was what prompted them to secretly plot Nichiren's destruction.

More Mongol emissaries arrived in Japan, sending the nation into a heightened state of crisis. Nichiren continued to remonstrate with important figures in the military government while at the same time strictly pointing out the errors of the True Word Precepts school. He showed no signs of slackening in his efforts.

IN 1271, a terrible drought continued to plague Japan, and the people's suffering and privation increased exponentially. With no solutions of its own, the Kamakura government ordered Ryokan of Gokuraku-ji to offer prayers for rain. When Nichiren learned of this, he sent a message to Ryokan through the latter's disciples: "If you can bring rainfall within seven days, I will become Ryokan's disciple. But if no rain falls, then Ryokan must take faith in the Lotus Sutra alone" (*see* WND, 808).

Ryokan accepted Nichiren's offer with tears of joy, convinced that he could make rain fall within one week. On June 18, Ryokan assembled more than 120 disciples and they prayed with a fierce, single-minded intensity.

But several days later there were still no signs of rain. Ryokan then called together several hundred more of his disciples and they continued praying, their voices resonating loudly through the air as they chanted the Pure Land school teaching.

When the agreed upon period of seven days had passed, not a drop of rain had fallen. In fact, instead, violent, destructive gales blew across the land. Nichiren sent a messenger to Ryokan with the message: "Come to me immediately as you have promised. I will teach the Law that causes rain to fall and the path that leads to Buddhahood" (WND, 809). Nichiren's words struck a bitter chord in Ryokan's heart, which was already putrefied with hatred. He was overcome with the feelings of humiliation and defeat of one whose mask of false authority has been ripped off to reveal absolute disgrace.

On hearing this message, Ryokan and his disciples wept with chagrin and trembled with rage. Ryokan requested an extension of another week and continued to pray for rain. But the false prayers of one who follows an erroneous teaching cannot be expected to bear fruit. No rain fell and the drought and devastating winds only grew worse. Ryokan's indisputable defeat was positive testimony to the validity of Nichiren's teaching from the standpoint of not only documentary and theoretical proof but also actual proof.

Ryokan, however, had no intention of honoring his promise to Nichiren. On the contrary, he only further stoked the flames of his resentment, hatred and envy, and conspired with the major temples of Kamakura to bring about Nichiren's downfall. In an effort to manipulate the government, they courted favor with the wives and widows of senior government officials, filling their ears with slanderous accusations against Nichiren. In this way, they deviously plotted to do away with Nichiren forever.

These women became the willing pawns of Ryokan and his cohorts, whom they ardently admired.

IN SLANDEROUS allegations, the corrupt priests of the various Buddhist schools accused Nichiren of putting a destructive curse on the nation. They also alleged he had declared that the late lay priests of Saimyo-ji and Gokuraku-ji—Lord Hojo Tokiyori and Lord Hojo Shige-toki, respectivelyhad fallen into the hell of incessant suffering. It was these lies that the priests told the wives and widows of high-ranking government officials. Incensed, the women demanded that Nichiren be dealt with and called on the leaders of the Hojo clan to have him beheaded or exiled. Their pleas spurred the military government into action.

On September 10, 1271, Nichiren was summoned to court and interrogated by Hei no Saemon, who was essentially in charge of the government's military, police and state affairs. Nichiren remained unperturbed as he responded to Hei no Saemon's questions, asserting "Every word is mine. However the statement about the lay priests of Saimyo-ji and Gokuraku-ji falling into hell is a fabrication. I had been declaring this doctrine [that the schools they belonged to lead to hell] since before their deaths.

"Everything I said was with the future of our country in mind. If you wish to maintain this land in peace and security, it is imperative that you summon the priests of the other schools for a debate in your presence" (WND, 765).

Nichiren went on to declare that the distinction between false and true teachings would then become clear. He also stated that if such a debate was not held and he was unjustly charged, then, in accord with the Buddhist teachings, within one hundred days, or within one, three or seven years after his condemnation, the disasters of internal strife and foreign invasion would occur. "Then you will regret what you have done!" (WND, 765) he proclaimed.

Nichiren turned his interrogation into an opportunity

to correct false views in light of the Buddhist teachings. Hei no Saemon was enraged. He felt as if he would burst with hatred and anger at Nichiren, who had boldly admonished him without showing the slightest hint of trepidation.

Nichiren was released, and on September 12, a day after returning to his dwelling at Matsubagayatsu in Kamakura, he wrote a letter of remonstrance to Hei no Saemon with the sincerest of intentions. It was filled with his genuine and earnest concern for the safety of the nation. But on that very day, a terrible incident occurred.

That evening, Hei no Saemon, leading several hundred armor-clad soldiers, set out for Matsubagayatsu. They were not heading into battle. They were going to arrest Nichiren. It was indeed a formidable procession to arrest a single, unarmed priest, and it was a sign of Hei no Saemon's great fear of Nichiren.

THE SOLDIERS' BEHAVIOR was out of the ordinary. At Hei no Saemon's command, they barged into Nichiren's dwelling like madmen with their eyes glaring and, shouting angrily, began wreaking havoc. After arresting Nichiren, Hei no Saemon's chief retainer, Shobo, snatched the scroll of the fifth volume of the Lotus Sutra, which Nichiren had tucked inside his robe, and struck him sharply across the face with it three times.

The fifth volume of the sutra contains the "Encouraging Devotion" chapter, which states that those who try to spread the Lotus Sutra in the Latter Day of the Law will be attacked with swords and staves. That Nichiren should have been struck with the scroll predicting this is testimony that he read the Lotus Sutra with his very life.

Some of the soldiers seemed to have gone insane as they unrolled the scrolls of the sutra and wrapped them around their bodies or trampled on them. It was a scene defying all rationality, in which the soldiers behaved as if they were intoxicated by devilish influences. At that moment, Nichiren's voice rang out powerfully: "How amusing! Look at Hei no Saemon gone mad! You gentlemen have just toppled the pillar of Japan" (WND, 766).

It was a great lion's roar. In an instant, a hush fell over the room. When the soldiers finally came to their senses, they carted Nichiren off to court again where Hei no Saemon sentenced him to exile on Sado. For the time being, he was to be held at the residence of Hojo Nobutoki, the governor of Musashi Province, whose lands included Sado Island. But in the middle of the night, Nichiren was placed on a horse and led away by soldiers. If he were really being sent to Sado, he would have been taken to the mansion of Nobutoki's retainer, Homma Rokuro Saemon, in Echi. The military government, while ostensibly sentencing him to exile, had in fact decided to behead him at the execution grounds at Tatsunokuchi under cover of darkness.

Nichiren had figured this out some time earlier. But because it was his first and foremost wish to give his life for the Lotus Sutra, he rode with dignity to his destiny. When they arrived at Wakamiya Avenue leading to Hachiman Shrine,[12] Nichiren stopped his horse, dismounted and called out toward the shrine: "Great Bodhisattva Hachiman, are you truly a god?" He then admonished Hachiman, one of the heavenly deities who are said to have vowed to protect the votary of the Lotus Sutra, declaring that if he failed to protect Nichiren, the foremost votary in all Japan, he would be severely rebuked by Shakyamuni for breaking his oath and rendering the scriptures false.

HOW AWESTRICKEN the soldiers escorting Nichiren must have been when they observed the great conviction and lofty state of being with which he rebuked Great Bodhisattva Hachiman. When the group arrived at Yui Beach, Nichiren sent a boy named Kumao to deliver a message to Shijo Kingo, who lived nearby.

Shijo Kingo had no doubt already learned of Nichiren's arrest and been desperately trying to think of some way to assist his mentor in this crisis. As soon as the message arrived, Kingo and his three brothers rushed off to the scene in such haste that they didn't even put on their footwear. When they reached Nichiren, he patiently explained to them his joy at giving his life for the sake of the Lotus Sutra. As the mentor, Nichiren continued to teach his disciples about Buddhism and offer them guidance up to the moment he was to be executed.

Deeply inspired by Nichiren's fearlessness in the face of death, Kingo felt incredible courage well up in his life. He grasped the reins of Nichiren's horse and walked along with his mentor to Tatsunokuchi. He was prepared to die at his side.

Eventually, the soldiers stopped and began to mill around in excitement. This was to be the site of Nichiren's execution. Strong as he was, Shijo Kingo broke down in tears as he said, "These are your last moments!"

Nichiren replied with firm resolve, "You don't under-stand! What greater joy could there be? Please smile." This admonishment rang both with limitless power and gentle, all-embracing compassion.

Before long, the preparations for the execution were completed and Nichiren was placed in position. He exuded an air of great dignity as he sat awaiting the blow. One of the soldiers unsheathed his sword. Just as he was about to raise it for the beheading, a brilliant orb shining as bright as the moon appeared in the pitchblack sky in the direction of Enoshima. It traveled from southeast to northwest, shedding light on all.

The radiant object illuminated the soldiers' faces, which were frozen with fear.

The executioner fell to the ground, his eyes blinded. Some fled as far as 330 feet away, some jumped down from their horses and huddled on the ground, and others crouched in their saddles. They were all terrified, and no one was prepared to carry on with the execution.

Nichiren's voice rang out clearly over the dark beach, "Why are you running away? Come closer, come closer!"

NO MATTER HOW Nichiren called to them, the cowering soldiers would not approach. His voice rang out again, "If you are going to execute me, do it quickly! Once day breaks, it will be an ugly business." But no one dared to lay a hand on him. Whatever the brilliant orb might actually have been, not even the force of the military government could kill Nichiren. He had received the solemn protection of the Buddhist gods as predicted in the Lotus Sutra, which states: "Swords and staves will not touch him" (LS14, 209), and "The executioner's sword will be broken to bits!" (LS25, 304).

This was proof that the devilish tendencies permeating the universe had been crushed and the life-state of the Buddha of the Latter Day of the Law manifested. It was at this moment that Nichiren, a common mortal, summoned forth the life of the eternal Buddha of limitless joy. In other words, he had cast off his transient status and revealed his true identity as the Buddha of the Latter Day.

Following the events at Tatsunokuchi, Nichiren was taken to the residence of Homma Rokuro Saemon at Echi. The leaders of the military government conferred again on what to do with Nichiren, but it took them a while to reach a decision. The fact was that he had committed no secular crime. He had only urged the government to distinguish between correct and incorrect teachings and had relentlessly pointed out the errors of the other Buddhist schools. The proper course would have been to recognize his innocence and release him, and indeed that was the opinion of some.

But during that period, Kamakura was hit with a number of cases of arson and a succession of murders, and rumors were flying about that these were the acts of Nichiren's disciples. In truth, however, these crimes were the work of Pure Land followers who sought to frame them. The government went so far as to blacklist more than 260 of Nichiren's followers. As a result, many of them were imprisoned, had their estates confiscated or were driven from their lands. It was an attempt by the authorities to do away with Nichiren and his disciples once and for all.

In early October, the military government finally reached a decision to exile Nichiren to Sado.

And so Nichiren's life on Sado began. The winter winds of Tsukahara blew fiercely and the snows were deep. Nichiren had only thin clothing and his supply of food was meager. His days were spent in cold and hunger. The locals were also antagonistic, seeing him as nothing more than an exiled villain. But Nichiren, joyed at having read the Lotus Sutra with his very being, chanted Nam-myoho-renge-kyo and recited the sutra in earnest. The flame of his determination to propagate the correct teaching burned ever brighter.

PURE LAND FOLLOWERS were also highly influential on Sado, and they despised Nichiren, who called for all to discard the Pure Land. A particularly fervent practitioner among them was a man named Abutsu-bo. When the elderly Abutso-bo learned that Nichiren had been exiled to Sado, he resolved to do away with this evil priest himself and went to Tsukahara immediately.

"Why do you slander the Pure Land?" Abutsu-bo demanded of Nichiren. With great compassion and warmth, Nichiren pointed out the errors of the teaching in light of the sutras, presenting an argument that was logical and reasonable. His words reflected integrity, dignity and depth of character.

Eventually, Abutso-bo's wish to harm Nichiren evaporated and he found himself listening to Nichiren's teachings in a completely new light. He discarded the Pure Land then and there and became Nichiren's disciple. From that time on, Abutsu-bo and his wife Sennichi-ama, whom he also persuaded to abandon the Pure Land, supported and protected Nichiren with sincere faith.

Evading the watchful eyes of the authorities, the couple continued to provide Nichiren with various necessities, such as food and paper. With the paper he received from them, Nichiren wrote a number of important treatises elucidating his major teachings while he was on Sado.

The priests of the Pure Land, Zen and Precepts schools on the island hated Nichiren with a vengeance and repeatedly conferred on how to deal with him. At first they drew up a plan to assassinate him, but Homma Rokuro Saemon, the deputy constable of Sado, strongly suggested that instead of killing him, they confront Nichiren in a religious debate.

Thus, on January 16, 1272, several hundred priests not only from Sado, but also from the provinces of Echigo, Etchu, Dewa, Shinano and Oshu, assembled at the Sammaido on Sado hoping to defeat Nichiren in debate. Voices rebuking him echoed throughout Tsukahara, and a rare tension filled the air.

Nichiren addressed the gathering, saying: "Silence, all of you! You are here for a religious debate." They were causing such a commotion that Rokuro Saemon and some of his subordinates grabbed the abusive Pure Land followers by the scruff of their necks and pushed them back.

At last the situation calmed and the debate began. Nichiren listened to what the priests of the various schools had to say and, after confirming their points, would ask questions of his own that keenly highlighted their errors. After one or two questions, the challengers would become stumped and start making mistakes in the scriptures and contradicting themselves.

NICHIREN'S REBUTTALS cut through his opponents' arguments like a sharp sword. Not even the great scholars of Kamakura were a match for him; what chance did these priests of shallow learning stand? Having all of their claims thoroughly refuted by Nichiren, some of them heaped abuse on him, while others were reduced to silence. Others, declaring the Pure Land to indeed be in error, took off their priestly robes on the spot, cast aside their prayer beads and wrote a pledge never to chant the Pure Land teaching again. This was the famous Tsukahara Debate, and it resulted in a number of priests, including the learned Sairen-bo (formally of the Tendai school), becoming disciples of Nichiren.

Soon after the debate, on February 11, 1272, a conflict erupted within the Kamakura government. This involved a plot to seize power by Hojo Tokisuke, the elder half-brother of the regent Hojo Tokimune and a shogunal deputy stationed in Kyoto at the time, and Hojo Noritoki. But Tokimune learned of the plot in advance, and on February 11, he attacked Noritoki and Noritoki's brother, Tokiakira, who was suspected of being involved in the conspiracy, at Nagoe in Kamakura. Then, on February 15, Tokimune laid siege to Tokisuke's residence in Kyoto.

This was a power struggle within the ruling Hojo clan, which set family members against each other. Just as Nichiren had predicted, the disaster of internal strife had occurred.

Awed by the accuracy of Nichiren's predictions, high-ranking leaders of the military government began releasing Nichiren's disciples who were being held in custody. In April 1272, Nichiren was moved from Tsukahara to the home of the lay priest Ichinosawa, a resident of Ichinosawa on Sado. Yet Nichiren remained under constant threat of assassination and continued to be treated with hostility.

Nichiren scribed some of his most important letters and treatises during his exile on Sado. Some thirty-nine of them, written from the perspective of the Buddha of the Latter Day of the Law, are included in the Japanese collection of the Daishonin's writings published by the Soka Gakkai. Among them are: "The Opening of the Eyes," which elucidates the object of devotion in terms of the Person; "The Object of Devotion for Observing the Mind," which elucidates the object of devotion in terms of the Law; "On Practicing the Buddha's Teachings"; "On the Buddha's Prophecy"; and "The True Aspect of All Phenomena."

Even while in exile, Nichiren's thoughts never

strayed from his disciples. The fact was that, after his near-execution at Tatsunokuchi, a number of his followers had abandoned their faith or had begun to doubt his teachings because they feared the harsh persecution they were sure to encounter. Some grew suspicious of Nichiren, questioning why, if he was the votary of the Lotus Sutra, he was being persecuted ceaselessly rather than enjoying a peaceful and secure existence. They concluded that his exile was a sign that the benevolent deities were not protecting him. They also wondered why those who persecuted Nichiren did not seem to incur any punishment. Cowardice and doubt ate away at their faith.

SOME OF THE DISCIPLES who became faint-hearted and lost their fighting spirit pointed an accusatory finger at Nichiren, saying: "Though the priest Nichiren is our teacher, he is too forceful. We will spread the Lotus Sutra in a more peaceful way" (WND, 306). This may seem perfectly reasonable, but it is actually nothing more than cowardice. Rather than challenging their weakness, these disciples shifted the blame to their mentor's methods of propagation, thereby justifying their own failure to engage in the struggle of a true disciple. Such is the modus operandi of people who grow corrupt and abandon their faith.

Nichiren's writings from Sado are alive with fatherly strength and compassion that seek to crush the cowardice and weakness in his disciples' hearts and teach them genuine faith. For example, the following passage from "The Opening of the Eyes" reveals his rock-solid determination to advance kosen-rufu in the face of all manner of obstacles: "Let the gods forsake me. Let all persecutions assail me. Still I will give my life for the sake of the Law" (WND, 280). This was a cry from the depths of Nichiren's being as he strove to quash the tendency of his easily swayed disciples to view faith as a mere means to gain personal security and receive protection from the Buddhist gods. He wanted to enable them to cultivate a perspective based on genuine faith and develop a boundless state of life. He thus warns: "Whether tempted by good or threatened by evil, if one casts aside the Lotus Sutra, one destines oneself for hell" (WND, 280).

Nichiren also writes: "Life is limited; we must not begrudge it. What we should ultimately aspire to is the Buddha land" (WND, 214). Here he is proclaiming that to dedicate one's life to the great vow to achieve kosen-rufu is itself life's eternal and ultimate purpose. And he states: "When an evil ruler in consort with priests of erroneous teachings tries to destroy the correct teaching and do away with a man of wisdom, those with the heart of a lion king are sure to attain Buddhahood" (WND, 302). In other words, struggling courageously when one meets great hardship is the key to attaining Buddhahood. This is the principle of obstacles lead to enlightenment.

Nichiren taught that encountering difficulties for the sake of the Law is an indispensable condition for attaining Buddhahood in this existence. He therefore calls on us to summon forth obstacles, viewing them as a source of tremendous joy and benefit. Nichiren himself joyfully expressed appreciation for his persecutors, for without them, he said, he could not have revealed himself as the votary of the Lotus Sutra.

Nichiren's teaching is one of transforming great adversity into great benefit and realizing supreme value in the process. It is a philosophy of creation that changes human life at the most fundamental level.

BASED ON the Buddhist scriptures, Nichiren Buddhism views persecutions encountered for the sake of the Law as proof of the correctness of our practice and a badge of honor. This is a philosophy that discovers life's true value in the effort to carry out our convictions based on the universal Law of life, without fearing any confrontation that may arise in the process. It is a humanistic philosophy of personal autonomy—the antithesis of the prevailing Japanese tendency to yield to the powerful and passively accept circumstances, abandoning the idea of justice and one's identity.

Under the worst of conditions on Sado, and even with a dire lack of paper, Nichiren wrote down his most important teachings in order to firmly secure a foundation of faith in the hearts of his disciples for all eternity.

After their defeat in the Tsukahara Debate, Pure Land priests continued to plot Nichiren's death. They appealed to Hojo Nobutoki, a highly influential figure behind the scenes, to do away with him. As a result, on three occasions, Nobutoki forged governmental decrees ordering a crackdown on Nichiren and his followers.

Nevertheless, Nichiren's disciples braved the long and perilous journey to visit their beloved mentor in his place of exile on Sado. The number of people on the island who took faith in the Lotus Sutra also continued to increase.

Nichiren knew that in order to save Japan, he would have to remonstrate with its leaders yet again. Observing the country's situation, he keenly felt that his opportunity was fast approaching. He was therefore determined to return to Kamakura. An official letter granting his pardon reached Sado on March 8, 1274.

The military government was terrified of an impending Mongol invasion and Japanese society was in turmoil. In addition, strange events, such as the sun appearing double in the sky, had taken place, increasing the anxiety of the people.

The regent Hojo Tokimune could no longer ignore the fact that Nichiren's prophecies were being fulfilled. Though he had sentenced Nichiren to exile on Sado based on the accusations of others, those charges had been completely without warrant. Tokimune must have also feared the occurrence of even greater calamities if he kept Nichiren in exile. Hence came his decision to pardon Nichiren.

When the Pure Land followers on Sado learned of this, they continued hatching schemes to keep Nichiren from returning to Kamakura, even plotting his murder. But all their machinations came to naught. On March 15, Nichiren departed from the Maura Bay on Sado with a fair wind carrying him home across the sea.

SHIN'ICHI thought back on his return journey to Niigata after his visit to Sado in 1960. He remembered how he had vowed to dedicate his life to kosen-rufu with the same determination that Nichiren Daishonin had felt when he declared: "Let the gods forsake me. Let all persecutions assail me. Still I will give my life for the sake of the Law" (WND, 280). And, since May 3 of the same year, the day he became third president of the Soka Gakkai, he had been firmly resolved to lead a life that embodied this passage.

Now, seven years later, Shin'ichi said to the Sado members who had gathered for a commemorative photograph in the Niigata gymnasium: "As Nichiren Daishonin clearly indicates, we are certain to face great persecutions. And in fact, things have gone far too smoothly until now. Persecutions will occur because the Soka Gakkai is the sole organization that is advancing kosen-rufu exactly as the Daishonin instructed.

"I hope all of you will become modern-day Abutsu-bos and Sennichi-amas, and, based on pure faith, continue to struggle throughout your lives toward the achievement of kosen-rufu on your island. The Daishonin is certainly aware of your activities.

"Let's meet again."

After saying his farewells, Shin'ichi was taken by car to the inn where he was staying. The road ran along the coast, and Shin'ichi was treated to a beautiful sunset spreading out over the Sea of Japan. The sky and sea both took on a hue of burning crimson. In contrast, the waves pounded the shore forcefully, sending golden spray high into the air.

Shin'ichi had told the Sado members that the Soka Gakkai would encounter great persecutions, and his sense that this was true was growing stronger every day, particularly since the Clean Government Party's entry in the Lower House.

Looking at the Daishonin's life, it was after he submitted "On Establishing the Correct Teaching for the Peace of the Land" to the nation's rulers that he was assailed by successive persecutions. This was because he had rebuked those in power and tried to correct their attachment to erroneous teachings.

The Soka Gakkai had established the Clean Government Party, which would now, with its representation in the Lower House, start making earnest efforts to realize a humanistic government based on Buddhist compassion. Insofar as this was an attempt to eradicate corruption in politics, it was equivalent to a remonstrance of the government. It was therefore only to be expected that plots would arise to prevent the Clean Government Party from carrying out its mission. Fully aware of this eventuality, Shin'ichi was determined to continue advancing forward, for he believed this was the path to Nichiren Buddhism's expansion into society.

In the distance, a boat made its way through the tossing waves, heading in the direction of the setting sun.

NOTES

1 Yumichi Takata (1909–51).

2 Retired Emperor Go-Toba (1180–1239): Reigned 1183–98. Go-Toba was placed on the throne at the age of three and remained the titular sovereign for fifteen years. A failed attempt to overthrow the Kamakura military government and restore authority to the imperial court resulted in his exile to the Oki Islands in 1221, where he spent his remaining eighteen years of life.

3 Emperor Go-Daigo (1288–1339): Reigned 1318–39. He was exiled to the Oki Islands when his plot to overthrow the Kamakura military government was discovered.

4 In Japan, it was traditionally believed that salt had purifying qualities and so it was thrown at unwelcome callers as a gesture of repulsion.

5 "The Great Hero Kusunoki": This is the popular name of a song originally titled "The Green Leaves of Sakurai." It was sung in the early days of the Soka Gakkai as an expression of the spirit of the mentor-disciple relationship.

6 Kusunoki Masashige (?–1336): Warrior chieftain who died supporting the Kemmu Restoration (1333–36), the ill-fated attempt of Emperor Go-Daigo to restore direct imperial rule following the overthrow of the Kamakura shogunate. He was later depicted in folk mythology as the supreme example of imperial loyalty.

7 Battle of Minatogawa: A battle fought on the river Minatogawa in Settsu Province (now part of Hyogo Prefecture), near present-day Kobe City.

8 Ashikaga Takauji (1305–58): A general of the Kamakura shogunate who turned against the government and supported Emperor Go-Daigo's Kemmu Restoration. Internal strife within the Go-Daigo regime, however, led to Takauji's rebellion against the emperor and subsequent defeat of the imperial

armies led by Kusunoki Masashige and others at the Battle of Minatogawa. Takauji then installed Emperor Komyo and established the Muromachi shogunate, which lasted more than two centuries.

9 Three calamities: Disasters said to occur at the end of a *kalpa*. There are two types: the three great calamities of fire, water and wind, which destroy the world itself, and the three lesser calamities of warfare, pestilence and famine, which result in the decline of human society.

10 Seven disasters: Disasters said to be caused by slander of the correct Buddhist teachings. The Medicine Master Sutra defines the seven disasters as: (1) pestilence, (2) foreign invasion, (3) internal strife, (4) extraordinary changes in the heavens, (5) solar and lunar eclipses, (6) unseasonable storms and (7) drought.

11 Toji Kagenobu: A steward of Tojo Village in Nagasa District of Awa Province and a devout follower of the Pure Land teachings. It was at Seicho-ji temple in that village in 1253 that Nichiren first declared his teaching of Nam-myoho-renge-kyo, strictly refuting the Pure Land school.

12 Hachiman Shrine: The principal religious facility for the god protecting the Kamakura regime. Hachiman was given the Buddhist title of Great Bodhisattva in 781, making him the first Japanese deity to receive this title.

Index

A

absolute happiness, achieving, 27, 41–42

Abutsu-bo, converting to Nichiren Buddhism, 329

action, 52, 177

Adachi family, 143

Adachi, Tetsuya, propagation efforts of, 143–44

advancement, driving force for, 281

adversity, changing, 8

Akaiwa, Mitsuko, Buddhist activities of, 134; challenges of, living new life in Argentina, 133–34; self-centeredness of, 135

Akizuki, Eisuke, 196

Alfonsín, Raúl (Argentine president), 141

altruism, and self-serving, 122

American serviceman, actual proof of, being released by NLF (National Liberation Front) soldier, 258

American youth division members, propagation activities of, 254

Anhembi Conference Center (São Paulo), congratulatory messages from countries for culture festival at, 67; culture festival at, 62, 65–67; Shin'-ichi's prayers for culture festival at, 64; venue of São Paulo culture festival, 56

Argentina, Seiichiro Haruki's visit to, 136–37; Shin'ichi's efforts to better friendship between Japan and, 141; Soka Gakkai leaders' visit to, 126

arrogance, 135

Asada, Katsumi, Shin'ichi on, about Kansai spirit, 228–29; Shin'ichi on, about postponing Kansai Culture Festival, 199–201

asura (demon), 112

B

Balaguer, Joaquin (Dominican president), 175

Bao Dai, (emperor of Vietnam), 231; ouster of, 233

Belaúnde Terry, Fernando (Peruvian president), 126

Bolívar, Simón (Venezuelan general) 85, 119–20

Bolivia, 117; Hiroshi Izumida's team to, 151–52; Hiroshi Yamagiwa's team to, 155–56; Japanese immigrants to, 154

Branco, Castelo (Brazilian president), 6

Brasília, 17

Brazil, independence of, 20; membership in, 22; politics

in, 67; Shin'ichi's first visit to, 2; Shin'ichi's resolve to advance kosen-rufu in, 4; Shin'ichi's unsuccessful third visit to, 56–62

Brazil Culture Center, 71

Brazil Grand Culture Festival, 80–83; "Juntos com Sensei" (Together with Sensei), 66; "A Paean of Peace to Our Land in the Twenty-first Century," 80; "Saudason a Sensei" (Welcome, Sensei), 82; Setsuko Saiki's display of emotions about the success of, 80

Brazilian members, participation in São Paulo sponsored culture events, 69–71; Shin'ichi's responsibilities to, 47–48; victory of, as pioneers of world wide kosen-rufu, 82–83

Brazilian secret police, Shin'ichi's interaction with, 37–38

Buddha, Nichiren Daishonin on, 112

Buddhism, power of, 48

Buddhist leader, actions of, 271; attitude of, 138; factors for receiving benefits for, 109; qualities of, 23, 109, 138

Buddhist study, Shin'ichi's approach to, 113

business, actual proof of Masayoshi Chiná's, 90; actual proof of Rosalia Harue Kishibe's, 104; actual proof of Tsutsui's family, 294; actual proof of Vicente Seiken Kishibe starting, 103–05

Butantan Institute, 45–46

C

Cambodia, invasion of, 261

capitalism, 280

card stunts, Kansai members and,

215; moving images in, 215–16; origins of, 214–15

Carioca (native residents of Rio de Janeiro), 19

central figure, Shin'ichi on, about risk of taking on all responsibilities by him-or herself, 115

Chida, Aoi, appointment of, 25

China, 232, 246; Shin'ichi's visit to, 69

Chiná, Masayoshi, 86, 95, 102, 108; appointment of, 92; life of, 87–89; propagation efforts of, 91

Chinese Civil War, 231

Chugai Nippo (newspaper), 277–78

Chugoku region, importance of, as model for kosen-rufu, 292–93

Chugoku Culture Center, 291; significance of, 292–93

Chugoku No. 3 Headquarters Leaders Meeting, 298

circumstance, forces for transforming, 135

Clean Government Party, 285; aim of, 12; candidates of, 278; expectations of, 272; religious groups actions against, 277–78; role of, 274–75; Shin'ichi's vision for, 279–80; significance of, 338. See also government, compassionate

Clean Government Political Federation. See Clean Government Party

Colonia Federico Chávez (Paraguay), Katsu Kiyohara's team to, 145–46, 150

Colonia Okinawa (Bolivia), Taro Kawaura's propagation efforts in, 154–55

Colonia Pirapó (Paraguay), Buddhist activities in, 145; immigrants, 145; Seiichiro Haruki's team to, 146–47

communism, 280

community, serving, 189

community centers, purpose of, 300

Constanza settlement meeting (Dominican Republic), Katsu Kiyohara's encouragement at, on unity, 172; Katsu Kiyohara's team to, 171–72

courage, Shin'ichi's encouragement to Yashuiro Saiki about, 78

cowardice, 7, 333

culture centers, 291

culture festival, history of, in Soka Gakkai, 192–93

D

Daibyakurenge, The, 149, 173, 285

defeat, cause for, 62; Shin'ichi on, 61

determination, Shin'ichi's encouragement to Konos on maintaining original, 21–22; single-minded, 216; strong, 94

devil king of the sixth heaven, 253

devilish functions, 76

dialogue, foundations for, 51

disability, Kitano Fumiki performs at Kansai Culture Festival despite, 217–18

disciples, doubt arises in Nichiren's, about persecutions of Nichiren, 333; persecution of Nichiren's, 328

Dominican members, Katsu Kiyohara's impression of, 172–73; Kiku Tadokaro's encouragement to, through letters, 174–75; Shin'ichi's concern for, 170–71

Dominican Republic, chapter established in, 172; Hiroto Muraki's emigration to, 163–64; Japanese immigration to, 159–61; Katsu Kiyohara's team to, 159, 170; kosen-rufu movement in, 169–70; repatriation program for emigrants in, 162; Shin'ichi's visit to, 175; Soka Gakkai members of parliament and, 161–62

Doryu, 319

E

earthly desires are enlightenment, 26

Eda, Kinji, appointment of, 300

education, Takata Yumichi spirit on, 289

Eisenhower, Dwight D. (US president), 233

election system, Soka Gakkai movement against, 276

Election System Council, 274

"Emerging from the Earth" chapter (Lotus Sutra), Kansai young women's division members performance and, 221

"Encouraging Devotion" chapter (Lotus Sutra), persecution of votary of Lotus Sutra in, 324

"The Entity of the Mystic Law," 184

era, creating new, 1

"ever victorious Kansai," birth of, 190–92. *See also* Kansai spirit

existentialism, 241

F

faith, 26; corrupt, 333; determining, 150; foundations of, 27; joyful, 308; persevering in, 114; purpose of, 41; Shin'ichi on, 109–10; Shin'ichi's encouragement to Niigata members on courageous, 302; Shin'ichi's

encouragement to Vietnamese members about, 259
falsehood, removing, 17
Figueiredo, João Baptista, (Brazilian president), 80; invitation to Shin'ichi, 71; Shin'ichi meeting with, 78
four sufferings, Nichiren's comparision of, to four metals, 307
Fuji Junior College, 289
Fukase, Koji, 255–56
Fukase, Michie, 255

G

Geisel, Ernest (Brazilian president), 57
Go-Daigo, Emperor of Japan, 293
Gohonzon, attitude when chanting to the, 111–12; power of the, 130; Shin'ichi's encouragement to Kazuya Okida about the power of the, 129–30; Shin'ichi's encouragement to S. G. Rice on power of the, 249
Gosho Lectures Compilation Committee, *Lectures on the Writings of Nichiren Daishonin* (Japanese), 184
Go-Toba, Emperor of Japan, 293
Goulart, João (Brazilian president), 6
government, compassionate, 280–81
goza, 131
Grand Main Temple, 179
Grand Reception Hall, 179
"The Great Hero Kusunoki," Josei Toda conveys the spirit behind, 312–13; Shin'ichi's encouragement to Sado youth division members about spirit of, 313; Shin'ichi plays melody of, for Sado youth division members, 312; story of, 312
guidance, personal, 158

Gunther, John, Shin'ichi's conversation with, 239

H

habu snakes, 46
Hachiman shrine, Nichiren's admonition to, 325–26
Hagi city (Yamaguchi Prefecture), Shin'ichi's visit to, 298
hardship, 302; Nichiren on, 334; Shin'ichi on, 27, 61
Haruki, Fumiko, 146
Haruki, Seiichiro, 86, 126, 135, 185
Haruki Yoji (father-in-law of Shin'ichi), 187
Hawaii, Shin'ichi's visit to, 181
health, actual proof of Yorie Tsutsui regaining, 294
Hei no Saemon (full name and title, Hei no Saemon-no-jo Yoritsuna), 319; Nichiren countering allegation and admonishment of, 323; Nichiren's remonstration with, 324
high school division meeting (Tokyo metropolitan area), Shin'ichi's feelings at, about soldier's execution, 237–38
Hiroshima, 292
Ho Chi Minh (Vietnamese political leader), 229–31; last words and death of, 261; poem to Vietnamese people by, 256–57
Ho Chi Minh Trail, 261
Hogan-bo, 319
Hojo Masamura, 318
Hojo Nagatoki, 317
Hojo Nobutoki, 325, 335
Hojo Noritoki, 332
Hojo Shigetoki, 317–18, 322
Hojo Tokimune, 318–19, 332
Hojo Tokisuke, 331–32

Hojo Tokiyori, 316–17, 322
Homma Rokuro Saemon, 315, 325, 328, 330–31
Honolulu, 123
hope, 281
human beings, 40
human revolution, 68, 254; Nichiren Buddhism teaches the path of, 40
Human Revolution, The, 226, 285

I

Ibrapuera Gymnasium (São Paulo), Shin'ichi's appearance and encouragement at, 78–80; venue of Brazil Grand Culture Festival, 78
idealism, 241
Ikeda, Hayato (Japanese prime minister), 272, 292
individual, determined, 297
Indochinese War, first, 231; peace conference ending, 232
Inside Asia (Gunther), 239
Inside Europe (Gunther), 239
Inside USA, (Gunther), 239
International Vietnam War Crimes Tribunal, Bertrand Russell and, 244
Inukai, Tsuyoshi (Japanese prime minister), 292
irresponsibility, Shin'ichi on, 110
Ito, Hirobumi (Japanese prime minister), 292
Izumida, Hiroshi, 3, 8–10, 22, 40–41, 43, 55, 95–96, 116, 190; complacency of, 44

J

Japan, mission of, 242
Japanese Brazilians, 10
Japanese politics, "Black Mist Scandal" in, 272
Johnson, Lyndon B. (US president), 245, 260

joy, source of, 27
judgments, mistaken, 44
Jujo, Kiyoshi, 5, 8, 22, 39–40, 94, 116, 198, 202

K

Kamakura government, internal strife within, 331–32; Kublai Khan's letter and, 318; Nichiren's remonstration with, for sponsoring prayers of false Buddhist schools, 319–21
Kansai, events of, serve as testimonials to history of kosen-rufu movement, 204
Kansai Culture Festival(s), behind-the-scenes activities at, 228; birth of, 193–94; Chiyoko Hanamura plea to hold, 198; commencement of, 206–07, 210; Eisuke Akizuki's skepticism to hold, 197–98; finale of, 224–27; high school division members and, 210–12; Jun Miki recalls, hope for Japan's future, 227; junior Fife and Drum Corps at, 207–09; Katsumi Asada's case to hold, 200; members preparation for, 226; preparations for, 203; Shin'ichi on, 199, 201, 205, 213, 227; significance of, 226–27; weather conditions at, 194–96, 201–02; women's division members dance at, 219–20; Yoshiiko Ohya's case to hold, 197; young men's division members gymnastics at, 222–24; young women's division members ballet at, 220–22; young women's division members card stunt at, 213
Kansai festival staff, Shin'ichi's appreciation to, 203

Kansai Headquarters leaders, 291
Kansai members, battling Typhoon No. 21, 189
Kansai spirit, Shin'ichi on, 228–29
Kansai young women's division members, Shin'ichi's poem to, 222
karma, transforming our, 27
Kasato maru (ship), 87
Kawaura, Taro, 152; life of, 153–54
Kawaura family, home of, 157
Kazumasa, Morikawa, 55
Kishi, Nobusuke (Japanese prime minister), 292
Kishibe, Rosalia Harue, 100; appointment of, 104; suspects Nichiren Buddhism, 102–03; tries Nichiren Buddhism, 104
Kishibe, Vicente Seiken, 100–01; appointment of, 104, 125; attempted suicides of, 102; Buddhist activities of, 103; determination of, 104; hardships of, 101; mission of, 124; encounters Nichiren Buddhism, 102; propagation efforts of, 105
Kishibe family, 108; Buddhist activities of, 106–07
Kiso Bushi (Japanese folk dance), 219
Kissinger, Henry, 264; Shin'ichi's meeting with, 265
Kitano, Fumiki, 216; Shin'ichi concern for, 218–19
Kiyohara, Katsu, 4, 41, 126, 142
Kobori, Yoshie, 137, 139; appointment of, 136; Shin'ichi concern for, 138
Kogane maru (ferry), 314
Kono, Masatada, 17; Shin'ichi praising, for increasing membership, 20
Kono, Misako, 17

Konos, 21–22; propagation activities of, 18–19
kosen-rufu, 76; actions for, 135; advancing, 21; benefits of dedicating one's life to, 110; beginning worldwide, 130; overseas members challenges of advancing, 107; path of, 2; persecutions and, 49; Shin'ichi praising Kazuya Okida for advancing, in Argentina, 139–40; Shin'ichi's activities for, 271; Shin'ichi's message at Brazil Culture Festival about advancing, 63–64
Koyama, Jorge, 73
Kushimoto Bushi (Japanese dance), 219
Kumao (Nichiren's messenger at Tatsunokuchi), 326
Kyodo News Service, Soka Gakkai members response to, smear campaign against Soka Gakkai in Latin American countries, 28–29
Kyonin-bo, 318

L
La Paz, 151
Land of Eternally Tranquil Light, place for kosen-rufu activities becomes, 150; Mitsuko Akaiwa recalls Shin'ichi's encouragement about, 134
Laos, invasion of, 261
Latin America, kosen-rufu in, 175
LDP (Liberal Democratic Party), and electoral system, 273
Le Duc Tho (Vietnamese diplomat), 264–65
learning, 290–91
"Letter from Sado," 183
life, Buddhist way of, 68; determining value of, 139; Nichiren

declares ultimate purpose of, 334; realizing brilliant, 307–08
life force, state of our, 110. *See also* Nam-myoho-renge-kyo
local elections, Clean Government Party in, 298–300
Los Angeles, 123, 137; Shin'ichi's visit to, 59
Lotus Sutra, Hei no Saemon (full name and title, Hei no Saemon-no-jo Yoritsuna) striking Nichiren with, 324–25; Nichiren's warning for discarding, 334; soldiers' handling of, 325
Lotus Sutra teachings, 11; three truths in, 240
Lower House, Clean Government Party candidates for, 273
Lower House elections 272; results of, 282

M

Major Writings of Nichiren Daishonin, The, publication of, 183. *See also Writings of Nichiren Daishonin, The*
Makiguchi, Tsunesaburo, 41, 43–44, 178, 251; journalist's false reporting on, as war criminal, 9
Mara, 253. *See also* devil king of the sixth heaven; devilish functions
materialism, 241
March 16, significance of, 64, 123
Matsushita, Masatoshi, 299 Metropolitan Theater meeting, Hiroshi Izumida giving the news at, about Shin'ichi's absence, 96–97; Hiroshi Izumida reading out Shin'ichi's message at, about advancing kosen-rufu in Peru, 97–98; scene at, prior to Shin'ichi's arrival, 96; "Song of Worldwide Kosen-rufu," 99
Miami, Shin'ichi's visit to, 56, 123
Middle Way, government based on, 241–42; philosophy of, 239–41; politician living in accordance with, 242
Mineko (wife of Shin'ichi), 45, 95, 185, 187
Minobe, Ryokichi, 299
misfortune, Nichiren on, 49
mission, Shin'ichi's encouragement to Soka Gakkai youth division members on, 180; Shin'ichi's message to Argentine members about, 136; youth and, 205
Miyaji, Shinshichi, 143, 146–47; Katsu Kiyohara's guidance meeting at home of, 147–49
momentum, creating, 269
Morro do Corcovado (mountain), 17, 19–20
Muraki, Hiroto, 170–71; benefits of, 166–68; Buddhist activities of, 168–69; encounters Nichiren Buddhism, 165–66; encouragement received by, to never give up, 166
Muraki, Isoko, 171
Muraki family, hardships faced by, 164–65
Myoren (mother of Nichiren), 317
Mystic Law, Nichiren on, about being outside your life, 68; Shin'ichi's poem to Peruvian members on being champions of, 123

N

Nagoya Culture Center, 291
Nakamura, Shutetsu, 154
Nakao, Kan'ichi, 169–71; Kiko Tadokora's encouragement to, through letters, 173–74

Nam-myoho-renge-kyo,
Shin'ichi on chanting, for
overcoming any deadlock,
110–11. See also Mystic Law
National Liberation Front
(NLF), emergence of, 234–35
New Year's leaders meeting, 279
New York, 137; Shin'ichi Yamamoto's health in, 1–3
New York Community Center,
Shin'ichi's visit to, 3
New York Times, 244
newspaper, organization, 114–15
Ngo, Dinh Diem (Vietnamese
prime minister), execution of,
235; rule of, 233–35
Nguyen, Thi Binh, 267
Nichiren Buddhism, 302, 335;
philosophy of, 241; three
truths in, 240; understanding,
184
Nichiren Daishonin, Abutsu-bo's
support to, 330; arrest of, 324;
Buddhist leaders' plot against,
320; corrupt priests allegation
against, 322–23; determination
of, 333–34, 336–37; disasters
predicted by, 323; Hojo
Tokimune pardons, 336; Izu
Peninsula exile of, 317;
Komatsubara persecution of,
318; led to Tatsunokuchi,
325–26; life in Sado, 316, 329,
335; Matsubagayatsu attack,
317; near-execution of, at Tatsunokuchi, 327; on "On Establishing the Correct Teaching
for the Peace of the Land,"
316–17, 338; Pure Land priests'
plot against, 335–36; religious
debate with, 330–31 (See also
Tsukahara Debate); "The
Opening of the Eyes," 333;
"The Rationale for Writing
'On Establishing the Correct

Teaching for the Peace of the
Land,'" 319; to Sado Island,
315; Sammaido shrine resi-
dence of, 316; significance of
near-execution of, at Tat-
sunokuchi, 328
Nichiren Daishonin Gosho Zenshu
(Collected Writings of
Nichiren Daishonin), 183
Nichiren Shu, 309
Niigata Community Center, history of, 300–01; opening ceremony of, 302–03
Niigata high school division
members, "Together With
Our Mentor," 303
Nikko, 315–16
Nixon, Richard (US President),
265; Shin'ichi's letter to, on
ending the Vietnam War,
262–64; "Vietnamization" policy by, 260–61
Nosaka, Sanzo, 292
Nova Era (Portuguese-language
Soka Gakkai journal), 32
nuclear disarmament, Josei Toda's
movement for, 29

O
"O Mundo Limpo do Senhor
Yamamoto" (The Clean
World of Mr. Yamamoto),
objective article titled, served
as rebuttal to criticism of Soka
Gakkai, 17
Ohya, Yoshihiko, 196; Kiyoshi
Jujo on, about starting time of
Kansai culture festival, 205–06
Okada, Ittetsu, 5, 7, 126, 172
Okamura, Fumiaki, 144
Okesa maru (ferry), 306
Oki Islands, 293; economy of,
295; Shin'ichi's encourage-
ment established the link of, to
Nichiren Buddhism, 297

Oki members, hardships faced by, 294–96

Okida, Kazuya, 135, 137–38; actual proof of, in flower business, 131–32; appointment of, 132, 141; Buddhist activities of, 141; life of, 128; loneliness of, 128–29; Mineko's hospitality to, 140; propagation efforts of, 130–31; resolve of, 140; vow of, 130

Okida, Mitsuko, 135; appointment of, 136, 141

Okinawa, in World War II, 264

Okoshi (Japanese sweet), 167

"On Establishing the Correct Teaching for the Peace of the Land," 184

"On Practicing the Buddha's Teachings," 184

"On the Buddha's Prophecy," 184

Osabe, Takao, 300

Osaka Rally, Shin'ichi's recollection of events at, 219

P

Pacaembu Gymnasium (Brazil), police surveillance of, 38; renting of, 38; Shin'ichi's visit to, 38

Panama, Shin'ichi's visit to, 59

Pão de Acúar (Sugar Loaf Mountain), 20

Paraguay, district and chapter formed in, 145; Japan's relations with, 142; Japanese settlers in, 143; Seiichiro Haruki's party's visit to, 142; Shin'ichi's visit to, 150

Parton, Albert E., actual proof of, as platoon commander for not losing single soldier, 250–51

peace, realizing true, 253–54

persecutions, Nichiren Buddhism and, 335; Shin'ichi's

encouragement to Sado Island members about, 337

persecutors, Nichiren appreciating his, 334–35

Peru, independence of, 118; kosen-rufu in, 125; membership growth in, 92; Shin'ichi's visit to, 85–87, 92–95, 99–100, 116–17

Peru Seikyo (newspaper), 116; launch of, 125

pioneers, 109; Shin'ichi on Misako Kono for being, 18; Shin'ichi on Peruvian members being, 108–09

Pizarro, Francisco (Spanish explorer), 85

politics, Soka Gakkai and, 11–16. See also Clean Government Party

Portugal, 17

power, Shin'ichi on Clean Government Party representatives about, 283–84

prayer, 116

pre-Lotus Sutra teachings, three truths in, 240

priesthood, behavior of, 107–08

propagation activities, challenges faced by Bolivian members about, 156–57; Shin'ichi's encouragement to Vietnamese members on, 259

Puerto Rico, 170

R

rain, 204–05

Record of the Orally Transmitted Teachings, The, 307

Reimei (Dawn), 114

religion, purpose of, 11, 292

"Reply to Kyo'o," study material for overseas members, 182

resolve, inner, 170

Rike, S.G., actual proof of, as

soldier to find out tour of
Vietnam was cancelled,
249–50; naval assignment of,
249; in Vietnam War, 248
Rimac (river), 92
Rio de Janeiro (Brazil), 1, 17, 21;
journalists' coverage of Shin'-
ichi's visit to, 23; Shin'ichi's
visit to, 4–24
Rodriquez Pedotti, Andrés
(Paraguayan President), 150
Run, Melos! (Dazai), 226
Ryokan, 319–20; defeat and
humiliation of, inability to
produce rain, 321–22;
Nichiren's challenge to, to
bring rainfall within seven
days, 321; slanderous
accusations against Nichiren
by, 322

S

Sado, history of, 309; Pure Land
followers in, 329; Nichiren's
link to, 303, 308–09; Nichiren's
writings in, 332; Shin'ichi's
visit to, 304–07
Sado Island members, 302; mission of, 309; resolve of, 310;
"Sado Okesa," 304; see off
Shin'ichi, 313–15; Shin'ichi's
concern for, 304
Sado young men's division
members, Shin'ichi's target for,
for securing the foundation of
kosen-rufu, 315
Sado young women's division
members, leader's criticism of,
dance performance, 311;
perfoms "Sado Okesa," 310–11;
Shin'ichi handling leader's
arrogance about, dance
performance, 311
Saigon, 257; Buddhist activities
in, 255; chapter establishment

in, 254; make up of Soka
Gakkai members in,
258–59
Saiki, Gloria S. *See* Saiki, Setsuko
Saiki, Ronaldo Y. *See* Saiki,
Yashuiro
Saiki, Setsuko, 45, 49, 68–69;
determination of, 48, 76; dis-
tress of, of Brazil police sur-
veillance on Shin'ichi, 46–47;
propagation activities of,
54–55, 71; resolve of, 62
Saiki, Yashuiro, 7–8, 23–24,
38, 40, 51, 58–59, 61–62, 64,
69, 98, 139; appointment
of, 25; determination of,
63; recollections of, of
Shin'ichi's previous visits
to Brazil, 77; Shin'ichi on,
about the growth of Brazilian
organization, 7
Saikis, 54; determination of, 50;
Shin'ichi on, about South
America Culture Festival, 37
Sairen-bo, converting to
Nichiren Buddhism, 331
Sakura maru, (ship), 87
San Francisco, Shin'ichi's visit to,
56–57, 59
San Juan de Yapacani settlement
(Bolivia), 153; Hiroshi
Izumida's team to, 157–59
San Martín, José de (Argentine
general), 117–21; Shin'ich's
vow to statue of, 122
Sanin Headquarters leaders,
Shin'ichi's photo session with,
293–94
Santa Cruz (Bolivia), Japanese
leaders visit to, 151–53; "Song
of Indomitable Dignity," 152
São Paulo, 17; Brazil secret police
surveillance of Shin'ichi's visit
to, 50; membership growth in,
55; Shin'ichi's visit to, 24–54;

Shin'ichi's visit to, after eighteen years, 78

São Paulo, community center, acquisition of, 25–26

São Paulo Municipal Theater, description of, 34; venue of South America Culture Festival, 29

Sato, Eisaku (Japanese prime minister), 272, 292

seeking spirit, 150; Shin'ichi's poem to Brazil-Kirishima group on, 72

Seikyo Graphic (magazine), 96

Seikyo Shimbun (newspaper), 67, 96, 149, 156, 173, 244, 254; launch of, 125

Seikyo Times (magazine), 182

Seki, Hisao (Clean Government Party Chairman), 305–06, 310; Shin'ichi on, to keep the Party uncorrupted, 282–83

self-centeredness, 135

Sennichi-ama (wife of Abutsubo), 329

Seven Bells, Shin'ichi's explanation of, 178–80

Shakyamuni, 298

shamisen (Japanese stringed instrument), 36, 304

Shijo Kingo, Nichiren admonishing, before near-execution at Tatsunokuchi, 326–27

Shiroya, Takeo, 126, 131, 135, 137–39; Josei Toda on, about going to Argentina, 127; life of, 127; propagation efforts of, 132; starts practicing Nichiren Buddhism, 128

Shiroyama, Kyoko, 91; appointment of, 92

single-party rule, Soka Gakkai youth division protests, 274

single-seat constituency system, consequences of adopting,

275; LDP (Liberal Democratic Party) postpones, 277; Soka Gakkai's action against, 276. *See also* single-party rule

society, cause for deadlock in, 280; transforming, 76

Soka Culture Center, 179

Soka Gakkai, benefits of knowing true value of, 7; Brazilian secret police views about, 5; and Brazilian society 50–51; correcting mistaken views of, 9; guidance of, 39–40; Hiroshi Izumida on journalist about false reporting of, 9–10; reason for Brazilian secret police surveillance of, 5–6; Shin'ichi meeting with journalist on false reporting of, 9; spirit of, 223, 296; theme of, in 1967, 270; theme and growth of, in 1966, 270; unbiased article headlines about, 45; unfair reporting of, after Brazil Culture Festival, 43; Zhou Enlai's aides deepen understanding of, by viewing footage of Kansai Culture Festival, 227

Soka Gakkai Argentina, growth of, 132, 135

Soka Gakkai Brazil, Brazilian secret police views about, 5–6; membership growth of, 7

Soka Gakkai United States, US media views about, 5

Soka Junior High School, 289–90

Soka Kyoiku Gakkai (Value-Creating Education Society), 178

Soka Senior High School, 289–90

Soka movement, 240–41

soldiers, postwar anxieties of, 252

South America Culture Festival, 29; media coverage of, 42–43;

"Season" dance performed at, by women's division members, 36; Shin'ichi attending, 35–38; Shin'ichi on Sakis about, 4, 37; *The Waltz of the Flowers* (Tchaikovsky) at, that accompanied young women's division members dance, 35. *See also* Brazil Grand Culture Festival; Anhembi Conference Center (São Paulo)
Soviet Union, 231–32
Steiner, Albert, antiwar activities of, 251; and draft board, 252
System of Value-Creating Pedagogy, The (Makiguichi), 178

T
Tabuchi, Katsunari, 55
Tahara, Kaoru, 60
Taisei Gakuin, 285; accreditation of, 289. *See also* Fuji Junior College
Takata, Yumichi, 286–87; death of, 289
Takehara, Katsumi, 151
Takehara, Masae, 151
Tanida, Shoichi, 202
Tanigawa, Ikuo, 146
Tao Gakuin. *See* Taisei Gakuin
Tenth Student Division General Meeting, 245
three obstacles and four devils, Nichiren Daishonin on, 7, 26–27
time, Shin'ichi on, 8, 270–71; Shin'ichi's encouragement to Niigata high school division members on using present, 303
Titicaca (lake), 86
Toda, Josei, 75, 123, 178, 180, 251, 305; birth anniversary of, 76; Shin'ichi working for, 287
Tojo Kagenobu, 318
Tokiakira, 332

Tokyo, 123; challenges faced by, 298–99; post World War II life in, 245–46
translation, challenge faced by *Peru Seikyo* (newspaper) on, 124–25; of Nichiren's teachings, 182; difficulties for editorial staff of *Seikyo Times* on, 182–83; Nikko Shonin on, 181
"The True Aspect of All Phenomena," 183
"The True Object of Worship," 183
True Word Precepts school, 321
truth, Shin'ichi's conversation with journalist about reporting, 9; stating the, 45
truth of non-substantiality, 239–40
truth of temporary existence, 239
Tsukahara Debate, 331
Tsutsui, Shigeyoshi, 294, 297
Tsutsui family, propagation activities of, 295
Tsutsui, Yorie, 297
twentieth century, Shin'ichi about, of war and conflict, 284
twenty-first century, Shin'ichi's vision for, to become century of life and hope, 284–85

U
Uda, Nobuhiro, 30–32, 38; confronts Brazil Secret Police, 30; Shin'ichi on, about becoming emotional, 31; Shin'ichi on, about having never give up spirit, 33–34
understanding, mutual, 23–24
University of Brasília library, 78
United Kingdom, 232
United States, 231–36, 238–39, 243–47, 250–55, 259–67; Shin'ichi's prayers from the, Vietnam War costs for the, 267

unity, 309; Shin'ichi on, 115; Shin'ichi's encouragement to Brazilian members on, 8; Shin'ichi's encouragement to Sado youth division members on, 310

V

Vaesken, Alexis F., 150
victory, realizing, 23; Shin'ichi on, 61, 64, 112
Vietnam, French involvement in, 231–32; Fukase family in, 266; history of, 230; Soka Gakkai's fund-raising events for refugees of, 266–67; unification of, 266; United States involvement in, 233
Vietnam War, 229–30, 236–37, 245, 254–55, 261–62; American members and the, 247–48; American members' realizations about the, 252–54; American university professors and the, 244; American youth division members on the, 244–45; casualties of the, 267; first Paris peace talks for ending the, 260; Gulf of Tonkin Incident in the, 235–36; Japanese Soka Gakkai members during the, 266; local Vietnamese members during the, 266; movements against the, 260; My Lai Massacre, 259–60; Paris Peace Accords ending the, 264–65; Shin'ichi's action towards ending the, 238; Shin'ichi's proposal towards ending the, 242–43; Shin'ichi's second proposal for ending the, 246–47; Tet Offensive, 256–57; Thant U's (Burmese diplomat) proposal for ending the, 247; US allies of the, 236

Vietnamese member, actual proof of, escaping fighting in the streets, 258; resolve of, to propagate Nichiren Buddhism, 256; unity of, 258–59

W

war, cause of, 268; Soka Gakkai's position on, 268
War and Peace: The Course of the Vietnam War (exhibition), 267
Weil, Simone, 177
women's division members, prayers of, likened to power of earth, 50
World Boys and Girls Art Exhibition, 267
world peace, achieving, 69; Nichiren Buddhism elucidates path to realizing, 79
Writings of Nichiren Daishonin, The, publication of, 183. See also Nichiren Daishonin Gosho Zenshu (Collected Writings of Nichiren Daishonin)

Y

Yabe, Koichi, 298–99
Yamagata, Aritomo (Japanese prime minister), 292
Yamagiwa, Hiroshi, 92, 126, 305
Yamaki family, 143
Yamaki, Haru, 144
Yamamoto, Shin'ichi, Argentine government award for, 141; "Atsuta Village," 75; attending "Toda University," 288–89; became third president of Soka Gakkai, 179; Brazil Secret Police surveillance of, 30; commute of, 186–87; conversation with Brazilian secret police officer, 51–53; determination of, 336; Dominican Republic government award

to, 175; educational background of, 285–86; graduation of, 291; guidance tours of, 297–98; Hiroshi Izumida views about, 23; home of, 185–86; Japanese member's impression of, 271; Jonan Industrial Association, 286; Kobayashi-cho home of, 187–88; meeting with Brazilian youth representatives, 73–75; Mineko's care of, during illness, 3; "The Moon Over the Ruined Castle," 75; Paraguayan government award to, 150; on serving

Josei Toda, 180; Shinano-machi home of, 188–89; sons of, 186, 187; "The Three Martyrs of Atsuhara," 75; titles conferred on, 125–26; Toyo Commercial High School, attends night school, 285; wedding of, 185; work experience of, 286–88; writing of graduation papers by, 289–90; and Yasuhiro Saiki's greeting, 78
Yoshikura, Ineko, 208–09
youth division general meeting, 238

More on Nichiren Buddhism and Its Application to Daily Life

The following five titles can be purchased from your local or On-line bookseller, or go to the Middleway Press Web site (www.middlewaypress.org).

The Buddha in Your Mirror: Practical Buddhism and the Search for Self by Woody Hochswender, Greg Martin and Ted Morino

A bestselling Buddhist primer that reveals the most modern, effective and practical way to achieve what is called enlightenment or Buddhahood. Based on the centuries-old teaching of the Japanese Buddhist master Nichiren, this method has been called the "direct path" to enlightenment.

"Like the Buddha, this book offers practical guidelines to overcome difficulties in everyday life and to be helpful to others. Readers will find these pages are like a helpful and supportive friend. I enthusiastically recommend it."
—Dr. David Chappell, editor of *Buddhist Peacework: Creating Cultures of Peace*
(Paperback: ISBN 0-9674697-8-3; $14.00;
Hardcover: ISBN 0-9674697-1-6; $23.95)

**Choose Hope: Your Role in Waging Peace in the
Nuclear Age** by David Krieger and Daisaku Ikeda
"In this nuclear age, when the future of humankind is imper-
iled by irrational strategies, it is imperative to restore sanity
to our policies and hope to our destiny. Only a rational analy-
sis of our problems can lead to their solution. This book is an
example par excellence of a rational approach."
—Joseph Rotblat, Nobel Peace Prize laureate
(ISBN 0-9674697-6-7; $23.95)

Planetary Citizenship: *Your* **Values, Beliefs and Actions**
Can **Shape a Sustainable World** by Hazel Henderson and
Daisaku Ikeda
"*Planetary Citizenship* is a delightful introduction to some of
the most important ideas and facts concerning stewardship
of the planet. I cannot think of any book that deals with more
important issues."
—Mihaly Csikszentmihalyi, author of *Flow:
The Psychology of Optimal Experience,* California
(ISBN 0-9723267-2-3; $23.95)

**Romancing the Buddha: Embracing Buddhism
in My Everyday Life** by Michael Lisagor
"*Romancing the Buddha: Embracing Buddhism in My Everyday
Life* is...a resource which provides excellent insights into
applying Nichiren Buddhism to the difficulties of daily life,
including depression, spousal illness, the challenge of raising
two daughters and the quest for happiness. An absorbing and
inspirational selection of vignettes touched with wisdom,
Romancing the Buddha is an impressive and welcome contribution to Buddhist Studies reading lists."
—Midwest Book Review
(Paperback: ISBN 0-9723267-4-x; $18.95)

Unlocking the Mysteries of Birth & Death . . . and Everything in Between, A Buddhist View of Life (second edition) by Daisaku Ikeda
"In this slender volume, Ikeda presents a wealth of profound information in a clear and straightforward style that can be easily absorbed by the interested lay reader. His life's work, and the underlying purpose of his book, is simply to help human beings derive maximum meaning from their lives through the study of Buddhism."
—*ForeWord* Magazine
(ISBN 0-9723267-0-7; $15.00)

The Way of Youth: Buddhist Common Sense for Handling Life's Questions by Daisaku Ikeda
"[This book] shows the reader how to flourish as a young person in the world today; how to build confidence and character in modern society; learn to live with respect for oneself and others; how to contribute to a positive, free and peaceful society; and find true personal happiness."
—Midwest Book Review
(ISBN 0-9674697-0-8; $14.95)

The following titles can be purchased at SGI-USA bookstores nationwide or through the mail order center: call 800-626-1313 or e-mail mailorder@sgi-usa.org.

Faith into Action: Thoughts on Selected Topics
by Daisaku Ikeda
A collection of inspirational excerpts arranged by subject. Perfect for finding just the right quote to encourage yourself or a friend or when preparing for a meeting.
(World Tribune Press, mail order #4135; $12.95)

For Today and Tomorrow: Daily Encouragement
by Daisaku Ikeda
Daily words of encouragement that are sure to inspire, comfort and even challenge you in your practice of faith. Great for the newest member and seasoned practitioners.
(World Tribune Press, mail order #4100; $16.95)

The Human Revolution, boxed set by Daisaku Ikeda
"A great human revolution in just a single individual will help achieve a change in the destiny of a nation, and further, can even enable a change in the destiny of all humankind." With this as his main theme, the author wrote his twelve-volume account of Josei Toda's life and the phenomenal growth of the Soka Gakkai in postwar Japan. Published in a slightly abridged two-book set, this work paints a fascinating and empowering story of the far-reaching effects of one person's inner determination. Josei Toda's awakening and transformation, his efforts to teach others the unlimited power of faith, his dedication in leading thousands out of misery and poverty, the efforts of his devoted disciple Shin'-ichi Yamamoto—within these stories we find the keys for building lives of genuine happiness.
(World Tribune Press, mail order #4182; $45.00)

The Journey Begins: First Steps in Buddhist Practice
A pamphlet on the basics of Nichiren Daishonin's Buddhism. Each step is discussed in very basic terms, but each plays an important role in your practice. For the new member, the points will help you build a foundation in your practice. Return to them again and again throughout your practice to help keep yourself on track and get the maximum benefit from your Buddhist practice.
(World Tribune Press, mail order #4138 [ENGLISH], #4139 [SPANISH]; $1.00)

My Dear Friends in America
by Daisaku Ikeda
This volume brings together for the first time all of the SGI president's speeches to US members in the 1990s.
(World Tribune Press, mail order #4104; $19.95)

The New Human Revolution
by Daisaku Ikeda
An ongoing novelized history of the Soka Gakkai, which contains not only episodes from the past but guidance in faith that we can apply today as we grow our movement here in the United States.
Volume 1 (World Tribune Press, mail order #4601; $12.00)
Volume 2 (World Tribune Press, mail order #4602; $12.00)
Volume 3 (World Tribune Press, mail order #4603; $12.00)
Volume 4 (World Tribune Press, mail order #4604; $12.00)
Volume 5 (World Tribune Press, mail order #4605; $12.00)
Volume 6 (World Tribune Press, mail order #4606; $12.00)
Volume 7 (World Tribune Press, mail order #4607; $12.00)
Volume 8 (World Tribune Press, mail order #4608; $12.00)
Volume 9 (World Tribune Press, mail order #4609; $12.00)
Volume 10 (World Tribune Press, mail order #4610; $12.00)
Volume 11 (World Tribune Press, mail order #4611; $12.00)

The Winning Life:
An Introduction to Buddhist Practice
Using plain language, this booklet gives a quick-yet-detailed introduction to a winning way of life based on Nichiren Daishonin's teachings. A perfect tool for introducing other to the benefits of practice.
(World Tribune Press, mail order #4105 [English], 4106 [Spanish], 4107 [Chinese], 4113 [Korean]; $1.00)

The Wisdom of the Lotus Sutra, vols. 1–6,
by Daisaku Ikeda, Katsuji Saito, Takanori Endo
and Haruo Suda
A captivating dialogue on the twenty-eight-chapter Lotus
Sutra that brings this ancient writing's important messages
into practical application for daily life and for realizing a
peaceful world.
Volume 1 (World Tribune Press, mail order #4281; $10.95)
Volume 2 (World Tribune Press, mail order #4282; $10.95)
Volume 3 (World Tribune Press, mail order #4283; $10.95)
Volume 4 (World Tribune Press, mail order #4284; $10.95)
Volume 5 (World Tribune Press, mail order #4285; $10.95)
Volume 6 (World Tribune Press, mail order #4286; $10.95)

A Youthful Diary: One Man's Journey From the
Beginning of Faith to Worldwide Leadership for Peace
by Daisaku Ikeda
Youthful inspiration for people of all ages. Through the tale
of the ever-deepening relationship between the young
Daisaku Ikeda and his mentor-in-life, Josei Toda, *A Youthful
Diary* is a compelling account of both triumphs and setbacks
on the road to establishing the foundation of today's Soka
Gakkai.
(World Tribune Press, mail order #4101; $23.95)